WORKSHOP PROCESSES
FOR MECHANICAL ENGINEERING TECHNICIANS

VOLUME II

GENERAL TECHNICAL SERIES

General Editor:

AIR COMMODORE J. R. MORGAN, O.B.E.
B.Sc., C.Eng., F.I.Mech.E., F.R.Ae.S., R.A.F. (Retd.)

Formerly
Director of Studies
Royal Air Force Technical College
and
Deputy Director, Educational Services, Air Ministry

Workshop Processes for Mechanical Engineering Technicians
(in two volumes)

R. T. PRITCHARD
C.Eng., M.I.Prod.E.

Engineering Drawing for Mechanical Engineering Technicians
(in four volumes)

Metric Examples in Engineering Drawing and Materials
(in four volumes)

H. ORD
M.I.E.D., M.I.Plant.E., A.R.Ae.S.

Other books of interest

T3 Workshop Technology for Mechanical Engineering Technicians

T4 Workshop Technology for Mechanical Engineering Technicians

R. T. PRITCHARD
C.Eng., M.I.Prod.E.

WORKSHOP PROCESSES

FOR MECHANICAL ENGINEERING TECHNICIANS

VOLUME II

R. T. PRITCHARD

C.Eng., M.I.Prod.E., Full Tech. Cert. C.G.L.I.,
Teacher's Cert. in Metalwork

Lecturer in Mechanical Engineering,
Garretts Green Technical College, Birmingham.
Examiner for the City and Guilds of London Institute,
The Union of Educational Institutions and
The Welsh Joint Education Committee

THE ENGLISH UNIVERSITIES PRESS LTD

Paperback edition ISBN 0 340 15254 0
Boards edition ISBN 0 340 15255 9

First printed 1963
Reprinted 1963, 1965
Second edition 1969
Third edition 1971
Reprinted 1972

The English Universities Press Ltd,
St Paul's House, Warwick Lane, London EC4P 4AH

Printed in Great Britain by
Hazell Watson & Viney Ltd, Aylesbury, Bucks

Editor's Foreword

THE new awareness of the imperative need to make the very most of our technical potential makes a foreword to this General Technical Series almost unnecessary, for it aims directly at encouraging young men—and women—to extend their interest, widen their knowledge, and improve their technical skills.

The City and Guilds of London Institute makes special provision for the technician to acquire a qualification appropriate to his Craft. The wide range of examinations now held under its auspices is ample evidence not merely of the need to cater for the technician but also of the growing desire of the Craftsman to improve his knowledge of his Craft. Many of the books in the present series will be related to syllabuses of the City and Guilds of London Institute, but this will not limit their use merely to preparation for the examinations held by that body. The aim is to encourage students to study those technical subjects which are closely related to their daily work and, by so doing, to obtain a better understanding of basic principles. Any study of this kind cannot fail to stimulate interest in the subject and should produce a technician with a clearer understanding of what he is doing and how it should best be done.

But although the series is intended to appeal, in the first instance, to students who are interested in the certificates offered by the City and Guilds of London Institute, that must be regarded as only the immediate aim. Those students who, as a result of their initial endeavours, find that they are capable of going further should aim at obtaining either a National Certificate in an appropriate field of engineering or, alternatively, a General Certificate of Education at a level appropriate to their potential attainment.

All the books in the series will be written by experienced and well-qualified teachers who are thoroughly conversant with the problems encountered by young men and women in studying the subjects with which their books deal.

J. R. M.

Author's Preface

In writing and illustrating this second volume, I have, wherever possible, attempted to emphasise and develop the basic principles and techniques laid down in Volume I. The first year of any course is perhaps, for the student, the most important one; it is not an end in itself but a stepping stone to further endeavour and success.

The principle of a single volume to cover each year of the course not only allows the student to see both the scope and the content of the year's work, but also enables the author to plan ahead, introducing ideas and principles ready to be expanded and enlarged in a later volume. I make, then, no apology for occasional reference back to Volume I on certain points in this volume, and I hope that teachers will not be afraid to adopt this technique.

The layout follows the same pattern as Volume I. It is intended as a class book for students, and once again an attempt has been made to keep the written text to a minimum and to make the fullest use of clear and informative diagrams. Drawings and diagrams are the language of workshop engineering; it is important that the student engineer makes continual and useful contact with them.

The first two chapters deal with the basic primary manufacturing processes of casting and forging, followed by the principles involved in the testing of metals, thus paving the way for the chapter on heat treatments, in which an attempt is made to correlate the structural changes with changes in physical properties. Measurement and inspection follow, together with further work on the centre lathe and drilling machine, and there is a final chapter on milling.

Once again, each chapter will require between three to four weeks of class work, and the questions at the end of each chapter will provide the student with a useful yardstick, allowing him to arrive at a measure of his assimilation of the chapter contents.

I am indebted to my proof-reader, Mr Brian G. Staples, M.A., F.L.A., for his valued advice and assistance, and to the City and Guilds of London Institute for permission to use the past examination papers in the Appendix.

Sutton Coldfield

R. T. Pritchard

Preface to Second Edition

SI Units

In May 1965 a Government statement was made as follows: 'British industries on a broadening front should adopt metric units sector by sector, until that system can become in time the primary system of weights and measures for the country as a whole. . . . the government hope that within ten years the greater part of the country's industry will have effected the change. . . .'

To this end, the International System (SI) of metric units only have been used in this volume. It is the opinion of the Author that the conversion of present-day Imperial units to SI units has no place in this text; the student must learn to think metric at all times, and this can be achieved only with complete disregard of Imperial units.

To assist the student, the more common SI units are given in the following table.

Physical Quantity	*SI Unit*	*Unit Symbol*
mass	kilogramme	kg
length	metre	m
area	square metre	m^2
volume	cubic metre	m^3
time	second	s
force	newton	N
temperature	°Celsius	°C

Note: All dimensions on mechanical engineering drawings are usually expressed in millimetres (mm)

Multiples and Sub-multiples

The following multiples and sub-multiples are used for all physical quantities.

Prefix	*Multiplying Factor*		*Symbol*
tera	1 000 000 000 000	$= 10^{12}$	T
giga	1 000 000 000	$= 10^{9}$	G
mega	1 000 000	$= 10^{6}$	M
kilo	1 000	$= 10^{3}$	k
hecto	100	$= 10^{2}$	h
deca	10	$= 10^{1}$	da
deci	0·1	$= 10^{-1}$	d
centi	0·01	$= 10^{-2}$	c
milli	0·001	$= 10^{-3}$	m
micro	0·000 001	$= 10^{-6}$	μ
nano	0·000 000 001	$= 10^{-9}$	n
pico	0·000 000 000 001	$= 10^{-12}$	p

The use of a prefix representing 10 raised to a power which is a multiple of ± 3 is preferred. For example,

2 000 metres = 2 kilometres = 2 km
0·001 metre = 1 millimetre = 1 mm
0·000 001 metre = 1 micrometre = 1 μm

Contents

1 The Casting of Metals

ENGINEERS have been casting metals for over three thousand years. The art of metal-casting consists in filling a cavity of the required shape with molten metal, producing on solidification a metal component having the desired shape.

This is undoubtedly the quickest and most economical method of producing a metal component, especially if it is of large size and com-

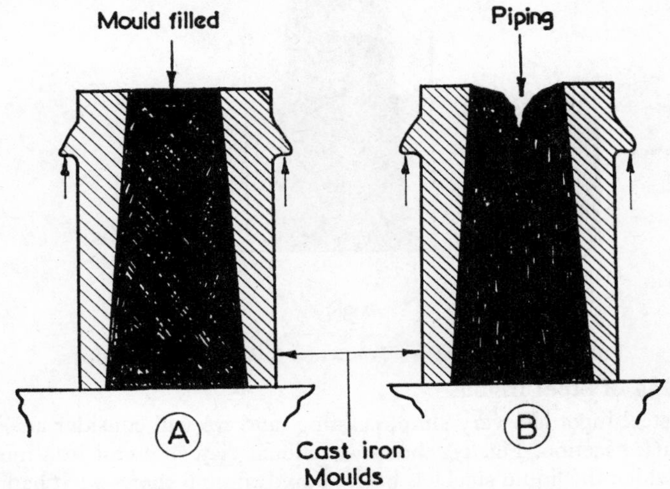

FIG. 1.—CASTING STEEL INGOTS.

plicated shape; yet for many years the art of metal-casting has been traditional, with much secrecy surrounding this vital and basic process. The importance of this basic hot-working process has now been appreciated, with foundry engineering rapidly developing into a skilled science, offering many opportunities to the competent technician.

It is not possible in the space of a single chapter to cover every aspect of metal-casting; but it is essential that the student has some knowledge of the principles and techniques underlying the science of casting. This knowledge will increase his respect for the foundry engineers, for it is their products that make possible the high quality required in all engineering components. It may not be appreciated that any component made from steel, be it a pin, perambulator, or press-tool, starts its life as a casting. Steel, made in a steel-making furnace, is cast into ingots. These steel ingots are essentially steel castings, and a bicycle frame that started life as a badly cast or faulty ingot may well prove unreliable. It is essential, then, to have a closer look at the casting of steel ingots.

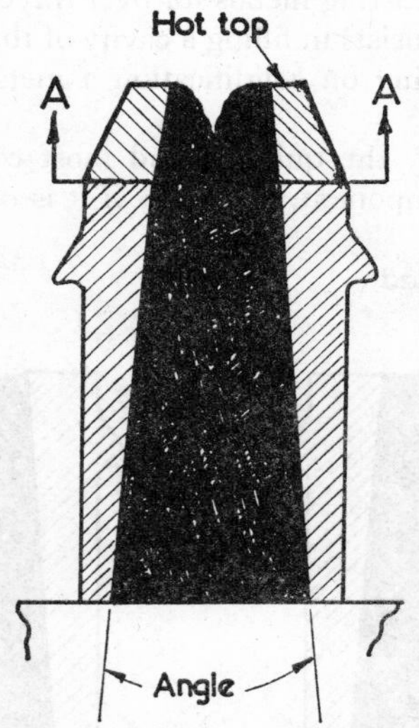

FIG. 2.—USE OF A HOT TOP WHEN CASTING STEEL INGOTS.

Casting of Steel Ingots

A steel ingot is a very simple casting, and we will consider an ingot of square section. Fig. 1A shows a sectional view of a cast iron mould, into which the liquid steel has been poured; fig. 1B shows what happens when the steel solidifies. Note that, owing to the contraction of the metal, a hollow or concavity appears at the top of the ingot. This effect is known as **piping**, and represents a serious defect in the casting. If this ingot is rolled into bar or sheet strip, this piping will be further elongated, and the finished product will be defective.

Fig. 2 illustrates how the problem is overcome. Note the separate mould at the top. This is called a **hot top**, and provides a reservoir of surplus metal. The piping is now contained within this hot top and, on removal from the mould, the ingot is cut at the line AA, shown in fig. 2.

Thus the defective portion is removed, leaving a sound and reliable casting.

Removal of the Ingot from the Mould

A very simple principle is adopted to ensure that the ingot is readily removed from the mould. Reference to fig. 2 will show that the cavity within the mould is tapered, or at an angle. This angle allows the mould to be lifted off the ingot without the ingot tearing or sticking. This principle is used and appreciated by young children who find much delight and pleasure in constructing sand-castles at the sea-side. The bucket acts as a mould for the damp sand; vertical movement of the bucket provides immediate clearance between the sides of the bucket and the moulded sand-castle. The principle is shown in fig. 3.

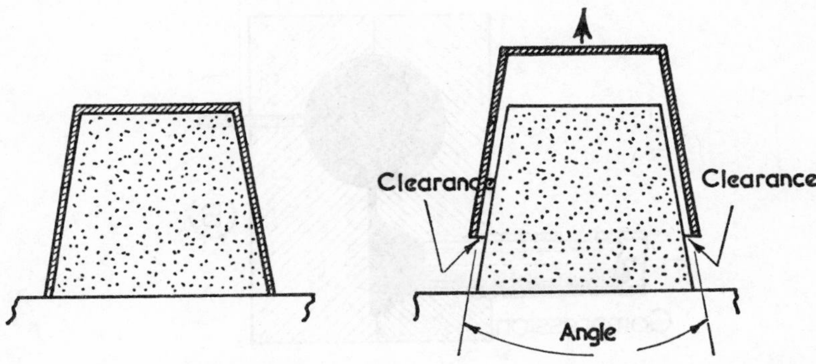

FIG. 3.—TAPER PRINCIPLE WHEN MOULDING.

Gravity Casting

When casting ingots the molten metal is poured into the mould, and it must be appreciated that it is the force of gravity which causes the liquid metal to fill the mould. A casting produced by pouring molten metal into a mould is known as a **gravity casting.** Gravity castings call for considerable technique and skill, and we shall deal with the main principles involved later on in this chapter.

Die Casting

Die casting involves the use of alloy steel moulds or dies. The use of these permanent dies allows the molten metal to be forced under pressure into the cavity between the dies, and very accurate, well-finished castings can be produced in this way. The external pressure forces the molten metal tightly against the cavity face, giving very accurate detail

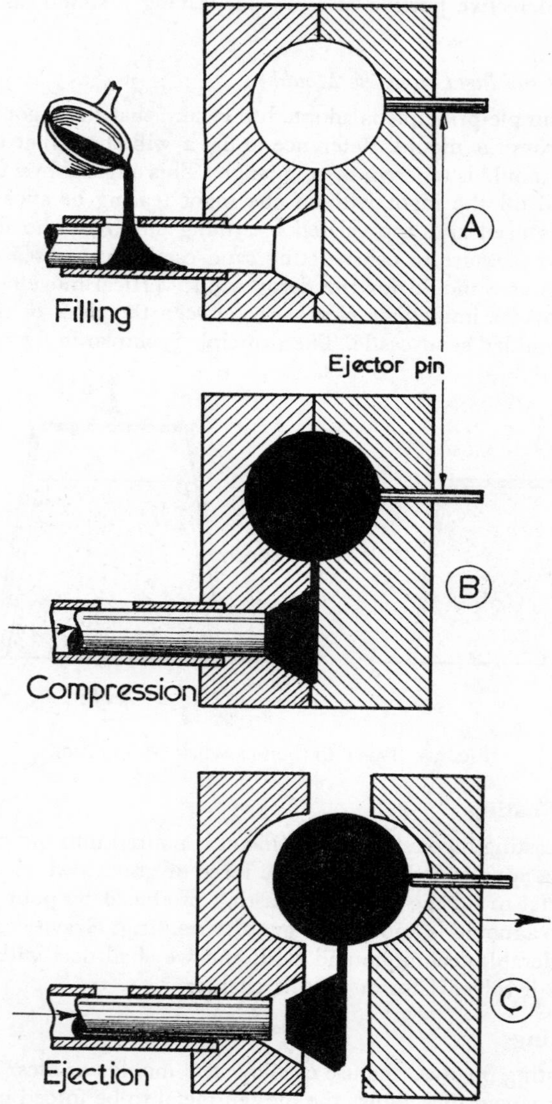

Fig. 4.—Stages in the Pressure Die Casting of an Aluminium Alloy Ball.

and smooth external finish, not possible with gravity casting. It is, of course, possible to carry out gravity die casting, by pouring molten metal into the dies, but the resultant casting will not have the exterior finish, accuracy, and detail of a pressure die casting.

Pressure Die Casting

Very high pressures are used in this process, and a piston, operated hydraulically or pneumatically, forces a measured quantity of molten metal into the die cavity. Several systems are in use, but essentially the principle remains the same. This is shown in fig. 4.

Filling

This may be done by hand from a small ladle, or the molten metal may be supplied by automatic methods. Fig. 4 shows the filling chamber receiving a charge of molten metal.

Compression

When filling is completed the piston moves forward and the metal is forced into the die cavity. This is shown at B. The pressure exerted by the piston will exceed 14 MN/m^2, calling for a strong rigid set-up.

Ejection

The dies are water cooled and held at a temperature of about 200° C, resulting in rapid solidification of the casting. A mechanical device opens the dies, and the ejector pin moves forward, ejecting the casting from the right-hand die, whilst a slight forward movement of the piston

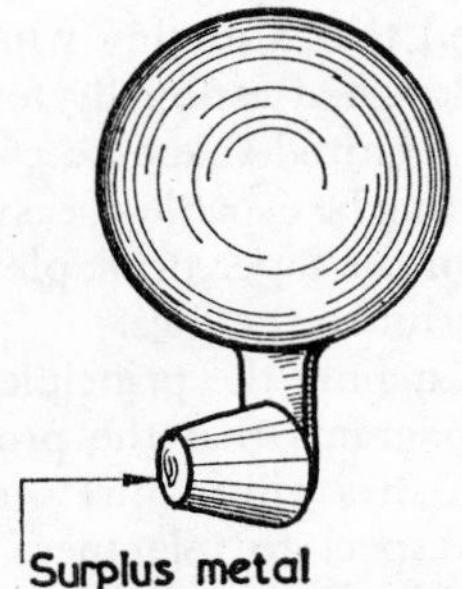

FIG. 5.—EJECTED PRESSURE DIE CASTING.

will eject the casting from the left-hand die. Note that a considerable amount of excess metal is attached to the finished casting, as shown in fig. 5. It will be necessary to remove this excess metal, returning it for remelting, and the casting will require slight trimming.

Advantages of Pressure Die Casting

Filling, compression and ejection represent a casting cycle, and die casting machines are available, capable of the automatic repetition of this cycle. This means that high output rates are possible, and a finished casting rate of a casting every four seconds is easily achieved with small intricate castings. The amount of machining required by a pressure die casting will be very small, and this is a most important feature, for machining is, perhaps, the most expensive method of producing an engineering component. Also the rapid cooling of the molten metal promotes a better and finer grain structure, giving added strength and reliability to the casting.

Limitations of Die Casting

Because the dies used in the die casting process are made from alloy steel, it is essential that severe heating of the dies be avoided. This means that metals used for die casting must possess relatively low melting points; zinc-based alloys are widely used, with the molten metal held at about 400° C during the die casting process. A zinc-based die casting will not have a high strength value, and cannot be used if the casting is to be subject to stresses. Stronger castings are produced from aluminium-based alloys, requiring a working temperature of about 650° C during the casting process.

A typical zinc-based alloy would have the following composition: zinc 96%, copper 4%; a typical aluminium-based alloy, aluminium 88%, silicon 11·95%, sodium 0·05%.

It is generally accepted that a casting which is to be produced by pressure die casting is designed especially for this process, for it is a basic condition that the required shape be contained in two half-dies, and that the solidified casting be capable of easy removal from these dies. Much use will be made of the taper principle mentioned earlier, if the casting is not to tear or stick to the dies.

Although fig. 4 shows mainly the principle of pressure die casting, it is evident from the diagrams that the process involves the use of precision equipment. The dies will require precision workmanship of a very high degree with respect to tolerances, alignment, and surface finish of the cavity faces. These dies will be expensive, depending on the size and intricacy of the casting; it is possible for a set of dies to cost around £2000. Die casting machines are also expensive. Once again the cost will depend on the type required, but one can be sure £5000 will not purchase a very impressive machine. The high initial costs of dies and machine represent the greatest limitation of the pressure die casting process. If this process is to be an economical proposition, a very large number of castings must be required. There are, however, many industries requiring large numbers of castings, and a good example is provided by the motor-car door handle.

The size of the casting also imposes a limitation, for large castings would require very high pressures, together with the problem of supplying and maintaining at the correct temperature a large continuous supply of molten metal.

Centrifugal Casting

We have shown in our discussion on pressure die casting that an external force other than gravity is an essential of the process. Most of us are familiar with the pull exerted by a heavy object rotated at speed, and this force may be utilised to press molten metal tightly against the inner face of a revolving mould.

Three principles are in use, and they are worthy of a short discussion.

True Centrifugal Principle

This is a very suitable method for the casting of large-diameter hollow pipes. The technique is illustrated in fig. 6. The mould will consist of a

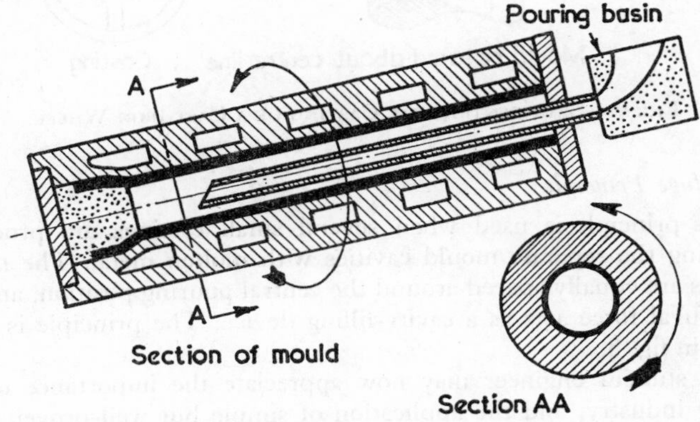

FIG. 6.—CENTRIFUGAL CASTING OF A LARGE-DIAMETER CAST IRON PIPE.

hollow water-cooled metal tube capable of being revolved at speed about its axis. This mould will be slightly inclined to the horizontal, causing the molten metal to take up a spiral path as it climbs up the inner diameter of the revolving mould. This metal will of course be forced tightly against the mould face, and on solidification a hollow casting will result. This is a popular method of producing large-diameter water pipes possessing a sound dense structure.

Semi-centrifugal Principle

This is shown in fig. 7. Unlike the true centrifugal castings in which there is no excess metal, semi-centrifugal castings will have excess metal at the poured end of the casting. The casting shown in fig. 7 is a simple wheel, and the rotation of the mould forces the molten metal outwards; cast iron wheels are readily produced in this way, possessing once again a sound dense structure.

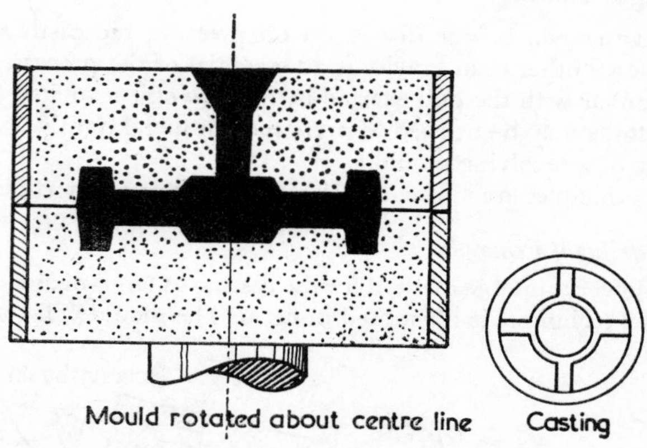

FIG. 7.—SEMI-CENTRIFUGAL CASTING OF A CAST IRON WHEEL.

Centrifuge Principle

This principle is used when several small castings are produced by filling the separate mould cavities with molten metal. The mould cavities are equally spaced around the central pouring position, and the centrifugal force acts as a cavity-filling device. The principle is illustrated in fig. 8.

The student engineer may now appreciate the importance of the casting industry, and the application of simple but well-proven principles. It must be remembered that molten metal is not the easiest of materials to handle, and an error of judgement may lead to serious and perhaps fatal consequences. It is true that when a casting is received for further machining, we are concerned wholly with the problems involved in machining the casting to the limits laid down in the drawing. We would do well to spare a thought for the skill, knowledge, and craftsmanship employed at the foundry to produce the casting, for true appreciation of the work of others instils an added interest in our own work.

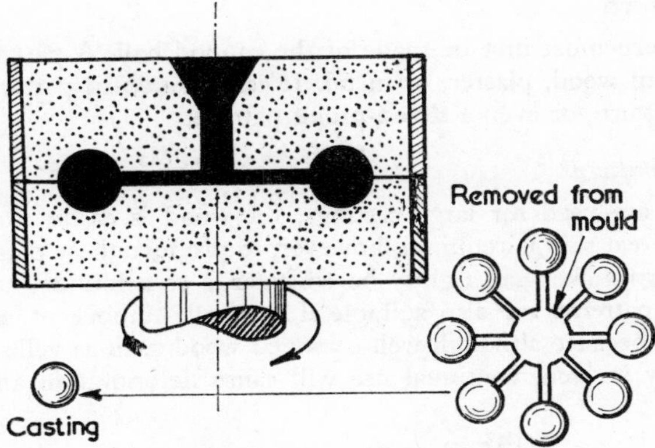

FIG. 8.—PRINCIPLE UNDERLYING CENTRIFUGE CASTING.

Sand Casting

The pouring of molten metal into a sand mould is known as **sand casting**, and this is an important and vital part of foundry work. This process is very suitable for producing castings of high melting point metals, such as cast iron and steel. The bed of a lathe, a milling machine table, the body of a shaping machine, are all examples of sand castings. A very great deal of skill, experience, and patience is involved in the production of castings such as these, and the finished casting will represent the combined efforts of a team of skilled craftsmen.

We may separate the manufacture of a sand casting into the following sections:

(i) making the pattern,
(ii) making the mould,
(iii) pouring the metal.

Each of the above processes has an important bearing on the accuracy and quality of the finished casting; "as the pattern goes, so goes the casting" is a typical foundry phrase, and only those actively engaged in the casting of molten metal appreciate the truth of this.

To illustrate the importance of each of the above processes, we will consider the sand casting of the component shown in fig. 9. This is a simple cast iron ball. Castings such as these were in very great demand about 400 years ago, at the time of the Spanish Armada, when countless thousands of cannon balls were required to arm our fleet.

Let us then go back in time, and see for ourselves how the foundry engineers cast these all-important cannon balls.

The Pattern

A pattern must first be made of the cannon ball. A pattern can be made from wood, plaster, or metal. It can be a **solid** pattern, a **two-piece** pattern, or even a **three-piece** pattern.

Wooden Patterns

These are used for large castings, for wood is easily worked and joined. Great skill is required, however, to produce these patterns, and the pattern-maker can rightly be considered as a foundry toolmaker. Wooden patterns are also suitable if a small number of castings is required, because although well-seasoned wood such as yellow pine or mahogany is used, continual use will cause deterioration and loss of

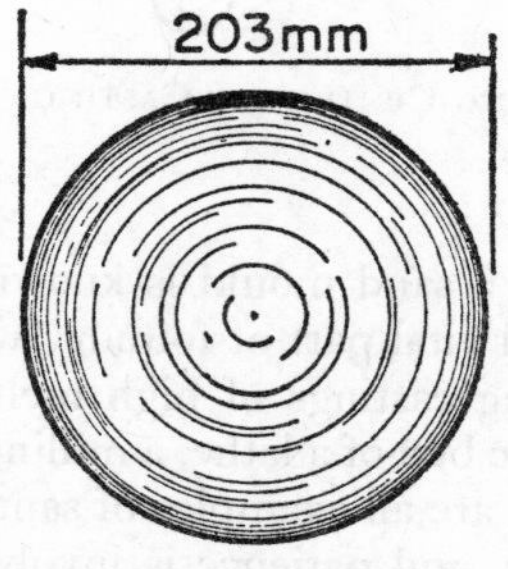

Fig. 9.—Cast Iron Cannon Ball.

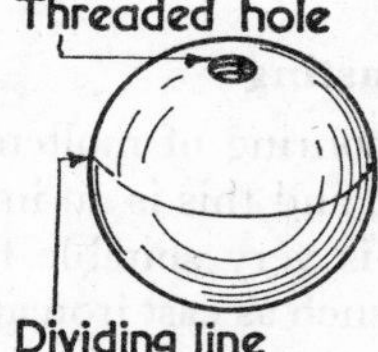

Fig. 10.—Metal Pattern for Casting Cannon Ball.

accuracy of the pattern. All wooden patterns will be well varnished to prolong their useful life.

Metal Patterns

Casting cannon balls provides a good example of the need for a metal pattern. Not only are cannon balls required in large numbers, but they must also be a reasonably good fit in the business end of the cannon, if maximum results are to be obtained. The use of a cast iron pattern will ensure that the castings will remain uniform in size, even after prolonged use of the metal pattern. A wooden pattern will, however, be made in order to cast the metal pattern.

The metal pattern is shown in fig. 10; note the dividing line and the threaded hole. Let us assume that the diameter of our cannon balls is to be 200 mm. Because of the shrinkage that will take place when the casting cools from the molten state to room temperature, it will be necessary to make the metal pattern of larger diameter to allow for this shrinkage. This presents no problem to the pattern-maker because he uses a special rule. A linear distance of 1·0103 metres on this rule would be equivalent to a distance of 1 metre on an engineer's steel rule, since the contraction rate for cast iron is 10·3 mm per metre.

Making the Mould

A 200 mm diameter cannon ball has a mass of about 29 kg, and this size will permit the mould to be made at the bench; the process is thus known as bench moulding. Moulding boxes of various sizes are available, and one will be chosen allowing reasonable space around the pattern. The top half of the moulding box is known as the **cope,** whilst the bottom half is known as the **drag.**

Stage 1

This is shown in fig. 11A. The cope is placed on the bench face upwards, and filled with sand. Sufficient sand is removed from the centre and the metal pattern is pressed in to the half-way line. Note in the diagram that the cope is provided with holes to accommodate location pins in the drag. When the cope is used in this way, as a preliminary method of supporting the casting, it is referred to as the **oddside.**

Stage 2

The drag is now placed and located on the cope and packed tightly with sand; the top face is smoothed or strickled off. This is shown in fig. 11B.

Stage 3

Both boxes are turned over and the cope or oddside removed. This operation leaves the drag in the correct position, with the pattern having the threaded hole uppermost. The top surface of the drag is now carefully cleaned over and lightly dusted with parting sand. This will prevent the cope from sticking to the drag. A rapping bar is inserted in the hole in the pattern, and the cope located on the drag, as shown in fig. 11C, and packed with sand.

Stage 4

The pattern must now be removed from the mould. A few taps on the rapping bar will loosen the pattern, permitting careful lifting off of the cope. A lifting hook is screwed into the threaded hole in the pattern, and the pattern lifted out. We must not forget that this pattern's mass is 29 kg, but its spherical shape will provide the essential taper principle mentioned earlier. Removal of the pattern gives us the shape required, and provision must now be made to allow this shape to be filled with molten cast iron. The reassembled moulding box is shown in

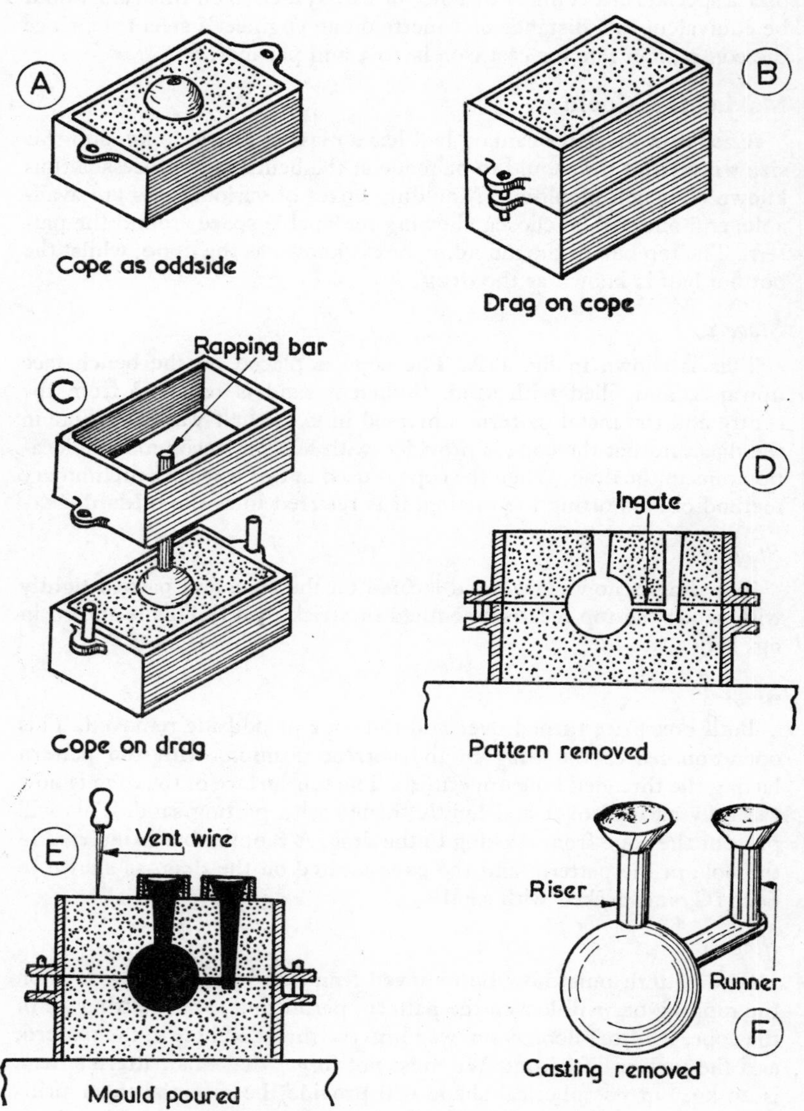

FIG. 11.—STAGES IN THE BENCH MOULDING OF A CAST IRON CANNON BALL.

fig. 11D, and it will be seen that provision has been made for the entry of the molten metal. This is achieved by using a cutter tube, which makes a neat hole in the cope. At the same time, provision must be made for the escape of gases, and a tapered hole is cut at the top of the cope. Note the small ingate cut in the drag; this allows the molten metal to flow into the mould cavity. The cope and drag are now ready for final assembly; the drag is placed on a sand bed on the floor of the moulding shop, together with the cope, dusted with some plumbago, a carbon or graphite compound.

Pouring the Metal

The liquid cast iron is poured from a ladle, and to assist the entry of the metal into the pouring or running hole, a large diameter bush is placed over this hole. A bush is also placed over the outlet hole; this allows feeding of extra metal as contraction takes place.

With the two half-moulds securely clamped together the mould is now ready for filling, and this important process is shown in fig. 11E. Pouring metal is a skilled job, the object being to ensure a steady constant stream of molten metal entering the mould. The sand will be damp, and the molten cast iron at about 1200° C. A considerable volume of hot gases must result from this combination and it is essential that these gases be driven out of the mould. As the level of molten iron rises they escape through the outlet at the top of the cope, and also through the vent holes pierced with the vent wire shown in fig. 11E.

On removal from the mould, and this means the destruction of the mould, the casting will appear as shown in fig. 11F. Note the runner and riser still attached to the casting. Because the cannon ball is cast iron, a sharp blow will remove these, and this excess metal can be remelted.

The cannon ball will now need **fettling**; this is the name given to the cleaning-up process required by all sand castings.

It is evident that the whole casting cycle must be repeated for each cannon ball to be produced, for as stated already the mould is destroyed in order to remove the solidified casting. It may come as a surprise to learn that in 1631 the town of Magdeburg was subjected to a bombardment of no less than 12 000 cannon balls a day during a two months' siege. It is certain that the foundries of that period must have been working at high pressure, and it is equally certain that the cannon balls were produced by gravity die casting. This means that cast iron dies were used, having cavities for two or more cannon balls. The great disadvantage of sand casting is that the mould, on which so much care and skill has been spent, must be destroyed in order to remove the casting. Nevertheless, provided a relatively small number of components is required, sand casting is still the cheapest and best process, for moulding sand is cheap and plentiful.

Hollow Castings

A cannon ball is a solid casting, but there are many instances when a casting may require a hollow portion. Fig. 12 shows a cast iron tailstock for a simple lathe. If this casting can be produced with a hole, say

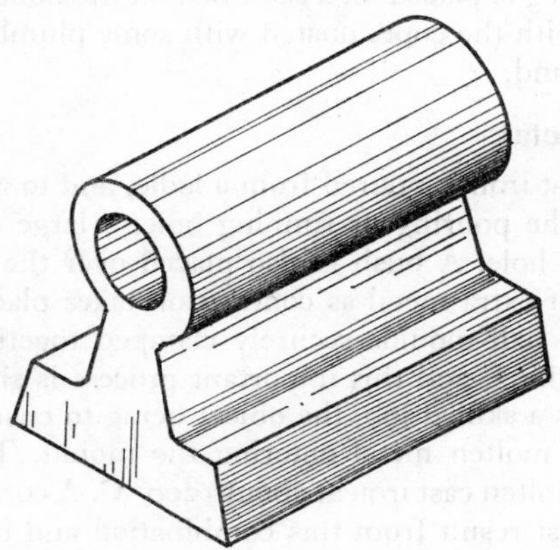

FIG. 12.—GREY CAST IRON CASTING WITH CORED HOLE.

6 mm less in diameter than finished size, then the machining time will be greatly reduced, lowering the manufacturing costs of the

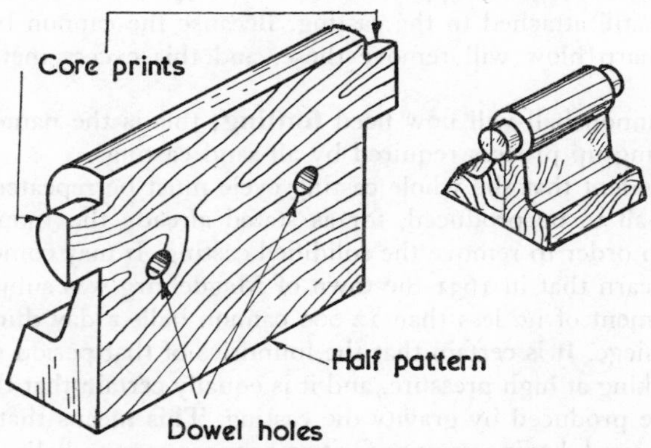

FIG. 13.—TWO-PIECE WOODEN PATTERN.

machined tail-stock. This casting will also require a **two-piece** pattern, and this pattern is shown in fig. 13.

The casting will now be known as a **cored** casting, and this means that a **core** will form an essential part of the mould. This core will require location in the mould; the end pieces shown in fig. 13 are known as **core prints**, for the core fits into the impressions left in the mould after removal of the pattern. Note the use of dowels to locate the two half-patterns.

We will now outline the stages involved in the casting of this tailstock.

Making the Core

The core is a separate part of the mould, and will be made in the core shop. The principle of core-making is very similar to casting; a mould will be required, and this mould will be filled with sand possessing an oil bonding compound. On removal from the mould the core will be baked in an oven, and this makes the core strong enough to be handled and stand up to the flow and pressure of the molten metal. At

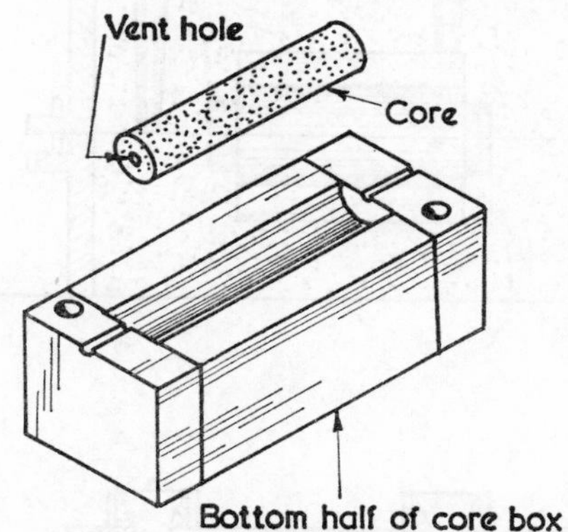

FIG. 14.—METHOD OF PRODUCING SIMPLE CORES.

the same time the core must be capable of easy removal when the casting has solidified. Although the cores are moulded, the moulds are more commonly known as **boxes**, and fig. 14 shows the tailstock core after removal from the core box. Note the vent hole in the core to facilitate the escape of gases.

Stage 1

The half-pattern containing the dowel holes is placed on a flat board, with the drag placed over it. The drag is packed or rammed with sand, strickled over, and the drag turned upside-down. This is shown in fig. 15A.

Stage 2

The other pattern half is now assembled to the half-pattern in the drag, the dowels providing accurate location. The cope is placed in position atop the drag, the joint face dusted with parting sand, and the

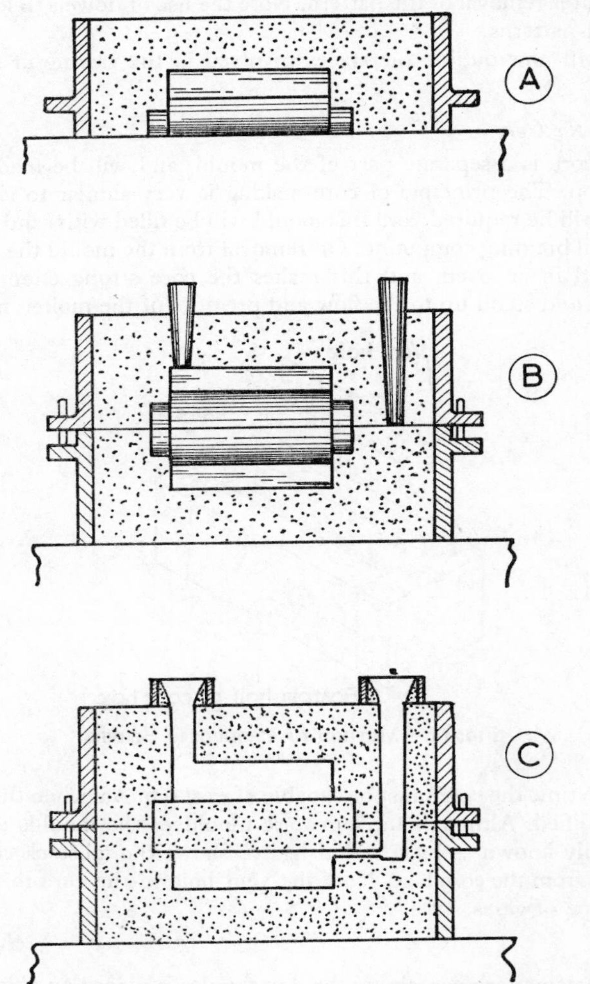

FIG. 15.—STAGES IN THE PRODUCTION OF A CORED SAND CASTING.

cope filled with sand and rammed. A sectional view of the assembled cope and drag is shown in fig. 15B. Note the use of ingate and riser pins. These are slightly tapered, and may be used instead of a cutting tube.

Stage 3

It is now necessary to insert the core and also cut a small channel or gate from the base of the runner into the mould. The cope is gently lifted off, the half-patterns lightly tapped and lifted out, and the core placed in position, after the ingate has been cut. Note that the core locates in the core prints. With the joint faces of both cope and drag smoothed up and dusted with plumbago, the cope is reassembled to the drag and securely clamped. A sectional view of the mould, ready for pouring, is shown in fig. 15C.

Stage 4

This will involve pouring molten cast iron into the mould, and as already stated great care is necessary. Any gases trapped within the mould will result in porosity or blow-holes in the finished casting. The presence of these faults may not be discovered until considerable machining has been carried out on the tailstock, and this means that much time and effort will have been wasted. We have seen in Volume I that the tailstock is an essential part of a centre lathe, and the machined surfaces will require a high degree of precision, if accurate work is to be turned between centres. The foundry plays an important part in producing castings that can be machined to precise limits, and there are many other aspects concerning casting techniques which may influence the quality of the finished casting. For example, if a large casting contains sections of varying thicknesses, the thin sections will solidify before the thicker sections, because of the small amount of metal present in a thin section. The larger mass of metal in a thick section will take longer to cool and must contract in the process. This contraction will set up stresses in the sections that have already solidified, which may lead to distortion of the casting, with the possibility of fracture when it is put into service.

In the same way, a badly-designed forging having a wide variation of section thickness will be subject to severe stress and distortion during the cooling process. This undesirable state of affairs can be removed by subsequent heat treatment of the castings and forgings, but the good designer ensures that as far as possible sudden changes in section thickness are avoided.

Moulding Sand

It must not be thought that the sand so abundant at the sea-side is suitable for mould-making. It is essential that moulding sand be strong enough to stand up to the flow and pressure of the molten metal, for this metal has the same weight as an equivalent solid mass. A bonding agent must be mixed with the sand, and clay is widely used, the high temperature of the molten metal causing the sand to fuse with the clay. Thus the loss of heat of the poured metal strengthens the mould, making it strong enough to stand up to the conditions imposed upon it, yet allowing fairly easy destruction on solidification of the casting.

Green Sand Moulding

This is the name given to the process adopted to produce medium-sized castings. The mould sand is damp, allowing a good impression of the pattern, and the metal is poured as soon as the mould is prepared. The use of machines for filling and ramming the moulding sand permits high production rates when castings are produced by green sand moulding.

Dry Sand Moulding

This process is used for large-size castings requiring a relatively strong mould capable of resisting the heavy pressure exerted by the molten metal. One of the great disadvantages of the casting process is that it is not until the finished casting is removed from the mould that any imperfections will be discovered. When castings of mass 20 000 kg or more are being produced, it is essential that the risks of failure be kept to a minimum, and the dry sand moulding technique reduces the probability of faulty castings. The moulds are prepared in the usual way, and are then baked or allowed to dry out. No moisture will be present in the mould, and this will reduce the existence of blow-holes in the finished casting. The casting will also possess better dimensional properties and a smoother finish.

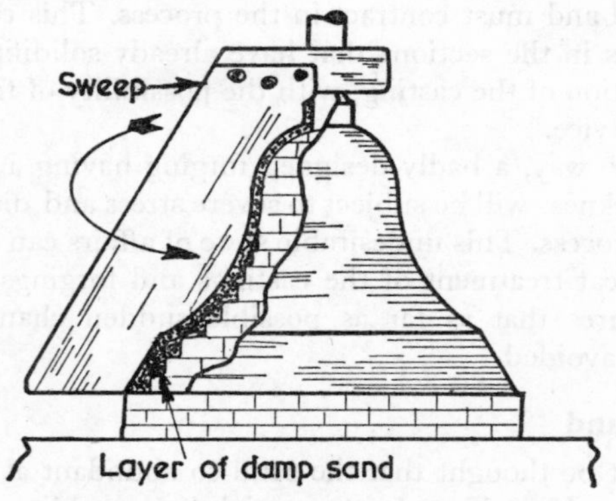

FIG. 16.—PRINCIPLE OF LOAM MOULDING.

Loam Moulding

This moulding process makes use of the generating principle described in Volume I. No pattern is required, as the contour is produced by rotary movement of the sweep. This is shown in fig. 16, which illustrates the loam moulding of a bell core.

Summary

Castings are the products of the foundry. They are produced by filling moulds with molten metal, and any metal that becomes liquid when heated sufficiently can be cast. Castings may be solid or hollow, and may be several grammes or several kilogrammes in mass. Low-melting-point alloys are readily pressure die cast in alloy steel dies, and the castings will possess excellent finish and close dimensional tolerances; further machining is not necessary in many cases. The manufacture of these dies demands a very high degree of skill and precision, as does the design and construction of die casting machines. These machines are in operation on the factory floor, and may well form part of a production line. We now see that not all castings are produced in the foundry, but we can be sure that the body of the die casting machine is a foundry product requiring much skill and precision in its manufacture.

Perhaps the first textbook on workshop processes was that written by Vannoccio Biringuccio in 1540, and the student is strongly advised to read this remarkable book, called the *Pirotechnia*. It will provide convincing testimony of the truth that although techniques change, principles remain. We will conclude this chapter on the casting of metals with an extract from Biringuccio's chapter on the art of metal casting:

"The outcome of this art is dependent upon and subject to many operations which, if they are not all carried out with great care and diligence and well observed throughout, convert the whole into nothing, and the result becomes like its name (cast away)."

QUESTIONS ON CHAPTER ONE

PART A

1. Explain what is meant by a gravity casting.
2. What is the essential difference between sand casting and die casting?
3. Explain with the aid of a neat diagram the principle underlying pressure die casting.
4. Make a neat sketch of a casting that could be produced using the true centrifugal principle.
5. What is the essential difference between a semi-centrifugal and a centrifuged casting?

6. Outline the stages necessary to produce a cast iron surface plate.

7. Define the circumstances that would determine whether a pattern is made from wood or metal.

8. Define the following terms:

(i) drag,
(ii) cope,
(iii) rapping,
(iv) strickling.

9. Make a neat sketch of a simple engineering casting that would require the inclusion of a core within the mould.

10. Describe briefly the stages necessary to cast a 4000 kg bronze bell.

PART B

Questions in this section after each chapter are reproduced by kind permission of the City and Guilds of London Institute, and the Welsh Joint Education Committee.

1. (a) List briefly the main points to be considered in deciding whether to employ casting or forging to produce a component. A particular component may be chosen to illustrate the points.

(b) Discuss the different reasons why it is a great advantage for both a casting and a forging to be as uniform as possible in Section.

C. & G. (1962)

2 The Forging of Metals

WE concluded the chapter on the Casting of Metals with an extract from Biringuccio's book. We will do well to open this chapter on the Forging of Metals with another extract, in which Biringuccio sums up the art of the ironsmith:

"It seems to me an art comprising great knowledge, for I know of no art or activity whatever, excluding the sciences and painting, that does not need this as its principal member. Therefore, in my opinion, if it were not for the nobility of the material, I would say that the smith working in iron should justly take precedence over the goldsmith because of the great benefit that he brings."

There is little doubt that this statement is as true today as it was when Biringuccio wrote it over 400 years ago. It is true also that because forging is generally associated with fire, smoke, grime, and noise, there is a tendency to belittle or ignore this important hot-working process.

We have seen, in Volume I, the advantages offered both in the strength of the finished forging and in the considerable economy of material achieved. The principle of hot rolling was outlined, and perhaps we can now point out that hot rolling is essentially a continuous forging process. We may define forging as a process whereby metal is forced into the shape required. It is important to appreciate that this process relies on the plastic flow of the metal under the influence of external pressure, and most metals have greatly increased plasticity when they are heated to a suitable temperature.

There is a very great demand for components that must stand up to conditions of fairly severe stress when in use, and good examples are provided by spanners, chains, connecting rods, and crank-shafts. All these components are produced by forging, and the following techniques may be adopted:

(i) hand forging,
(ii) drop forging.

Hand Forging

Mention was made in Volume I of the skill of the blacksmith and his striker when producing finished components from red-hot steel. It is important to appreciate that all forging is essentially an extension of the blacksmith's art, and modern techniques make extensive use of mechanical or hydraulic principles to provide the forces necessary to coerce the heated steel into the required shape. The art of forging consists in persuading or encouraging the metal to flow, and not forcing it into shape by the application of violent and severe blows or pressures. Brute force is always linked with ignorance, and ignorance leads to damage and destruction. The application of brute force during a forging process must result in severe stressing of the forged steel, not to mention undue stressing of the devices adopted to produce these severe forces. It is evident that the force available to the blacksmith is limited to the muscular ability of his striker, and a large forging will require large forces if the flow of metal is to be achieved before the metal cools.

Forging Hammers

The use of a forging hammer makes available a steady and continual source of power. It is in effect a mechanical or automatic striker, and fig. 17 illustrates a forging hammer in use about 200 years ago. Note the water wheel; a very popular device in much use before the advent of steam power. Rotation of this water wheel raises the heavy wooden beam, attached to which there is a heavy hammer. As the wheel rotates the hammer falls, and the metal is struck a considerable blow. Note that the work rests on an anvil, and if the maximum advantage is to be gained from the momentum of the falling hammer, then it is essential that this anvil be of very solid construction, at least twenty times as heavy as the hammer or tup, as it is often called. It is essential also that the anvil rests on a massive foundation.

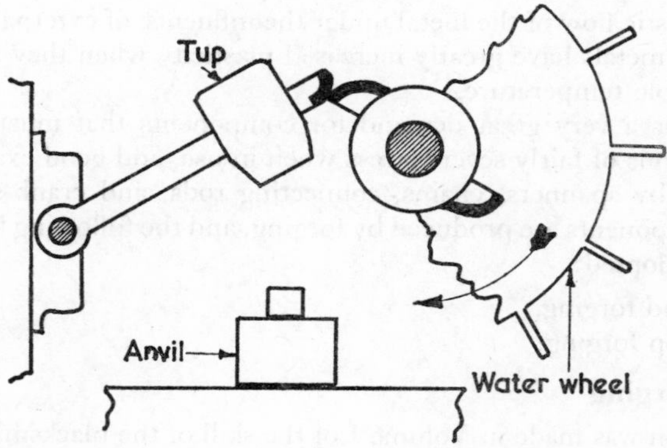

FIG. 17.—PRINCIPLE OF AN EARLY FORGING HAMMER.

Although this mechanical device provides the necessary power to work the heated metal, forgings produced at this tilt hammer are still classified as hand forgings. It is the blacksmith who controls the flow and direction of the metal, and this principle still holds good irrespective of the means adopted to provide the necessary power. There is little doubt also that the blacksmith's striker, released from muscular bondage, is given the job of controlling the water wheel, and in this way we see the gradual transformation of the manual worker into a machine operator.

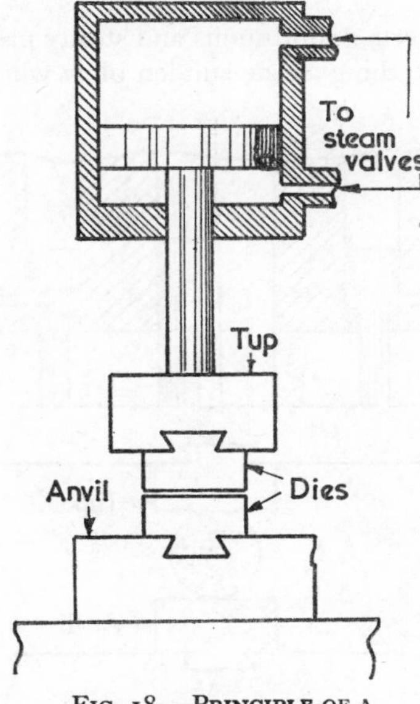

FIG. 18.—PRINCIPLE OF A SIMPLE STEAM FORGING HAMMER.

If we study this tilt hammer a little closer we will see also that although the design is ingenious, reflecting great credit on the engineers who designed and made it, it has its limitations. The force of the falling tup, relying on gravity, will be of a constant value; this means that variation of the blow is not possible. It was a practical engineer called Nasmyth who provided a vastly superior forging hammer. The principle of this hammer is illustrated in fig. 18, and it can be seen that the motive power is provided by steam. Suitable control of the valves permits a wide variation of the force of the blow given by the tup, and a popular demonstration of the versatility of this machine consisted in placing an egg in a wineglass on the anvil, and using the tup to crack the shell with no damage to the fragile wineglass. The next demonstration consisted of the placing of a white-hot ingot on the anvil, whereupon the tup descended with great force, calculated not only to scare the wits out of the interested onlookers, but also to rattle the crockery in every house within two miles.

This principle of the double-acting steam hammer is still in wide use for the manufacture of medium-sized forgings, and the use of this hammer still constitutes hand forging.

Forging Presses

A forging press exerts a continuous and steady pressure on the metal. This is not the same thing as the sudden blow which is given by a tilt

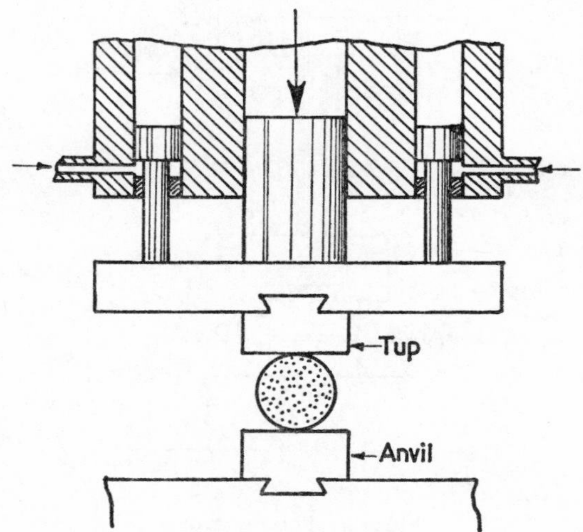

FIG. 19.—PRINCIPLE OF A FORGING PRESS.

or steam hammer. Forging presses are used for large or heavy work, and the forces exerted by these presses may exceed 200 MN. We have seen that the action of a forging hammer consists in striking the metal a sudden blow. If a large-diameter shaft were forged in this way the outside layers would flow into the required shape, but the mass of metal at the centre of the shaft would move very little. The use of a forging press removes this difficulty, as the metal is subject to a squeezing action, and the movement of the metal is reasonably constant throughout the whole section of the work.

The principle of a hydraulically operated forging press is shown in fig. 19, and such a press in operation works smoothly and quickly, with little noise or vibration. This is quite different from the noise and vibration, together with flame and smoke, associated with the forging hammer. To stand in a forging shop is not unlike standing in a battlefield. The impact of the falling tups shakes the very ground. Sawdust is often thrown on the white-hot steel to prevent sticking to the anvil or tup, and the impact of the tup provides a spectacular display of flame and smoke; it is difficult to appreciate that the metal is being coaxed or encouraged to change its shape. This, as stated earlier, is essentially the basic principle underlying successful forging, and one must not be misled by the apparent display of violence during the forging of a component with a forging hammer.

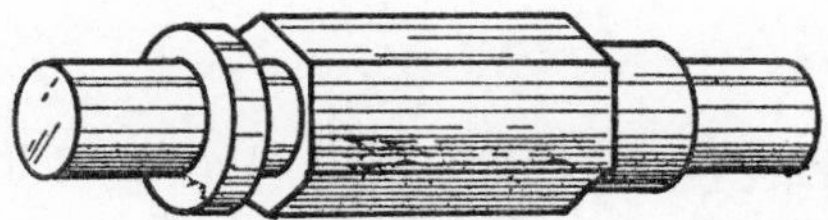

FIG. 20.—80 000 kg FORGED SHAFT.

Hand Forging at a Forging Press

It is a sobering thought to realise that a large forging of mass 200 000 kg will be hand forged in a forging press. Although the force exerted on the work may exceed 200 MN, the whole forging operation is under the control of one man. He is called the **forge master**, and he directs a team of skilled operatives who control the mechanisms that lift, move, and rotate the metal between the anvil and the ram.

Fig. 20 shows a steel shaft of mass 80 000 kg forged from a steel ingot. An experienced forge master, assisted by his team of helpers, can produce this component to a remarkable degree of accuracy, and because a forging press is used the operation takes place in an atmosphere of comparative silence. With expressive movements of his hands the forge master directs the movements of work and ram; square, rectangular, hexagonal, and circular sections are readily produced on the forging.

The finished forging will of course require machining; although the part is already of the approximate shape, machining is necessary to ensure that the forged shaft will possess the required dimensional accuracy and alignment to give efficient and trouble-free service.

Drop Forging

If a very large number of medium-sized forgings is required it is certain that they will be drop forged. This principle is not unlike die casting, because two half-dies will be used; one attached to the tup and the other attached to the anvil. They will, of course, be in close alignment, and the downward impact of the tup forces the metal into the cavity contained within the two half-dies. This principle is often referred to as **closed die forging.**

Closed Die Forging

A forging hammer or a forging press may be used; the latter is invariably used for heavier forgings such as railway wagon wheels. A railway wagon wheel can be produced in under four minutes from a white-hot steel billet. Although several stages are involved the essential principle is illustrated in fig. 21, which gives some idea of the forces

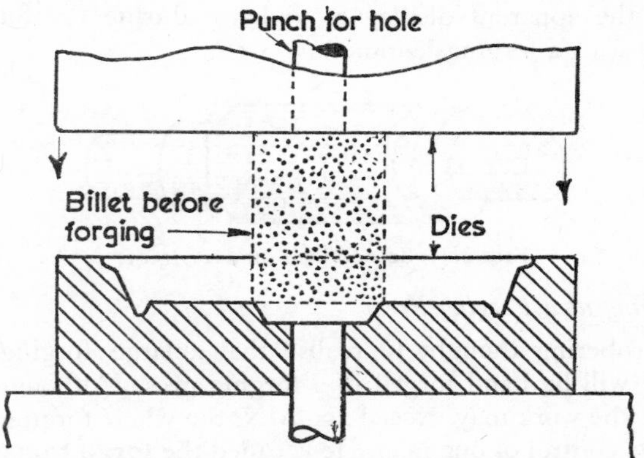

FIG. 21.—CLOSED DIE FORGING PRESS USED IN THE MANUFACTURE OF WAGON WHEELS.

involved together with the flow of metal. It is true that the experience and skill of the forge master are no longer required for this type of forging, for the wheels are now mass-produced. Much skill, however, has been employed in the manufacture of the steel dies, together with the arrangement of the handling equipment. The supervision of the mass-production process and the efficient working of the machinery used are the responsibility of a skilled and competent technician.

It is essential that the whole process works smoothly, with the forging passing quickly from stage to stage, losing little heat; for speed of operation is an important factor in all forging processes.

Forge Hammer Drop Forging

This a popular method of producing medium-sized forgings, and once again two half-dies are used, one fixed to the tup and the other fixed to the anvil. The heated metal is now struck a series of blows until the operator is satisfied that the required metal flow has taken place. Considerable skill is required by the operators of these machines, for once again speed is an essential factor.

All good spanners are drop forged, and we will now outline the essential stages required to produce strong and reliable spanners. Fig. 22 shows why an open spanner must be made as strong as possible; the nut, in resisting the tightening torque, imposes severe stresses across the planes shown as AA in the diagram, and a forged spanner will be greatly superior to one machined from the solid, or produced as a steel casting, because of the grain flow shown.

Making the Dies

Two half-dies will be required, each containing a half-cavity of the spanner. These dies are made from blocks of medium carbon or alloy

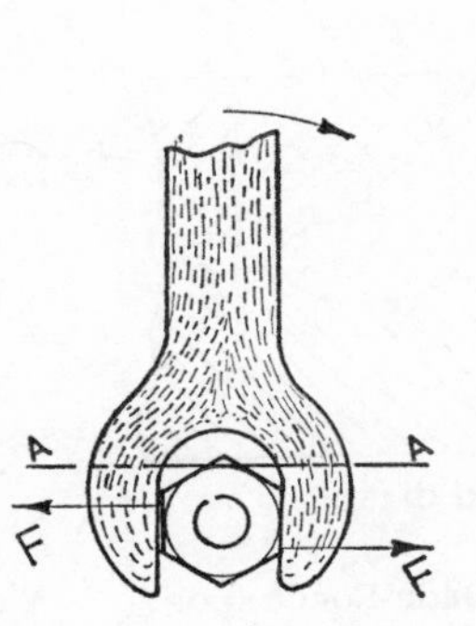

Fig. 22.—Forces Acting on an Open-ended Spanner.

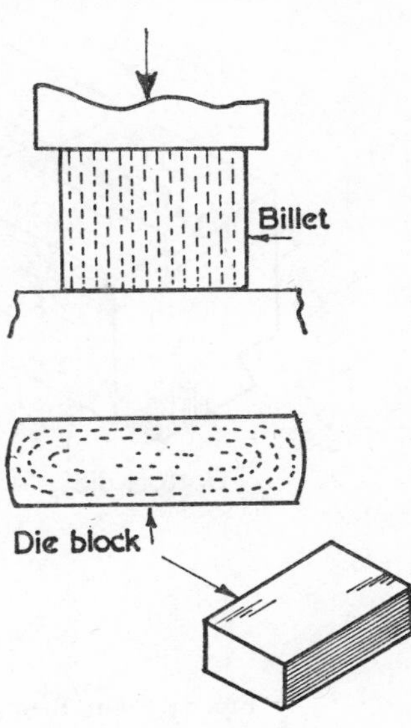

Fig. 23.—Forged Die Block.

steel, and because they must stand up to very severe working conditions of impact, stress, and abrasion, they are firstly forged from a billet or ingot. Fig. 23 illustrates the additional strength gained by the die block as plastic flow of the metal takes place. The cavities are now machined, and this operation is more commonly known as **die sinking**. This is a highly skilled job, requiring much patience and knowledge, and extensive use will be made of suitable machine tools, although it is inevitable that a considerable amount of hand work will be necessary to give the dies a smooth polished finish. When the die-sinker is satisfied with the finished job he will clamp both halves together and pour molten lead into the cavity. On solidification the lead pattern will be removed and then carefully measured and checked to ensure that the dimensions are within the limits laid down in the drawing.

Fig. 24 shows a pictorial view of the bottom die. A cross-sectional view is also shown, and it will be seen that the profile of the spanner is further extended with a narrow recess or gutter. The purpose of this additional space is to accommodate the excess metal of the blank from which the spanner will be forged. It is not possible to obtain the exact

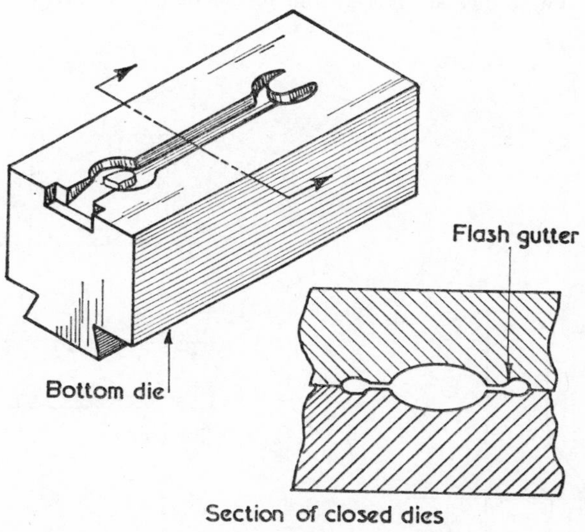

FIG. 24.—DIE BLOCKS USED IN THE DROP FORGING OF SPANNERS.

size of the blank required to fill the cavity completely, and to ensure absolute filling the blank must possess a greater volume than the finished spanner. The gutter provides an outlet for this excess metal, which is known as the **flash**. Thus on removal from the dies the spanner will be surrounded with this flash, and a further operation will be required to remove this surplus metal. This operation is known as **cropping** and is carried out immediately after the drop forging, a cropping press being situated close at hand. The principle of cropping is shown in fig. 25.

Pre-forming

It must not be thought that a rectangular bar is placed between the dies; this is not in accordance with our stated principle of forging which must consist in encouraging the heated metal to flow into the required

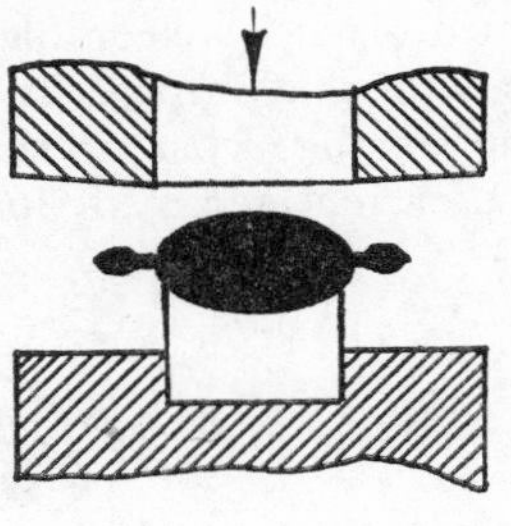

FIG. 25.—PRINCIPLE OF FLASH REMOVAL BY CROPPING.

shape. A rectangular bar would possess too great a volume of metal, and very little desired flow would take place. It is essential that a pre-forming operation be carried out on the metal prior to drop forging the finished spanner, and this pre-forming will also be a forging operation.

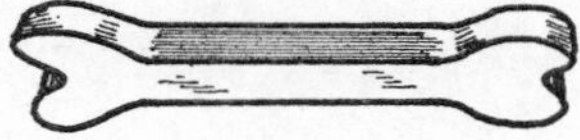

FIG. 26.—PRE-FORMED BLANK FOR FORGED SPANNER.

Fig. 26 shows the pre-formed blank, and it will be seen that the pre-forming operation has produced a workpiece of the approximate shape.

For the final drop forging, accurate alignment of the dies is essential, and this is achieved with the use of a "dummy" spanner. Sawdust is often thrown on to the workpiece as the tup falls, preventing the sticking of the workpiece to the top die. It must be remembered that the forging must be of such a shape that it is capable of easy removal from the dies, and this means that the taper principle, so essential when casting metals, must also be used when forging metals using closed dies.

Bar Forging

In our consideration of the forged spanner we have assumed that a suitably heated pre-formed blank has been placed on the bottom die, a pair of tongs being used for this purpose. It is, however, possible to forge spanners from long lengths of bar; in this case the ends will be heated and pre-formed, then reheated ready for final forging.

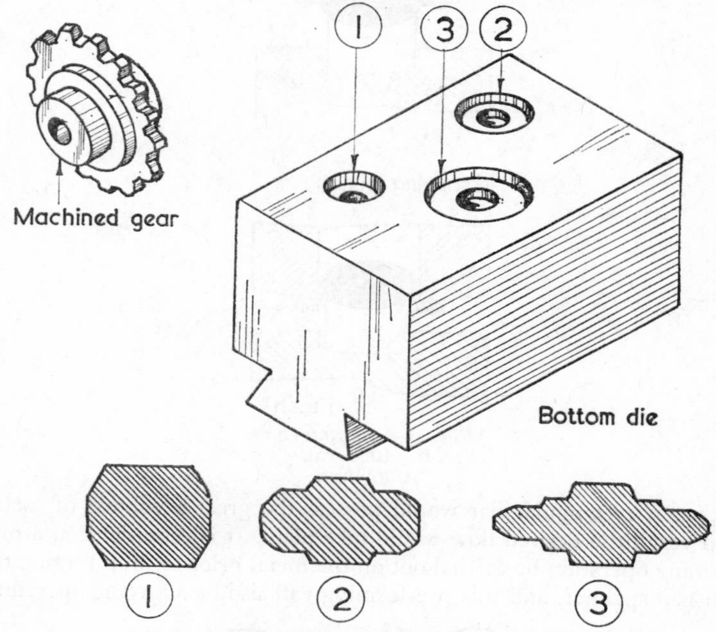

FIG. 27.—MULTI-IMPRESSION FORGING DIE.

Multi-impression Dies

Provided a component is of relatively simple shape, it can receive pre-forming operations in the same dies used for the finishing operation. This means that the die blocks will contain several cavities, each calculated to bring the workpiece to the approximate shape ready for the next impression. This technique permits high production figures, as the operator is able to move the workpiece, using a pair of tongs, from one impression to another, the workpiece losing very little heat in the process.

Fig. 27 shows the principle involved, and illustrates the mass-production of forged gear blanks. The amount of metal left for machining will be relatively small, and gears made in this way will be capable of standing up to conditions of severe stress. This is due to the flow of the grain during the forging process, and fig. 28 shows the comparison between a forged gear and one machined from a solid bar. Note that we have taken a cross-sectional view across a tooth; it is evident that the forged tooth, by virtue of the grain flow, is better able to withstand the pressures exerted under conditions of severe loading.

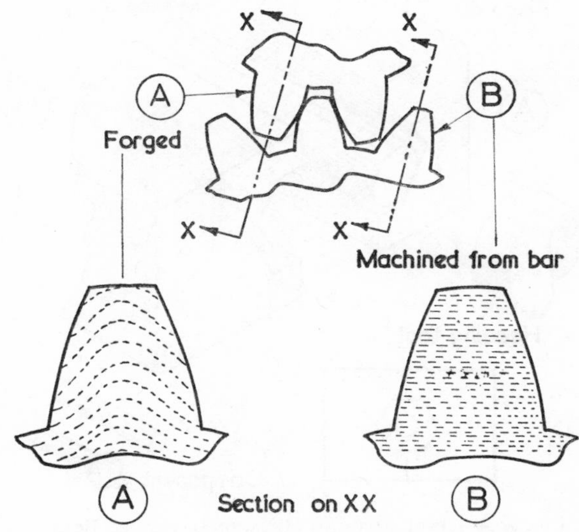

FIG. 28.—GRAIN FLOW IN A FORGED GEAR BLANK.

Most metals can be forged provided they are not hot short. All the ferrous metals excepting cast iron are amenable to the forging process. All the carbon steels, alloy steels, and non-ferrous metals such as brass, copper, and aluminium alloys, may be brought to the required shape by forging. It must be remembered that forging dies represent a considerable initial cost, together with the forging hammer or press, and it is essential that a large number of components be required if the process is to be an economical proposition.

Upset Forging

The principle of upsetting was shown in Volume I, whereby an increase in cross-sectional area is gained by the application of a vertical force, causing swelling out of the heated portion of a bar of metal. Not only does the component gain added strength, but the necessity for a considerable amount of machining is removed. This principle has been applied to the manufacture of the much-used engineering bolt for many years, and it differs little from the forging processes described, except that the bolt is forged by horizontal movement of the forming die. This forming die is sometimes known as a **heading tool**. Fig. 29 illustrates the essential technique. The work is inserted after heating

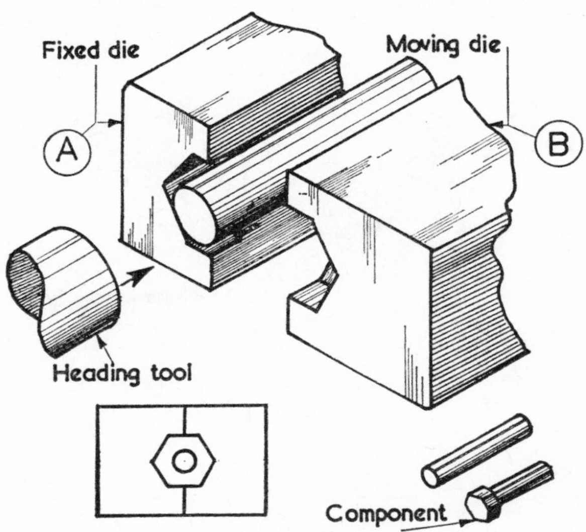

FIG. 29.—UPSET FORGING HEXAGONAL-HEADED BOLTS.

between the gripping jaws shown as A and B. As the moving jaw B closes, the heading tool comes forward and forces the metal into the cavity between the dies A and B. The amount of metal left for forging is controlled by the use of a simple stop, and this amount must be carefully calculated as no flash is produced in this process. At the completion of the forging stroke the heading tool returns, and the gripping die B moves back. This permits quick removal of the headed bolt, and the forging cycle is repeated.

More complicated shapes may be upset forged by adopting a similar technique to the method described for the drop forging of gear blanks. This means that the shape will be produced in successive stages, the work being passed on from one set of dies to another. A good example is provided by the manufacture of the popular socket wrench or socket spanner. We have seen in fig. 22 that the tightening of a nut with an open-ended spanner results in the application of two opposing forces, which tend to open the spanner. A loose-fitting open-ended spanner may well open enough to cause slipping or rounding of the nut, and this often results in injury to the operator's hand. Fig. 30 shows the advan-

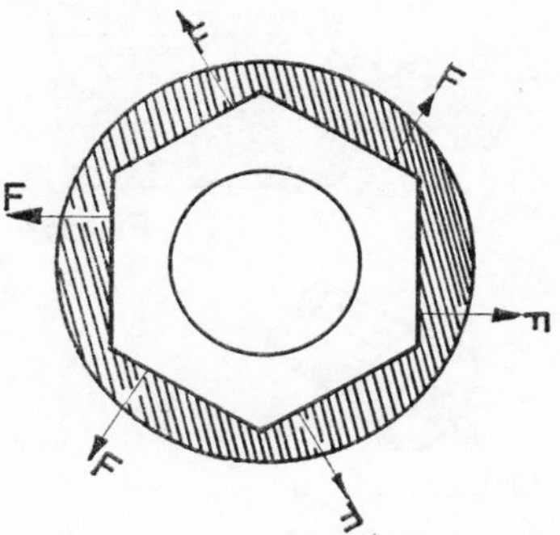

FIG. 30.—FORCES ACTING ON A SOCKET SPANNER.

tages of the socket spanner. Note that instead of two forces there are now six forces of smaller value, and these will be evenly distributed around the perimeter of the spanner. With the use of a socket spanner

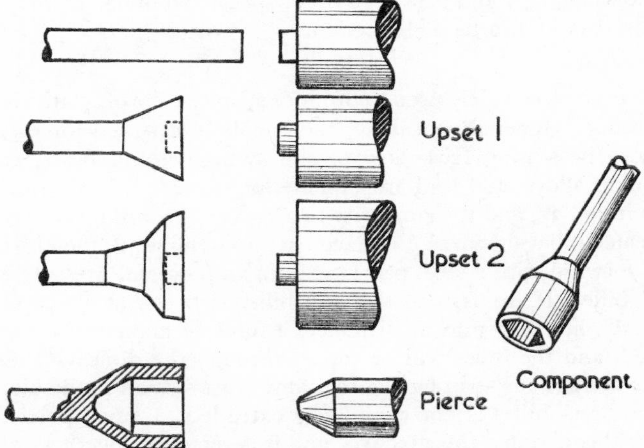

FIG. 31.—STAGES IN THE FORGING OF A SOCKET SPANNER.

having a forged head, the risk of slipping or rounding of the nut is considerably reduced, although care must be taken not to shear the bolt being tightened. The upset forging stages necessary to produce the socket spanner are shown in fig. 31.

Extrusion

Metals may be extruded either hot or cold. In both cases the metal is subjected to pressure, causing the metal to flow into the desired shape. The principle involved may be compared to the squeezing of grease out

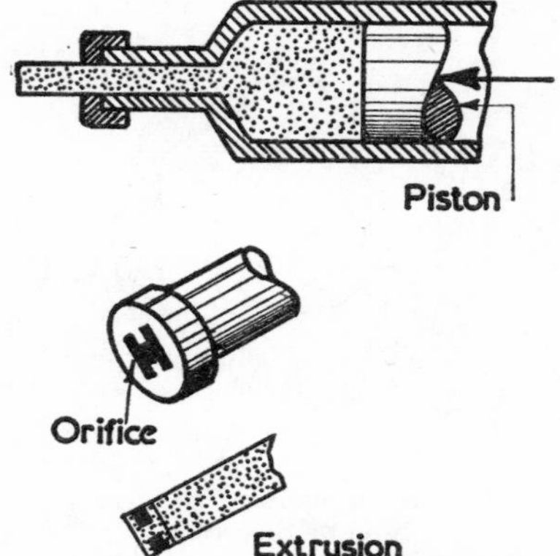

FIG. 32.—PRINCIPLE OF EXTRUSION.

of a grease gun; the ribbon of grease emerging from the nozzle of the gun will have the same shape as the orifice of the nozzle. Thus if the orifice of the grease gun possessed the shape shown in fig. 32, the ribbon of grease would also be of H section.

Hot Extrusion

This process is widely used to produce strip or tube of relatively complex section. Generally speaking, the metals best suited for extrusion are those possessing fairly low tensile strengths, and brass, copper, aluminium alloys, and lead are suitable for extrusion. The principle is shown in fig. 33, and the similarity to a grease gun will be clearly seen. The heated billet shown as A is placed in the container B; the ram C now moves forward with a steel pad D exerting a powerful pressure on the heated billet. If we assume that the billet is brass, at a temperature of 750° C, and 125 mm in diameter, a force of about 7 MN will be required, and the brass will be forced through the die cavity, emerging as a continuous strip having the same cross section as the die. Note that the brass billet is not completely extruded. A small portion will remain; this is called the **discard**, and it is removed together with the die. Very high production rates are possible when extruding; for example a brass billet with a mass of about 55 kg can be extruded into a suitable section 7 metres long in under 20 seconds. In this way quite complicated sections can be produced which would not be possible by hot rolling because of the intricacy of the section. Typical extruded

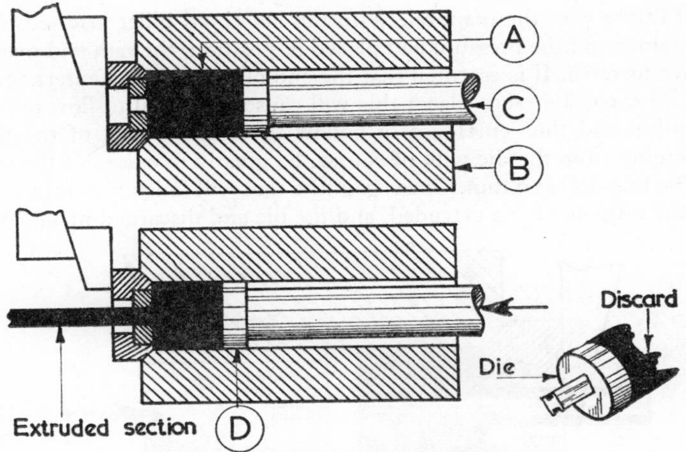

FIG. 33.—EXTRUDING BRASS SECTION.

sections are shown in fig. 34, demonstrating clearly the wide range of sections possible by the extruding process.

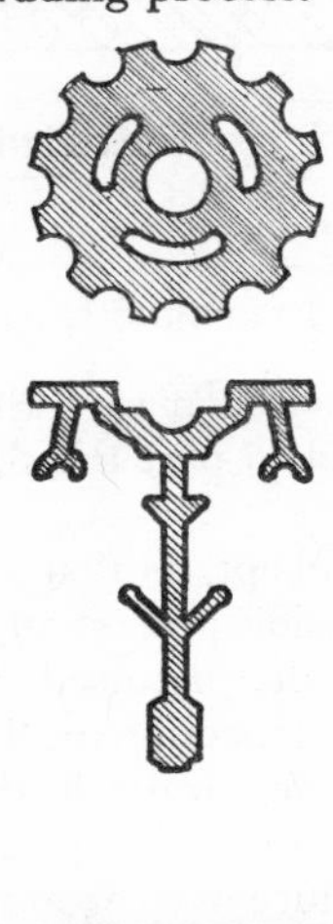

FIG. 34.—TYPICAL EXTRUDED SECTIONS.

Extruding Tubes

Hollow sections or tubes are readily extruded, and the principle adopted is shown in fig. 35. A hollow or cored billet will be used; note the fixed mandrel or forming bar attached to the ram with the pressure pad fitting over the mandrel. With the hot cored billet inserted in the container and the pressure pad placed in position, the ram and mandrel move forward. It is essential that the end of the mandrel enters the die before extrusion takes place; this will cause the metal to flow over the mandrel and thus emerge as a hollow tube. The speed of the metal emerging from the die will, of course, be greatly in excess of the speed of the mandrel and ram. Once again the ram will finish its stroke before all the billet has been extruded, and the die and discarded metal will be

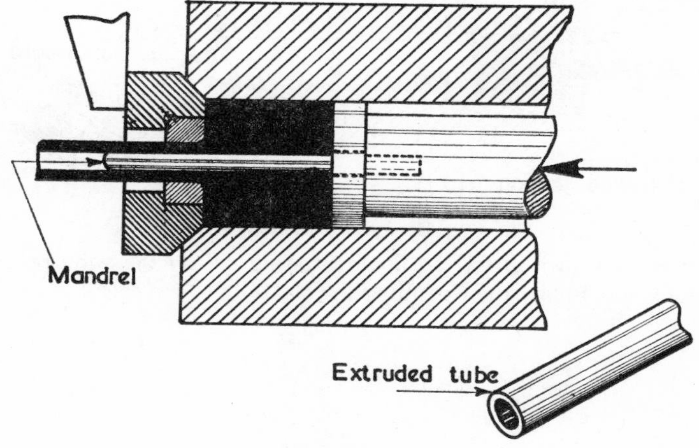

FIG. 35.—EXTRUDING HOLLOW TUBE.

removed using shears or a circular saw. Small sections may allow the use of a hammer and chisel to part the die and discard from the extruded section.

A stock of similar dies is kept, so that a new pre-heated die can be inserted, allowing the extrusion process to continue whilst the discard is being removed from the die just used. It must be appreciated also that the whole process is generally mechanised, with a continuous supply of heated billets automatically loaded into the containers, and the pressure pad also automatically placed in position. Thus one extruding machine can produce over 6500 m of tube in a working day. We must not forget, however, that provision must exist for the continuous heating and supply of the billets, and that the extruded sections will require a further straightening process.

Impact Extrusion

In all the forging processes described above, the metal is heated to promote greater plasticity, thus allowing the shaping or forming of the metal as required under the influence of a sudden impact or continuous pressure. There are some metals, however, notably tin, aluminium, and lead, which possess extreme plasticity in the cold state, and this allows them to be impact extruded. Thin metal containers can be impact extruded at high speed; typical examples of such containers are lipstick tubes, cigar tubes, and shielding cans for radio components. Aluminium is the metal used, and it is supplied to the impact extrusion machine in the form of small discs or slugs.

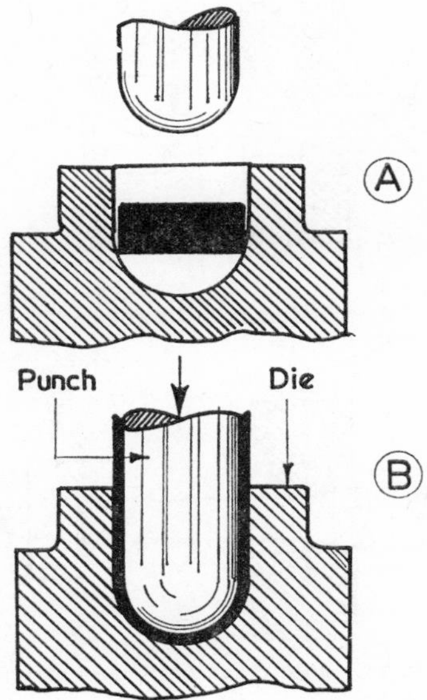

FIG. 36.—PRINCIPLE OF IMPACT EXTRUSION.

The principle is illustrated in fig. 36. Both punch and die must be hard, with highly polished working faces. Fig. 36A shows the aluminium slug in position with the punch ready to descend. Fig. 36B shows what happens when the punch strikes the slug. Note that the metal flows between the punch and the die, and this clearance determines the wall thickness of the tube. The punch returns to its starting position after the impact, and the spring-loaded ejector pad ejects the extruded tube off the forming punch. The speed of this operation is such that it is almost impossible to see, with the naked eye, exactly what is taking place, and together with automatic loading and ejection, fantastic output figures are achieved. It can be said that the speed of deformation exceeds the speed at which the metal work-hardens, and this accounts for the very high degree of cold working achieved during the impact extrusion process. As in all other cold-working processes the finish is superior to that obtained when hot working.

Wire Drawing

This is another cold-working process, and once again plastic flow of the metal is obtained whilst the metal is in the cold state. Essentially, as with impact extruding, it is a form of cold forging. Wire drawing,

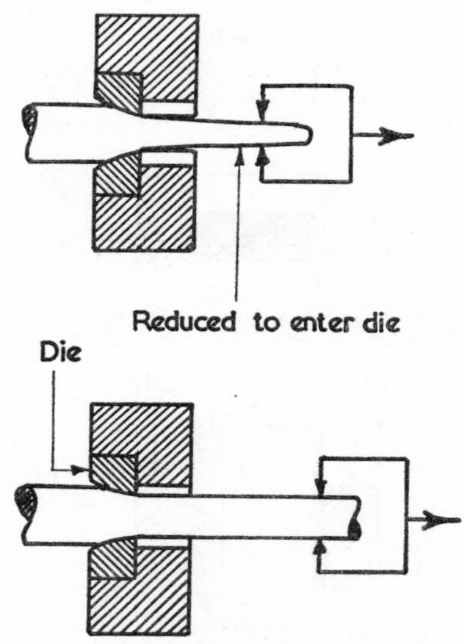

FIG. 37.—PRINCIPLE OF WIRE DRAWING.

however, is a much slower process, and several reduction stages are necessary to produce wire of small diameter. The process consists in pulling metal rod through a hard and highly polished die, and the principle is illustrated in fig. 37. It is first necessary to reduce the wire so that it will pass through the die, and special machines are used for this purpose. The reduced end after insertion in the die is now gripped, and a steady continuous pull is applied. It must be appreciated that the metal must possess not only ductility, but also a considerable amount of strength if it is to resist fracture, and that because of the relative slowness of the operation, work hardening will take place.

Summary

The forging of metal, like the casting of metal, is an important and essential part of the engineering industry. Both were carried out in biblical times, and both processes are mentioned in the Bible. We opened this chapter with an extract from the *Pirotechnia* of Vannoccio Biringuccio in which he extols the art of the ironsmith. All forging is essentially an extension of this ancient and time-honoured art, and represents the foundation stone on which the whole of our modern engineering structure has been built. It cannot be stated too often that the primary purpose of all engineers is to shape metals, and it is important that this be done in the most economical and efficient way, producing a component that will give reliable and trouble-free service.

We have seen that the stronger ferrous metals must be heated in order to increase their plasticity or ability to flow under the influence of heavy blow or sustained pressure. Several different types of machines are in use, operating either mechanically or hydraulically. In all cases the object is to coax the metal into the required shape, with much added strength gained due to the grain flow of the metal. We have seen, too, that some of the weaker non-ferrous metals can be extruded at high speed, whilst the stronger non-ferrous metals can be drawn, in the cold state, into wire.

It is evident that the properties of metals which enable them to be worked in this way are of great importance to the engineer, and these properties, together with the principles involved in their testing, will form the content of our next chapter.

QUESTIONS ON CHAPTER TWO

PART A

1. Make a neat sketch of an engineering component produced by a forging process, and explain why forging has been chosen as the method by which the component has been brought to shape.
2. What is the essential difference between hand forging and drop forging?
3. Make a neat sketch of an early type forging hammer. What are the limitations of the type chosen?
4. What is the difference between a forging press and a forging hammer?
5. What factors must be considered before deciding to produce an engineering component using the drop forging technique?
6. Describe, with the aid of neat diagrams, how the excess metal is accommodated during the drop forging of an open-ended spanner.
7. Explain what is meant by upset forging. Sketch an engineering component that would be produced by this process.
8. Draw a typical section of an aluminium alloy that would be hot extruded. Make a neat sketch also of the extruding die.
9. With a neat diagram, explain the principle of impact extrusion. What sort of components are suitable for this cold forging process?
10. Give **two** important physical properties that a metal must possess if it is to be cold drawn into wire.

PART B

1. (*a*) Drop-forging is a manufacturing process often used to produce components which are subject to severe stresses. Describe briefly the technique of drop-forging.

(*b*) State two reasons why certain components cannot be produced by the drop-forging process.

W. J. E. C. (1963)

3 The Testing of Metals

It is not enough that an engineering component be produced to the required shape, within the limits laid down in the drawing, and possessing the necessary surface finish. All these factors, difficult as they are to achieve in practice, will come to nothing if the component is unable to stand up to the sort of conditions it is likely to meet when put into service.

Perhaps the first consideration with regard to any engineering component is the metal from which it is to be made. Not only must the chosen metal possess the properties that will make it reliable when put to use, but also, as we have seen in the preceding chapter, it must possess properties that will allow the most economical manufacturing process to be used. Casting, forging, and cold working all require the metal to have suitable physical properties, if these processes are to result in rapid and efficient production of the component.

Before we test for anything it is vital that we know what we are testing for, and we will now outline the main physical properties of metals which are of concern to us as engineers.

Ultimate Tensile Strength

A great number of engineering components are subjected to tensile loads. Fig. 38 illustrates the process of ingot pouring at a steelworks. The ladle, containing 80 000 kg of liquid steel at a temperature of 1600° C, is supported by a chain, and this chain takes the total weight of the ladle of molten steel. The lives of the men whose work it is to fill the ingot moulds depend on the tensile strength, not only of the chain, but also of the lifting hook. This is only one instance when the lives of men depend on the ability of metal to stand up to heavy loads, for there are many occupations in which the worker depends on the strength of metal to ensure his safety.

We may define the tensile strength of a material as its ability to withstand tensile loads, and the more able a metal is to withstand tensile loading, the higher will be its tensile strength. It is important for engineers to know exactly how much a metal can be loaded in tension before it fractures, and we will refer to fig. 38 in order to show the principle involved. Let us assume that the forged lifting hook has a cross-sectional area of 5000 mm², and that this section represents the weakest part of the hook. This is shown on the diagram as diameter D, and will be equivalent to just under 80 mm dia. This means that a load of 80 000 kg, equivalent to a force of 80 000 × 9·81 newtons, acts on an area of 5000 mm², resulting in a tensile stress of 157 N/mm².

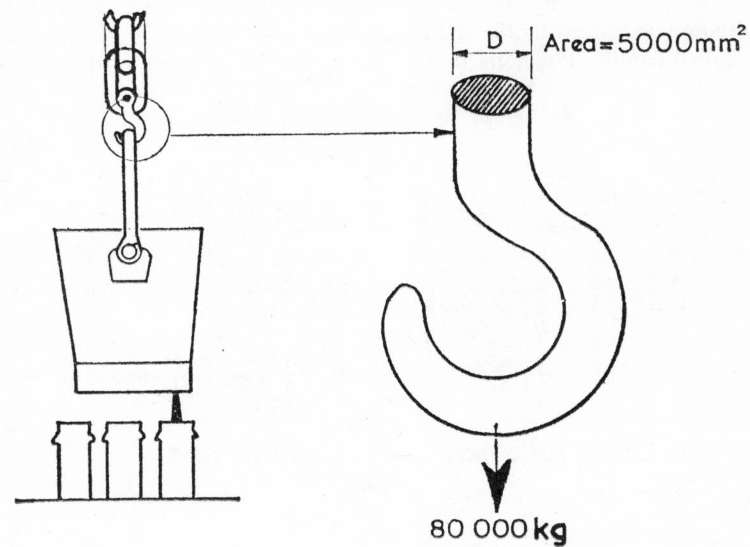

FIG. 38.—CHAIN AND LIFTING HOOK IN TENSION.

Now the ultimate tensile strength of any metal is the force that will pull apart a bar of metal having a cross-sectional area of 1 mm²; this force expressed in newtons, and the generally accepted value for wrought iron is given as 300 N/mm². If the lifting hook shown in fig. 38 is forged from wrought iron, then it will stand a load about twice as great as the one we are placing on it. We may say, in other words, that it has a **safety factor** of 2, and it is extremely doubtful whether such a low safety factor would be permitted, when one considers the consequences that would result from the sudden breakage of this lifting hook at the commencement of an ingot-filling operation.

We have seen in Volume I that threaded fasteners, such as nuts and bolts, set screws and studs, are widely used to join metal parts together. All these devices are subjected to tensile loads during the tightening process, and depending on the pitch of the thread, together with the spanner length and force used, the stretching load can reach a very high figure. Fig. 39 shows a typical set-up involving the use of a nut and bolt.

Note that part A and part B are held tightly together because the metal of the bolt **resists** the stretching load; this brings us to a most important physical property of metals.

Elasticity of Metals

The parts A and B are held tightly together because the bolt, although stretched by the tightening load, is attempting to return to its original length. The condition is identical in all respects to the device

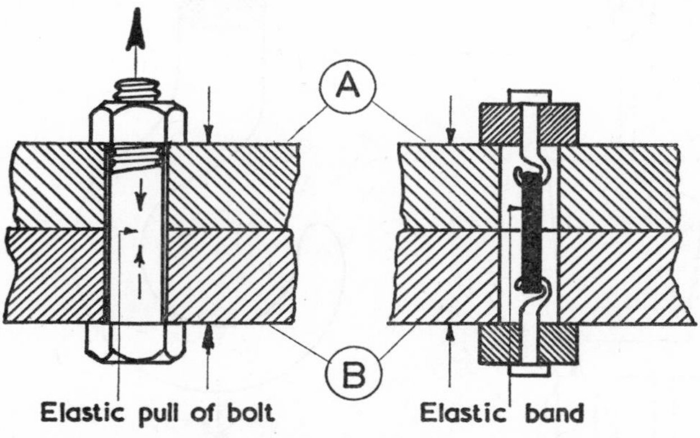

FIG. 39.—COMPONENTS HELD TOGETHER WITH THE ELASTIC PULL OF STEEL.

also shown in fig. 39, where two parts are held together by an elastic band in tension. We see now the importance of elasticity in an engineering metal, and we may define the elasticity of a metal as its ability to return to its original shape after deformation under the influence of an externally applied load. The flexing of a good quality engineers' steel rule will provide ample testimony to the elastic properties of high-quality steel. All engineering assemblies possess a degree of elasticity. Steel bridges, bicycle wheels, the wings of a jet air liner, all possess the ability to flex or bend when they are subjected to loads, yet return to their normal shapes on removal of the load.

Ductility of Metals

Metals that can be easily bent, twisted, or stretched in the cold state are said to be **ductile.** This is an important property, for it allows the rapid and economical manufacture of a great number of components. We have seen in Chapter 2 that wire is produced by drawing or pulling through a hardened and polished die, a reduction in diameter taking place. Since this process is carried out whilst the metal is in a cold state, a metal must possess a good degree of ductility if it is to be drawn into wire.

The body of a motor car is made up of several sections that have been formed from mild steel sheets using large press tools, and once again it is the ductility of mild steel that allows the shaping, say of a car roof, to be achieved in a matter of seconds. It is a great advantage if engineers can shape or form components from strip or sheet, for this allows the

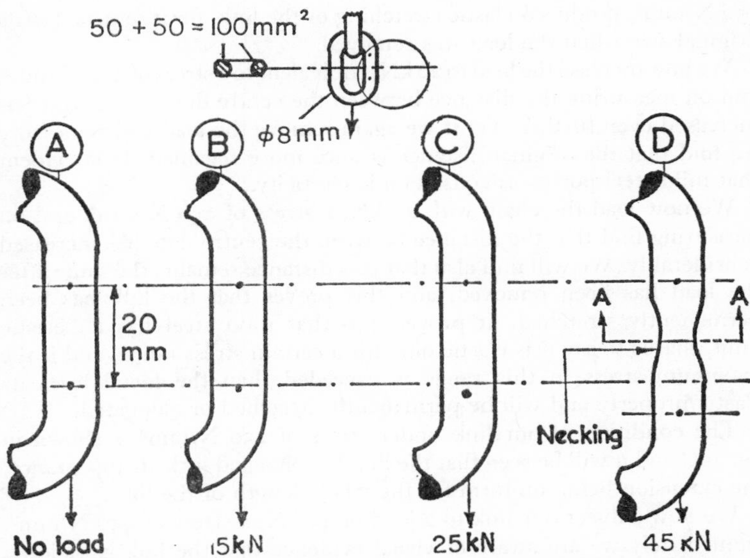

FIG. 40.—BEHAVIOUR OF A CHAIN LINK UNDER INCREASING TENSILE LOADS.

use of press tools, and the sheet or strip metal can be purchased from the steelworks which specialise in this type of product.

We may, then, define the ductility of a metal as its ability to undergo deformation in the cold state without fracture.

Effect of Increasing Tensile Loads

Fig. 40 gives a close-up of a chain link. Let us assume that the link is mild steel and has been forged and welded using 8 mm diameter bar. The cross-sectional area of the bar is about 50 mm² so the effective area supporting a load will be about 100 mm². We have also made two small centre dots 20 mm apart and these are shown in fig. 40A. The saying that the strength of a chain is in the weakest link is perfectly true, so we will assume that this particular link illustrated in fig. 40 is the weakest link in the chain which we are about to load.

Fig. 40B shows the behaviour of this link when the chain is taking a load of 15 kN by supporting a mass of about 1500 kg. We see at once that the distance between the centre dots has increased slightly, proving that the link has stretched. If we now remove the load and remeasure the distance between the centre dots, we will find that they have returned to their original position. Thus the extension caused by the 15 kN load acting on an area of 100 mm², a stress of 15 000/100 = 150 N/mm², produced elastic stretching of the link, for it returned to its original size when the load was removed.

We now increase the load to 20 kN, equivalent to a stress of 200 N/mm², and on measuring the distance between the centre dots find that it has increased even further. Yet if we again remove the load and remeasure we find that the original distance is once more regained. It is evident that mild steel possesses considerable elasticity.

We now load the chain with 25 kN, a stress of 250 N/mm², and on measuring find that the distance between the centre dots has increased considerably. We will find also that this distance remains the same after the load has been removed, and this proves that the link has been permanently stretched. It proves also that mild steel has an elastic limit, that is to say it is elastic only for a certain stress range, and if the maximum stress in this range is exceeded then the metal loses its elastic property and will be permanently stretched or elongated.

The condition of our link under stress of 250 N/mm² is shown in fig. 40C and it will be seen that the link has changed little in appearance, the extension being uniform for the whole length of the link.

We now subject our link to a load of 45 kN, a stress of 450 N/mm². Immediately we are aware of visual evidence that the link is yielding under the influence of the 450 N/mm² stress, for there is, as shown in fig. 40D, a distinct reduction in diameter. This is known as necking, and is a certain indication that the breaking point is close at hand. It is certain also that a link in this condition would be most dangerous; because of the reduced diameter shown at AA, the stress is increased and the link is likely to give way under a lower load than that which produced the necking condition.

Periodical inspection of all chains is carried out at regular intervals, and no chain must be loaded beyond its elastic limit. Even so, every time a chain is used to lift a load it suffers elastic stretch, and thus continual lifting will work-harden the links, and it may be necessary to carry out an annealing operation.

Tensile Testing

It is evident that engineers must know the actual figures at which a metal loses its elasticity. We need to know also the precise load required to fracture a metal, and the amount of permanent deformation before final fracture or failure takes place. Tensile testing machines are used for this purpose, and it is important that the student appreciates that the purpose of a tensile testing machine is to determine, under laboratory conditions, the exact behaviour of metal under the application of increasing stresses.

The three most important figures obtainable from a tensile test on mild steel are:

(i) the elastic limit,
(ii) the percentage elongation,
(iii) the ultimate tensile strength.

The conduct of this test is very similar to the observations we carried out on our mild steel chain link, except that actual values will be required. Let us assume that we are to carry out a tensile test on mild steel.

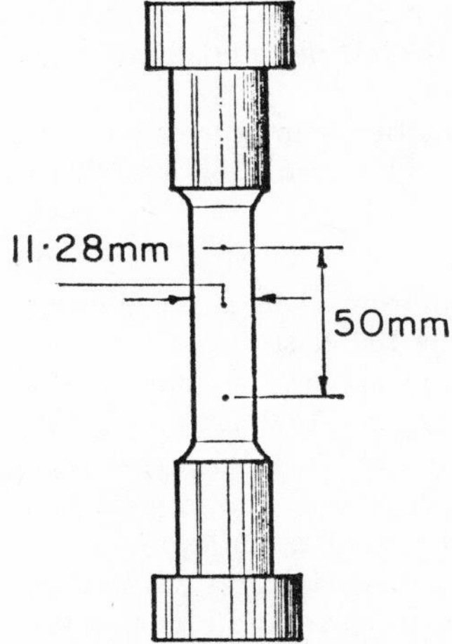

FIG. 41.—TEST PIECE USED FOR TENSILE TESTING.

The Test Piece

This is our first requirement, and a typical test piece is shown in fig. 41. Great care will be required in the machining of this test piece, in regard to both dimensional accuracy and quality of finish. Note the two small centre dots at a distance of 50 mm apart. Note also that the test piece has a centre portion of reduced diameter. This diameter must be 11·28 mm, with a corresponding area of 100 mm^2.

There are several types of testing machines in use, but in all cases the test piece is carefully aligned in the machine, and an axial load is applied. In effect the test piece is to be slowly pulled apart, with careful measurement of the increase of the centre dot distance, together with careful observation of the load causing this extension.

Plotting the Load-Extension Graph

The best way of showing how change in load affects the extension of the test piece is to plot a graph of extension against load. In this way a clear picture will emerge, having much greater value than a tabulated set of results. A measuring device will be fitted to the machine to allow accurate readings of the extension of the distance between the centre dots. At the same time it will be necessary to read off the loads producing the measured extension, and provision will exist for this by means of a calibrated dial, or the relative position of a weight in relation to a fixed scale. A series of increasing loads is applied to the test piece, and the corresponding deflection produced by each load measured and recorded. This continues until the test piece finally fractures, usually with an impressive noise or crack.

A typical graph resulting from a tensile test is shown in fig. 42, and we will now consider the information available from this graph.

The Elastic Limit

It will be seen that from O to A the plotted line is straight. This straight line represents the elastic range of the steel under test; provided the load does not exceed the value shown as W_1, the steel will return to its original length. For a test piece of 11·28 mm diameter, this load will be about 25 kN, and this means that a mild steel bar of 100 mm^2 cross-sectional area will possess the property of elasticity provided the tensile stress does not exceed 245 N/mm^2.

The steel will, of course, be in a stressed condition, and we can consider this stress as an equal and opposite reaction to the load producing this stress. It is this state of stress which provides the necessary tightening force required in a mild steel bolt if parts are to be held firmly together. We may now define the elastic limit of mild steel as the greatest stress at which the property of elasticity is retained. For mild steel the elastic limit is indicated at point A on the graph, and will be equivalent to 247 N/mm^2.

The Percentage Elongation

If we refer back to the graph, it will be noted that from A to B considerable extension takes place for little or no load. The steel is no

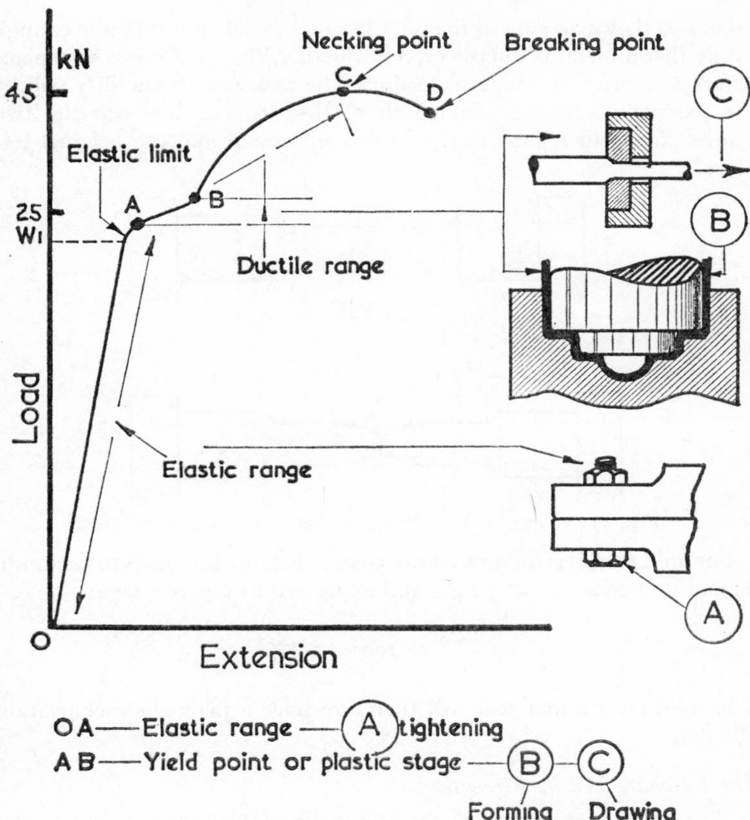

FIG. 42.—LOAD-EXTENSION GRAPH, AND ITS PRACTICAL VALUE IN ENGINEERING MANUFACTURE.

longer able to regain its original length. The elastic limit has been exceeded and the metal now suffers permanent stretching, or, in other words, **ductile extension** takes place. The metal now yields under the influence of the increased load; this stage in the behaviour of the metal is referred to as its **yield point**, and is shown on the graph as point B. Further loading causes increased extension, until at C the specimen begins to neck, and at this point we have reached maximum load. This necking results not only in further extension, but also in reduction of diameter, and the final fracture will take place at a reduced load.

It is necessary that engineers must be able to have a measure of ductility; the illustrations alongside the graph indicate two manufacturing processes that make use of the ductility of a metal, and it is not enough to say that a metal is ductile or very ductile. Fig. 43 shows a test piece before and after breakage in testing. The measure of ductility will be the percentage increase in length of the distance between the two centre dots with regard to the broken specimen and the original test piece.

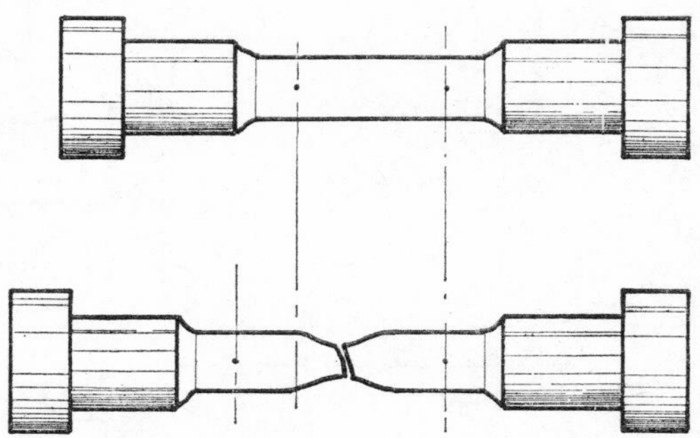

FIG. 43.—TENSILE TEST PIECE BEFORE AND AFTER TESTING.

For mild steel it is found that the 50 mm distance increases to 62·5 mm. Thus the increase is 12·5 mm, and expressed as a percentage:

$$\frac{12\cdot5}{50} \times 100 = 25\%$$

The mild steel under test will therefore have a percentage elongation of 25%.

The Ultimate Tensile Strength

This will be equivalent to the maximum stress induced in the steel at the highest point of the graph. We see from the graph that the load will be 45 kN; thus the ultimate tensile strength for mild steel will be 45 000/100 = 450 N/mm².

The Value of the Tensile Test

Perhaps the student will now appreciate the value of the tensile test. By taking samples of metal, and subjecting them to the tensile test described above, engineers are able to determine:

(i) the elastic limit of the metal,
(ii) the percentage elongation,
(iii) the ultimate tensile strength.

All these properties are of great importance with regard to the ability of the metal not only to stand up to the stresses imposed on it in service, but also to be brought to the required shape in the most economical way.

The Hardness of a Metal

The hardness of a metal may be defined as its ability to withstand abrasion or indentation. This is an essential property required by all cutting tools. We have seen in Volume I that the removal of metal is achieved by a shearing action, and this is true whether the tool is used at the bench or in a machine tool. Whilst the metal being removed deforms or shears under the application of the cutting force, the tool remains unaffected. It is, in effect, harder than the metal or material being cut; thus a wooden knife is able to shear or cut paper, whilst a stiff piece of paper will remove a small portion of butter. We see now that hardness is relative; there are soft woods and hard woods, soft pencils and hard pencils, soft or ductile metals and hard metals.

Testing for Hardness

There are several simple tests which may be carried out in the workshop to determine the relative hardness of metals. Let us use a new file on brass, copper, lead, mild steel, and silver steel or gauge plate. Setting each in the vice, we make about 20 filing strokes, care being taken to use uniform pressure and length of stroke upon each of the metals in turn.

If the metal test pieces are of the same thickness, say 3 mm, we will find on measuring the height of the test piece after filing that the order of maximum metal removal is as follows:

(i) lead,
(ii) copper,
(iii) brass,
(iv) mild steel,
(v) silver steel.

Note that we attempted to keep the energy requirements, or filing effort, constant for each test piece; thus the amount of metal removed in each case will depend on the hardness of each metal, or its ability to resist the abrasive action of the file. It is possible to measure each filed piece in turn and arrange the metals in order of relative hardness.

Fig. 44 illustrates the technique and likely results. This, perhaps, is not a very accurate test, for soft metals are likely to cause **pinning** of the file, that is to say small particles will fill the spaces between the file teeth and thus reduce the cutting efficiency of the file. We can, however, overcome this defect by using a file especially designed for soft metals, for example a rasp, or dreadnought.

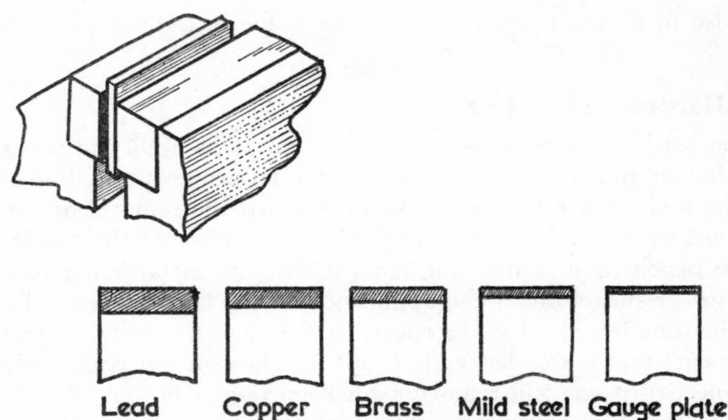

FIG. 44.—PRACTICAL HARDNESS TESTING OR RESISTANCE TO ABRASION.

Hardness Testing by Indentation

For this simple demonstration we will require the same test pieces used for the file test, and also a ball-bearing of about 6 mm diameter. Commencing with the two hardest metals, silver steel and mild steel; these are placed between two smooth vice-jaws, with the ball-bearing inserted between the two metals. The vice is now tightened so that the

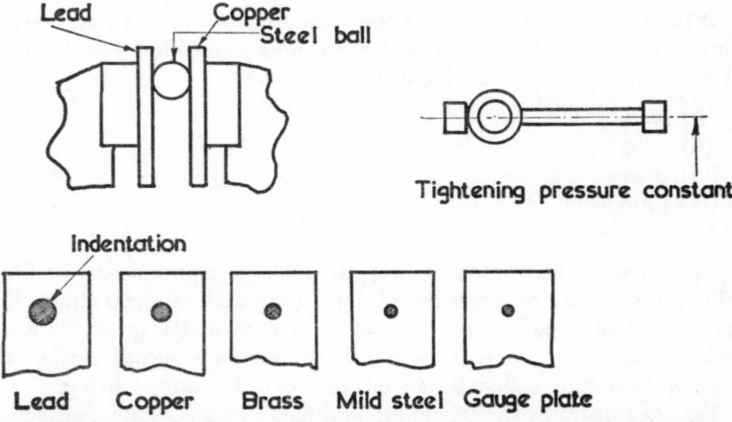

FIG. 45.—PRACTICAL HARDNESS TESTING OR RESISTANCE TO INDENTATION.

tommy-bar reaches a vertical or horizontal position. The test pieces are now removed, and it will be found that each will have a small indentation. As we have already stated that the hardness of a metal is its ability to resist indentation, the hardest metal will have the smallest indentation. The process is now repeated for mild steel and brass, brass and copper, then copper and lead.

This testing technique is illustrated in fig. 45, and once again likely results are shown. Note that in bringing the tommy-bar to the same position when tightening, we have attempted to keep the tightening pressure or load constant. It is possible to measure the diameters of the impressions produced by the ball-bearing and arrive at some relative hardness figures. For example, if the diameter on the copper test piece is twice the diameter on the mild steel test piece, then we are justified in assuming that mild steel is twice as hard as copper.

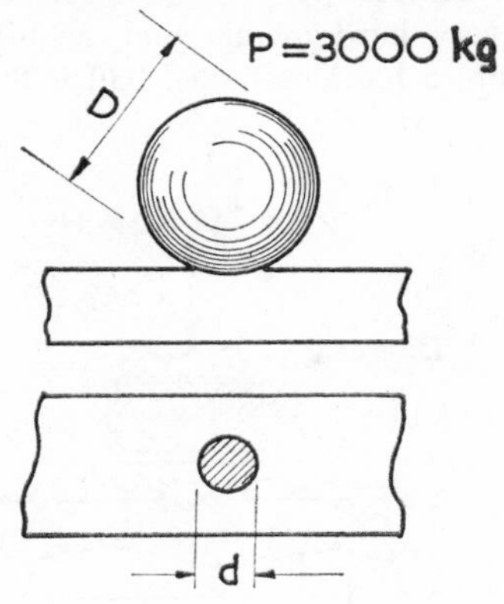

D = Dia of ball
d = Dia of impression
P = Applied load

$$\text{Brinell Number} = \frac{\text{Load}}{\text{Area}}$$

$$\text{Brinell N}^{\circ} = \frac{P}{1{\cdot}571\,D\left(D - \sqrt{D^2 - d^2}\right)}$$

FIG. 46.—PRINCIPLE OF THE BRINELL HARDNESS TEST.

The Brinell Hardness Test

This principle of determining the hardness of a metal by measuring the indentation produced under a constant load is widely used in engineering, and was devised by a Swedish engineer, Dr. August Johan Brinell. The principle is shown in fig. 46, and consists in pressing a hardened steel ball of 10 mm diameter into the metal under test, using a "load" of 3000 kg. The diameter of the impression is measured by a graduated microscope and the hardness number calculated from the following formula:

$$\text{Brinell Hardness Number} = \frac{\text{Load}}{\text{Spherical Area of Indentation}}.$$

The mathematical expression of the above formula is given in fig. 46, although this is seldom worked out in actual practice. Tables are supplied giving the appropriate hardness number in terms of the diameter of the spherical indentation.

When testing very hard metals such as high carbon steel in the hardened condition, a hardened steel ball will deform and inaccurate results will be obtained.

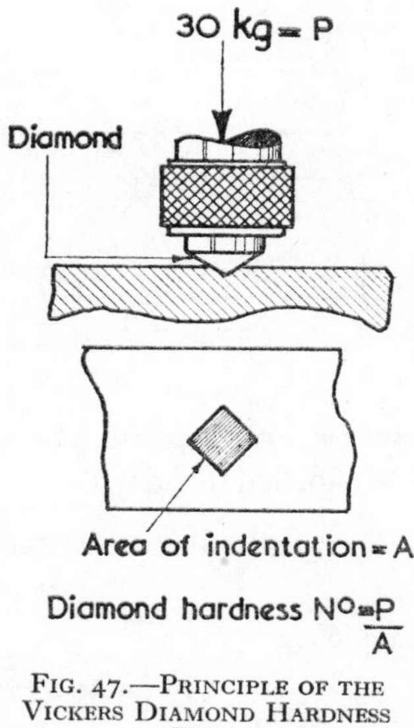

FIG. 47.—PRINCIPLE OF THE VICKERS DIAMOND HARDNESS TEST.

The Vickers Diamond Hardness Test

This test makes use of a diamond having the form of a pyramid. This diamond is capable of making an indentation in the hardest of steels, and is always used in the testing of the many types of cutting tools used in engineering manufacture. The technique is illustrated in fig. 47, and once again a constant load is applied to the specimen under test.

The diamond hardness number is given by the following formula:

$$\text{Diamond Hardness Number} = \frac{\text{Load}}{\text{Area of Indentation}}.$$

Once again a set of tables is provided giving the hardness number in terms of the distance across the diagonals, and a microscope is used to determine this distance to a close degree of accuracy.

The Rockwell Hardness Test

This differs in principle from the hardness tests previously described because the hardness of the metal under test is now determined by the depth of penetration of a radiused diamond indenter. A hardened steel ball may be used for softer metals, and the reading of the hardness is quickly obtained from a calibrated scale or dial. This dial has two scales; the B scale is used for the hardened steel ball, and the C scale is used for the diamond. The calibration is such that the harder the metal, the higher is the reading or Rockwell number. This type of machine permits rapid determination of hardness, and is much used on production work. The principle is illustrated in fig. 48.

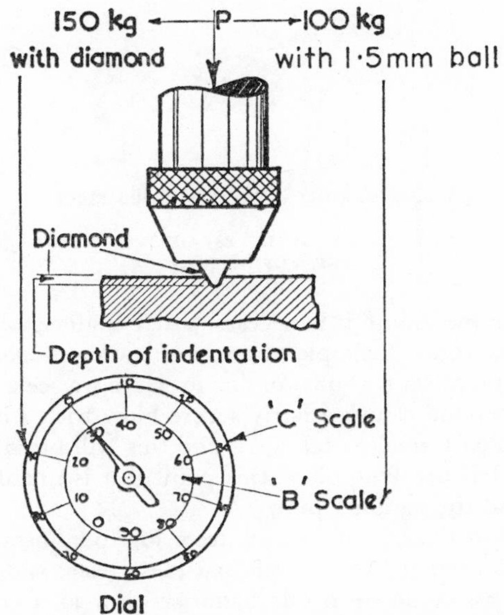

FIG. 48.—PRINCIPLE OF THE ROCKWELL HARDNESS TEST.

All the machines described will involve care and patience in their use if accurate results are to be obtained, and the student is strongly advised to read the excellent and informative instruction manuals supplied by the makers of these machines.

The Toughness of Metals

The toughness of a metal may be described as its ability to stand up to sudden blows or shocks without fracture. The head of a hammer or sledge is a good example of a component that must be able to stand

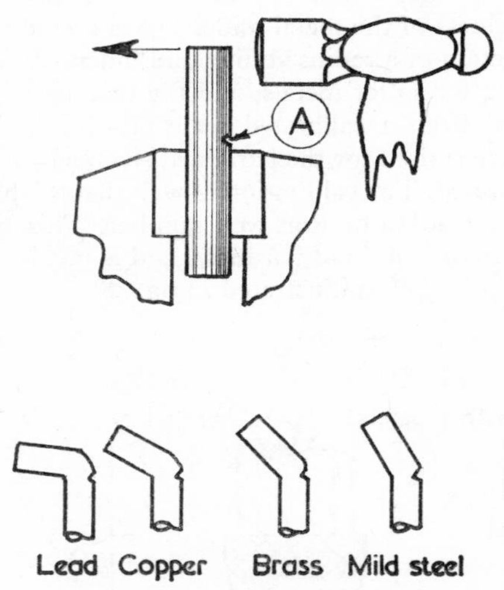

FIG. 49.—PRACTICAL TEST ON THE TOUGHNESS OF METALS.

up to such treatment, and it is necessary that engineers have a relative measure of toughness. A simple example of testing for toughness using a simple workshop test is shown in fig. 49. Here we see a mild steel bar placed in a vice, and struck a fairly severe blow with a hammer. Note that we have filed a small notch at A, and this will provide a source of weakness, the bar breaking off at this point if it is unable to stand up to the impact of the hammer blow.

It is possible to carry out simple tests for toughness on the same metals that we used for our simple hardness tests, shown in fig. 44, and provided we could keep our hammer blow at a constant value, the angle of bend would be an indication of the toughness of the metal under test. A very similar principle is used in the Izod Impact Test.

The Izod Impact Test

In this test the metal test piece is subjected to a violent blow imparted by a heavy pendulum. The principle is illustrated in fig. 50, and it will be seen that the pendulum falls freely under the influence of gravity when the stop is released. If the angle of the pendulum before release is ϕ, then the pendulum when released will swing so that at the end of its swing it will be at almost the same angle. If now a test piece is placed at A, in the path of the pendulum, energy will be required to bend or break the metal of the test piece, and this must result in a smaller angle

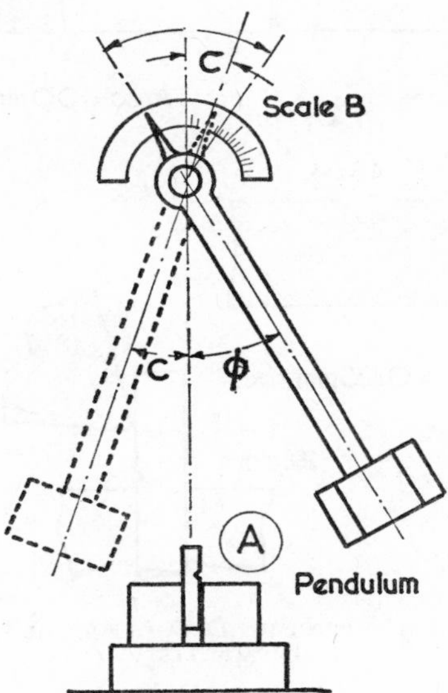

Fig. 50.—Principle of the Izod Impact Test.

of upward swing of the pendulum. Thus the energy lost by the pendulum will be the energy required to bend or break the test piece, and this amount can be read off on the scale B. A free-moving pointer will be used, and this pointer will be moved through the arc C as the pendulum rises and will remain in position when the pendulum swings back. The smaller the angle of arc moved through by this pointer, the tougher will be the material; the scale is calibrated in joules.

In this way, the relative toughness of a metal can be expressed in terms of joules. The specimen test piece will require careful and precise preparation, and a typical specimen is shown in fig. 51. Note that four tests can be performed on each specimen.

Brittleness

A brittle metal breaks easily when subjected to a sudden blow. This, of course, is the opposite to toughness, and therefore the Izod Impact Test will also provide a measure of brittleness. Engineers have little

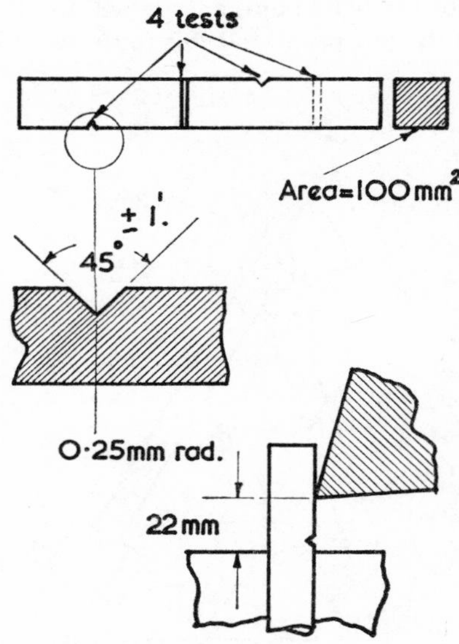

FIG. 51.—SPECIMEN DETAILS FOR THE IZOD IMPACT TEST.

use for brittle metals, but it must be appreciated that hardness is often accomplished only at the expense of brittleness, and this means that the cutting tools used in engineering manufacture must be handled with some care.

Mechanical Properties of the More Common Engineering Metals

The table on p. 57 gives some of the mechanical properties of the more common ferrous engineering metals.

Summary

The testing of metals is an important part of engineering. In this chapter we have attempted to show the basic principles involved when

Metal	*Elastic Limit* (N/mm^2)	*Percentage Elongation*	*Ultimate Tensile Strength* (N/mm^2)	*Brinell Hardness Number*	*Izod Value (joules)*
Wrought iron	154	30	300	100	92·92
Cast iron	—	—	170	200	—
Mild steel	247	25	460	130	40·68
Nickel-chrome steel	926	22	1235	400	81·36

testing for tensile strength, elasticity, ductility, hardness, and toughness. There are many other tests carried out on metals, both destructive and non-destructive. A destructive test means that the specimen or test piece is destroyed in the process of testing, as in the tensile testing machine. The preparation of test pieces that are to be used for mechanical testing demands a high degree of skill and knowledge, and the accuracy of the test will depend in a large degree upon the dimensional accuracy and finish of the test piece. This is important and vital work, and is exactly the sort of work a technician may be called upon to perform. The testing machines are expensive, requiring skilled manipulation, and there is the probability that some calculations will have to be made, together with the tabulation of results, and a concise report on the findings of the test. A technician who is familiar, not only with the principles of the testing process, but also with the need and use of the test in connection with the manufacture of engineering components, will find greater interest in his work, and may rightfully consider himself as an important and essential contributor to engineering skill and progress.

QUESTIONS ON CHAPTER THREE

1. Explain what is meant by the "elastic limit" of a metal. Why is elasticity essential if a threaded fastening device is to be used to hold two parts tightly together?
2. What is the essential difference between elasticity and ductility?
3. Describe briefly the behaviour of a mild steel test piece given a destructive test in a tensile testing machine.
4. Describe the principles by which engineers arrive at a measure of ductility.
5. Make a neat sketch to illustrate a manufacturing process that relies on the ductility of the metal to be processed.
6. Why is it essential that test pieces conform to the specifications laid down?
7. Make a neat sketch of an engineering component that would be tested for hardness before being put into service, describing briefly the principle underlying the process of hardness testing.
8. Why is it necessary to use a diamond when hardness testing a milling cutter?
9. Define the term "toughness". Describe briefly the principle adopted when testing the toughness of a metal.
10. Make neat sketches of typical specimens for:

    (i) tensile testing,
    (ii) impact testing.

4 Heat Treatments

THE object of all heat treatment processes is to improve the properties of the metal undergoing the heat treatment, thus making it more suitable for either the manufacturing process, or the conditions that the finished component must stand up to. It is important to appreciate that the physical or mechanical properties of a metal are directly related to the structure of the metal. If we change the structure, then it is certain that a change in the properties of the metal will also take place, and this simple principle is the basis of all heat treatment processes.

A simplified line diagram, fig. 31, Volume I, indicated some practical workshop heat treatment processes, together with the temperatures at which these processes are carried out. Reference back to this diagram will show that the only difference between hardening, normalising, and annealing is in the rate of cooling of the heated metal. It is evident, then, that the cooling rate has an important effect on the structure of a heated metal.

Importance of the Cooling Rate

We are all familiar with the decorative effect produced by frost on a window on a cold winter's morning. Perhaps we are not so familiar with the simple fact that the behaviour of water when changing from liquid to solid or ice is similar in many respects to the behaviour of a metal when changing from liquid to solid. The difference is one of temperature only.

Let us take a closer look at two frosted windows, shown in fig. 52 as A and B. Each window possesses a different frost pattern. At A we see a pattern of large ice crystals, whilst at B the pattern is made up from a large number of small crystals. These are familiar sights, and the student, if he is to become an efficient and capable engineer, must develop an enquiring mind. Interest is the spark that sets afire the flames of learning, for without interest there is no education. What are the conditions that have brought about the variation of crystal size?

If we remember that all metals possess a crystal structure, and that the properties of the metal are related to the structure, then we may learn a great deal from our frosted windows.

Window A

The large ice crystals have been brought about by a **slow fall** in temperature to below freezing point. This results in large crystals, for they have ample time in which to develop, and the process of crystal formation is shown in fig. 52.

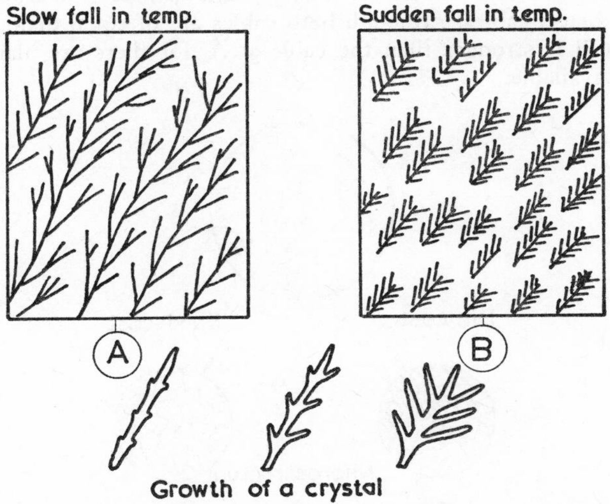

FIG. 52.—EFFECT OF COOLING RATE ON THE SIZE OF ICE CRYSTALS.

Window B

The large number of small crystals have been brought about by a **sudden fall** in temperature. If the temperature falls quickly to below freezing point then the water must change into ice, and this can only be achieved by the rapid formation of a large number of small crystals.

Thus the difference in crystal size has been brought about, not by a difference in temperature, but by a difference in the rate of cooling or freezing.

Metals behave in exactly the same way. If liquid metal is poured into a mould and allowed to cool slowly, a large crystal or grain size will result, whilst rapid cooling of a liquid metal will produce a small or fine grain structure.

Grain Size and Strength

Let us consider the component produced in the pressure die casting process illustrated in fig. 4 (Chapter 1). The dies are made of steel; the high thermal conductivity of steel will result in rapid solidification or freezing of the aluminium alloy, and the casting will have a small crystal or fine grain structure. If this casting were produced using the alternative process of sand casting, the low thermal conductivity of sand would result in slow cooling of the molten aluminium alloy, and the solidified casting would have a large crystal or coarse grain structure. Both these structures are shown in fig. 53, and a comparison is made with stranded steel cables. Although both cables are of equal diameter, the cable at B is stronger than the cable at A, for there are many more strands available.

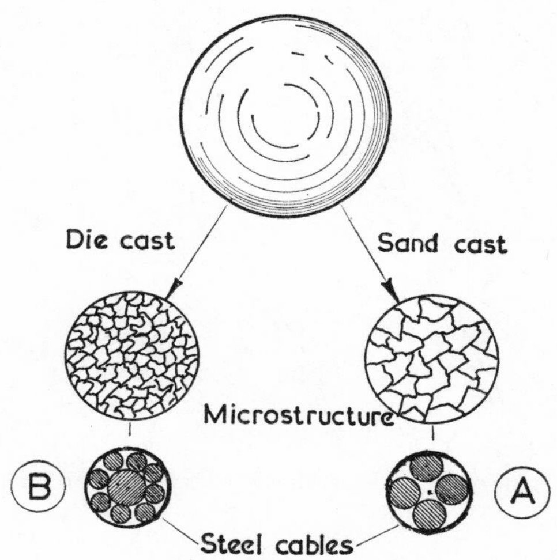

FIG. 53.—CRYSTAL STRUCTURES OF SAND AND DIE CAST COMPONENTS.

Thus the pressure die casting process will produce not only well-finished accurate castings at high production speeds, but also stronger castings than those produced by the much slower sand casting process. In this way considerable economy of metal can be achieved; an important factor when very large numbers of castings are to be produced.

Chill Cast Phosphor Bronze

This is another good example of how engineers improve the mechanical properties of a metal in order to produce a more reliable component, and at the same time achieve both economy of material and a reduction of the manufacturing cost. Fig. 54 illustrates the principle involved. The phosphor bronze bush is shown at A, whilst at B and C we see the alternative methods of manufacture.

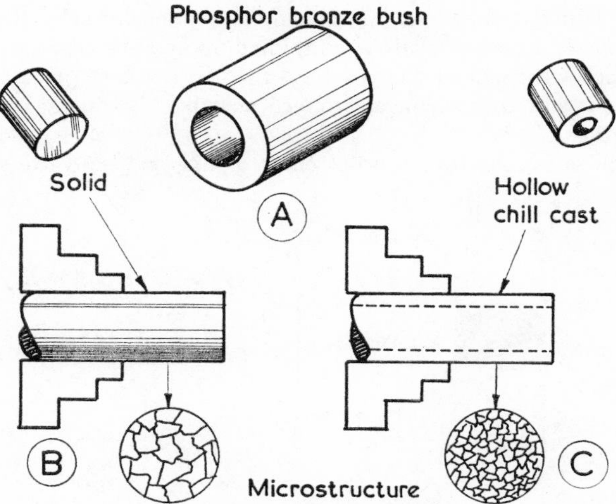

FIG. 54.—ADVANTAGES OF BEARING BUSHES MADE FROM CHILL CAST PHOSPHOR BRONZE.

At B the bush is to be made from sand cast solid bar, and this will involve a considerable amount of machining, with much metal removed in the process.

At C the bush is machined from chill cast hollow bar. Not only are we able to produce the bush with much less machining, but also the cost of the metal will be less, for all metal is bought by weight, and the chill cast bar will weigh a great deal less than a solid bar of equivalent length. Because the chill cast bar possesses a finer grain structure it will be stronger than the solid sand cast bar, and thus the bush shown at C will give longer and more reliable service.

The examples given above illustrate the advantages to be gained in the primary process of casting. The object is to improve the mechanical properties of the metal so that the casting is better able to stand up to the sort of conditions it will meet when put into service. We have seen in Chapter 1 that most steel products begin life as a steel casting, poured into and then removed from an ingot mould. This steel ingot will have a relatively coarse structure, with the possibility of impurities at the crystal boundaries. It is important to appreciate that the process of hot rolling brings about considerable improvement in the mechanical properties of the rolled steel, by closing up the structure and reducing the grain size.

There are, however, several heat treatments that are carried out in engineering workshops. The essential practical techniques underlying hardening, tempering, normalising, and annealing were described in Volume I, together with a simplified temperature-process chart. No mention was made of the structural changes that take place, bringing about the required mechanical properties such as hardness, toughness, and ductility.

We will now construct another chart or diagram, and this time we

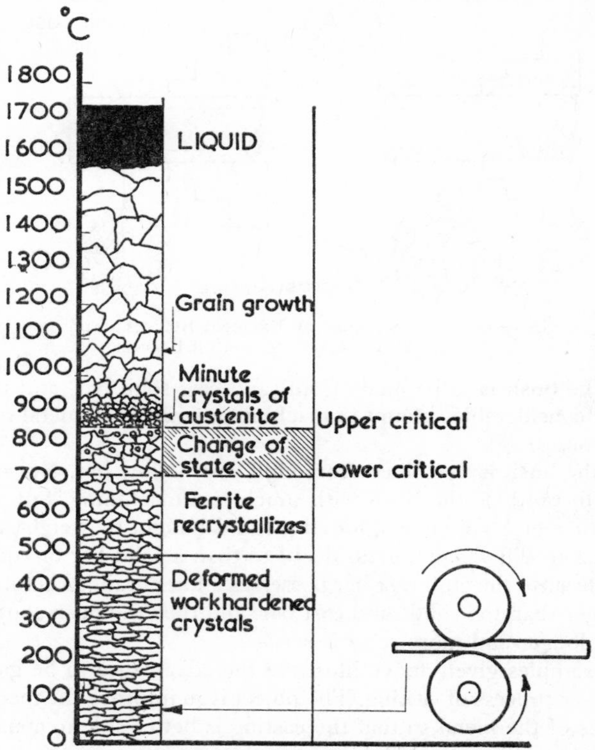

FIG. 55.—EFFECT OF HEAT ON THE CRYSTAL STRUCTURE OF BRIGHT MILD STEEL.

will be concerned with the structural changes that take place when a piece of bright mild steel is slowly heated to say 1200° C. Once again the temperature is plotted vertically, and the completed diagram is shown in fig. 55.

Effect of Heat on the Structure of Bright Mild Steel

Bright mild steel is produced by a cold rolling process, resulting in distortion or elongation of the grain structure and work-hardening of the steel. The ultimate tensile strength and hardness will increase whilst the percentage elongation will fall, the steel becoming less ductile.

The diagram shows that no structural change will take place on heating the steel until a temperature of 500° C is attained. At this point the ferrite will recrystallise, and a certain amount of **stress relief** will be gained.

Stress Relieving

Because mild steel contains over 90% ferrite, considerable stress relief is possible by heating the steel to just over 500° C. This relatively

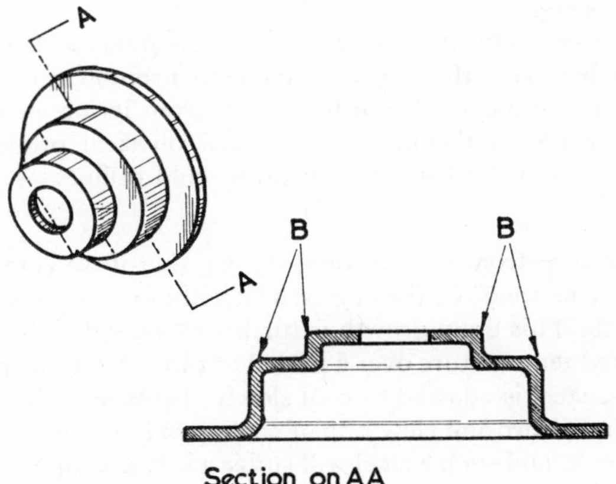

FIG. 56.—CLUTCH HOUSING REQUIRING STRESS RELIEVING.

low temperature not only allows the process to be carried out at low cost, but also prevents scaling of the component. Fig. 56 shows a clutch housing produced by press tools from bright mild steel strip. This operation, involving the use of a hardened steel forming punch and die, permits a very high rate of production, with no wastage of metal, but the steel will be further work-hardened in the forming process. This clutch housing will be subject to considerable stress in service, and there exists the danger that fracture may occur at the bends shown at B in fig. 56.

Stress relieving will remove this danger, and it is a relatively simple matter to pass the components through an electrically heated furnace, at 550° C, the whole operation being continuous and efficient, with no scaling of the component.

Normalising

Reference back to fig. 55 shows that at 720° C we reach a temperature known as the **lower critical temperature.** At this point a change of state begins to occur in the steel, and a new structure begins to form. This change of state will be completed at about 850° C, and this temperature is known as the **upper critical temperature.** This new structure consists of minute crystals, and at this point the steel is non-magnetic. It is a simple matter to carry out a practical test to prove this; heat a piece of mild steel to bright cherry red, place on a steel plate and hold a bar magnet over it. At this temperature the steel will not be attracted to the magnet, but as the steel cools to dull red it will attach itself to the magnet.

It is, however, with the minute or small crystal size that we are concerned. We have seen that a small crystal size promotes greater strength, and allowing the metal to cool in still air from its upper critical temperature restores to the metal its normal physical properties. Thus normalising removes all stresses set up by cold rolling.

Refining

It will be seen from the diagram, fig. 55, that if we continue to heat the steel, say to 1000° C, the crystal size will increase; this is known as grain growth. This grain growth is further increased if the steel is held at an elevated temperature over a period of time. A serious position now arises if this steel is allowed to cool slowly; because of the combination of high temperature and slow rate of cooling, a large coarse grain structure will result, and such a steel will suffer a severe drop in its impact or Izod value. This means that the steel is very likely to fracture without warning when struck a sudden blow; in other words it is now relatively brittle.

Perhaps a practical engineering example will help to illustrate the principle involved. Fig. 57 shows the spanner used as a forging example in Chapter 2. It is certain that these spanners will be drop forged in quantity, and it may well be that the finished spanner is thrown, on completion of the drop forging, on to a pile of previously forged spanners. Thus we have a large number of white-hot spanners cooling together. This represents a large mass of heated metal, and must result in very slow cooling of all the spanners. Slow cooling from an elevated temperature produces, as we have stated, a large coarse grain structure, with the result that these spanners may prove brittle when used.

If we now refer back to our heat treatment diagram, fig. 55, we see once again that at the upper critical temperature a fine minute grain structure emerges at the completion of the change of state as the steel passes through the critical range.

Provided the steel has not been permanently damaged by serious overheating or **burning**, the change of state indicated will always take place, and the ideal structure will return at the upper critical temperature of the steel.

If the spanners are reheated to the upper critical temperature, and allowed to cool in air, the normal structure will return, as will the normal Izod value. It is possible to quench the spanners in oil and thus increase the cooling rate, producing a finer grain structure and also a stronger spanner; this is the true refining process. Fig. 57 shows the difference

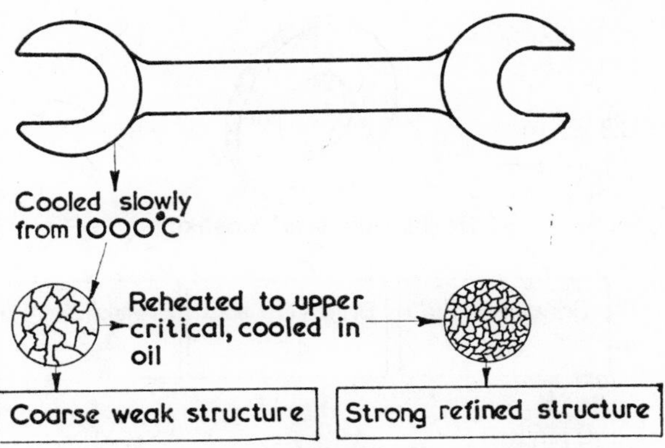

FIG. 57.—REFINING A FORGED SPANNER TO IMPROVE STRENGTH.

in grain structure between a slowly cooled forged spanner, and one that has been refined.

Annealing

The object of annealing is to render the steel as soft as possible, or to give it maximum ductility. The procedure is identical to normalising with regard to the temperature to which the steel must be taken. We see from the diagram, fig. 55, that the steel must be taken to the upper critical temperature and then allowed to cool as slowly as possible. This is best achieved by turning off the heat supplied to the furnace when the component to be annealed has been allowed to **soak**; this means that the whole mass of the component is at the required temperature. The component is allowed to remain in the furnace, cooling slowly as the furnace loses heat. The slow rate of cooling induces a fairly large grain structure, the metal also losing some of its tensile strength and hardness, but there will be a rise in the percentage elongation. The following practical demonstration will clearly illustrate the considerable increase in ductility achieved by annealing bright mild steel.

Obtain two bright mild steel washers, say with 12 mm diameter holes. Heat one to bright cherry red, or in a small furnace to 850° C, and allow to cool in the furnace. Alternatively the washer can be buried in lime in a small container. Polish the washer when it is cool enough to be handled, and carry out a hardness test on both the annealed washer and the untreated washer. There will be a marked difference in the hardness values. It is possible to obtain equivalent tensile strengths

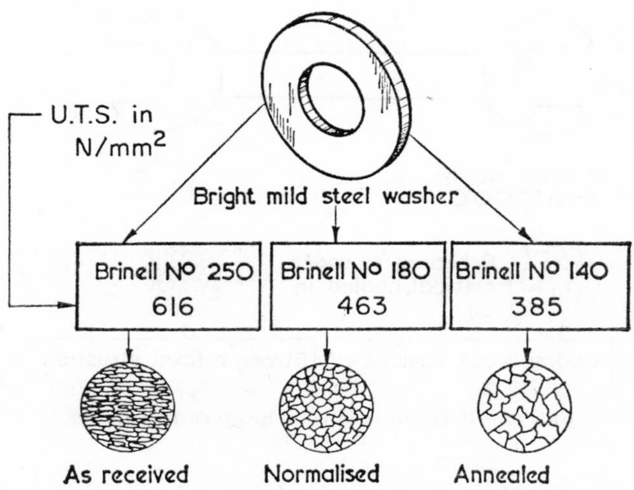

FIG. 58.—VARIATIONS IN THE PHYSICAL PROPERTIES OF A MILD STEEL WASHER FOLLOWING HEAT TREATMENT.

from tables, and it will be found that there is a marked difference in these also. The untreated washer may now be heated to 850° C and allowed to cool in still air. On testing for hardness the value will differ from the two previous results, as will the equivalent tensile strength. This demonstration is illustrated in diagrammatic form in fig. 58, and it will be seen that the variation in physical properties is due to the variation in grain structure.

Perhaps a more practical and more entertaining demonstration can be carried out using some 150 mm nails. Place about half a dozen of these nails in a suitable metal pipe and attempt to seal up the ends with clay or something similar. Place in the fire before going to bed, and in the morning remove the nails from the pipe. The purpose of this pipe is to prevent severe scaling of the nails. This is inevitable if the nails are placed singly in the fire, and as we wish to polish the annealed nails it is essential that the scaling be kept to a minimum. The nails can be polished using a drilling machine or lathe, the object being to make these annealed nails indistinguishable from untreated nails. Put a tiny centre-dot on the annealed nails, and the stage is now set for the entertainment side of this practical heat treatment demonstration. You may now display your powers of strength by bending a 150 mm nail with your bare hands in front of your friends. Now let someone try to repeat your feat, but take great care to give them an untreated nail. It is most unlikely that this cold-drawn and severely work-hardened nail will be bent out of straight for it will require an exceedingly strong grip to achieve even slight bending; yet it will be found a relatively simple matter to bend the annealed nail through 90°.

We see now the considerable changes in the physical properties of metals that can be brought about by changing the grain size, and in this way, suitable heat treatment processes play a great part in the manufacture of engineering components.

Perhaps the most important of all heat treatment processes is the hardening of suitable steels. A very great number of cutting tools are used in the manufacture of engineering components, and the essential physical property required by all cutting tools is hardness, together with a certain degree of toughness. It is true that the use of high carbon steel for the removal of metal is limited to those operations that involve little or no rise in temperature. If high-speed metal removal is required, as in turning or drilling, then high-speed steel will be used, and the following description of the theory of hardening applies only to **high carbon steel.**

The Hardening of High Carbon Steel

The hardening of high carbon steel can only be properly understood if reference is made to the iron-carbon equilibrium diagram. An equilibrium diagram shows the structural changes that take place when an alloy is allowed to cool slowly from the molten state. Carbon steel can be considered as an alloy of ferrite and carbon, and the amount of carbon present determines the type of carbon steel. The iron-carbon diagram is somewhat complicated; so we will first consider a much simpler diagram, namely the lead-tin diagram. These metals form the popular alloy known as soft solder, much used for the rapid and cheap joining of metal parts. The diagram is shown in fig. 59. We have plotted percentage lead and tin on the horizontal line AB, whilst the vertical lines AC and BD represent temperature in degrees Celsius.

The Lead-Tin Diagram

We are not concerned with the methods and techniques necessary to construct this diagram, but only with its value to us as practical engineers or practising technicians. The principles of soft soldering were dealt with in Volume I, but no mention was made of why plumbers' solder is always used for wiped joints, or tinman's solder for lapped joints. Careful study of the diagram shown in fig. 59 will not only serve to make clear the choice of the best solder for the particular type of joint required, but also assist us to understand the diagram used for carbon steels.

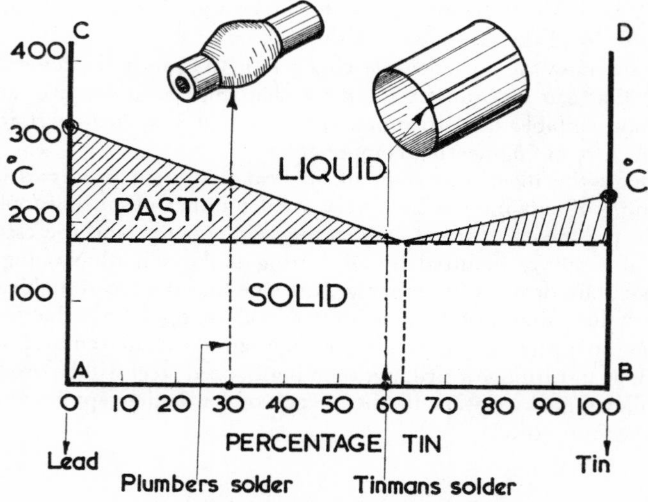

FIG. 59.—THE LEAD-TIN EQUILIBRIUM DIAGRAM.

The melting point of tin is 232° C, and this point is shown on the vertical line BD. The melting point of lead is 327° C, and this point is shown on the line AC. Note that the melting point of any solder is easily found by projecting a vertical line from the particular solder required; thus the melting point of plumbers' solder is 260° C and the melting point of tinman's solder 185° C. Below the horizontal dotted line equivalent to 183° C all the solders become solid, but the shaded portion represents a stage at which the solder is pasty or spongy. We see now that plumbers' solder has a considerable pasty stage, allowing the plumber to shape or wipe the spongy solder to produce the joint shown in the diagram. On the other hand, tinman's solder has a very small pasty stage, the solder rapidly solidifying. This is very suitable for the joining of metal parts, allowing high soldering speeds with no time wasted in waiting for the solder to freeze or solidify.

The diagram also shows clearly that the melting point of tinman's solder is below that of plumbers' solder, and less heat will be required. We must, however, remember that tinman's solder is expensive, and before a solder is chosen for a particular job, we can be sure that the diagram will be studied with care, for as we have seen there is much useful information to be gained from it.

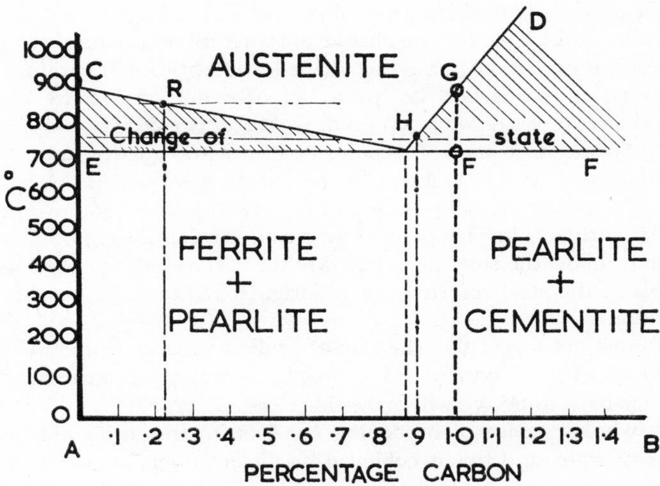

FIG. 60.—PART OF THE IRON-CARBON EQUILIBRIUM DIAGRAM.

The Iron-Carbon Equilibrium Diagram

This diagram provides the essential information required for the correct heat treatment of all carbon steels. It is used in the same manner as the lead-tin diagram, except that the steel remains in the solid state whilst the structural changes take place. Fig. 60 shows part of the iron-carbon diagram, and it is essential that this diagram be used in conjunction with fig. 55. The horizontal line AB represents percentage carbon and the vertical line AC temperature in degrees Celsius. Reference back to fig. 55 shows that a change of state begins at just over 700° C, and this is shown in fig. 60 as the line EF. This is the **lower critical temperature**; at this point the carbon begins to dissolve into the ferrite. Note that the lower critical temperature is the same for **all** carbon steels.

The line CD is the **upper critical temperature**; at this point the change of state is complete, and a new non-magnetic structure exists. This structure is known as **austenite**, named after the famous metallurgist, Sir William C. Roberts-Austen. Note that the upper critical temperature varies for different carbon steels, and we may compare this diagram to the lead-tin diagram which also indicates the different melting points of varying compositions of lead and tin.

Practical Use of the Iron-Carbon Diagram

Let us consider the hardening of a piece of silver steel with a carbon content of 1%. The structure of this steel will consist of pearlite and cementite, and we see that no change of structure occurs until the point F is reached on the diagram. This is the lower critical temperature, and at this point the carbon begins to dissolve into the ferrite. As the temperature increases we reach point G, the upper critical temperature for 1% carbon steel, and at this point we have a new austenitic structure. This change of state has taken place whilst the steel passed through the range of temperature between F and G, and this range is known as the **critical range.** The change of state requires a certain period of time; if we now allow the steel to cool slowly the reverse change of state will take place, the steel returning to its original structure of pearlite and cementite.

We must not forget that the rate of cooling will determine the grain size, producing a normalised, refined, or annealed structure, and reference back to fig. 55 will make this clear.

The whole essence of hardening consists in preventing the return change of state, and this is achieved by violent quenching of the steel from its upper critical temperature. In this way no time has been allowed for the reverse change of state to take place, and the original structure cannot be regained. This means that a new structure must result, and this structure is known as **martensite**, named after another famous metallurgist, Adolph Martens. Martensite is a highly stressed, hard and brittle structure, having a Brinell hardness number of about 700, or 68 on the Rockwell Scale C. Steel in this condition is seldom used in the workshops because of its extreme brittleness, and is usually subjected to a tempering process which increases the toughness of the steel at the expense of some loss of hardness. A description of practical tempering was given in Volume I, in the chapter on Heat Treatment, the tempering range being shown there in fig. 31.

Although we have stated that the essential conditions for the hardening of carbon steel consist in heating the steel to its upper critical temperature, and then quenching violently using cold clean water, in actual practice carbon steels in excess of 0·8% carbon are heated to just above their lower critical temperature; the object of this is to avoid the large grain size obtained if the steel were heated to its upper critical temperature.

We see now the value of the iron-carbon diagram, and provided it is used in conjunction with fig. 55, it is possible to determine with accuracy the correct temperatures for the efficient heat treatment of carbon steels.

Carburising

Carburising consists in giving low carbon steels an outer case of high carbon; therefore a carburised component will possess a tough core together with a hard case. Several methods of carbon addition are in use, and they may be summarised as follows:

(i) surrounding with a carbonaceous material,
(ii) immersing in a carbon salt,
(iii) exposing to a carbon atmosphere.

In all cases the component will be at its upper critical temperature, and the depth of carbon penetration will depend mainly on the time the component is subjected to the carburising process.

The choice of the carburising method will depend on several factors, namely:

(i) depth of case,
(ii) size of component,
(iii) rate of production.

Superficial Hardening

A component requiring a relatively thin case of high-carbon steel is best carburised in a liquid cyanide bath, and this process is known as **superficial hardening**. This process offers many advantages:

(i) no scaling will take place,
(ii) small parts can be held in a suitable metal basket,
(iii) large parts can be suspended in the molten salt with little risk of distortion,
(iv) the components may be quenched immediately they are removed from the molten salt.

The salts used are mainly mixtures of sodium cyanide, sodium carbonate, and sodium chloride, and the salt is kept at about the upper critical temperature of the low carbon steel from which the component is made. Generally speaking the rate of carbon penetration will be about 0·25 mm per hour of immersion in the molten salt, although after the first two hours there is a marked decrease in the amount of carbon penetration. Because of this it is not an economical proposition to attempt deep penetrations, and the liquid salt technique is best suited for small amounts of case-hardening, say within the range of 0·25 mm to 0·5 mm.

The technique is illustrated in fig. 61, a simple forced draught gas-fired furnace being employed. The pot may be cast iron or alloy steel, and it is essential that the fumes from the molten cyanide be vented outside through the roof of the heat treatment shop. Great care must also be taken to ensure that there is no water or moisture present on the component when it is immersed in the molten salt, as this will lead to a minor explosion resulting in the eruption of molten cyanide from the

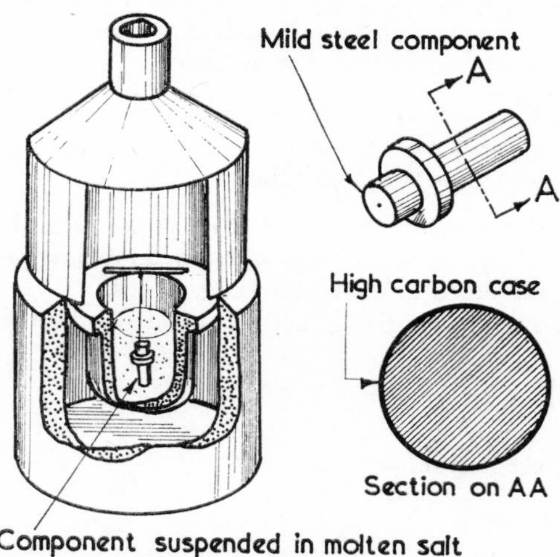

FIG. 61.—SUPERFICIAL HARDENING USING A SALT BATH.

pot. Great care must also be taken when handling the cyanide salt, for it is extremely poisonous, giving off a lethal gas when brought into contact with water. All parts to be case-hardened in the cyanide pot must first be pre-heated to remove any traces of moisture and the cyanide salt must be kept under lock and key. It is essential also that the prescribed antidote for cyanide poisoning be close at hand, together with full instructions regarding its use.

Note the component used in fig. 61; this is a mild steel pillar intended for use in a press tool. The depth of case will be about 0·25 mm, and it will be suspended as shown in the molten salt for about an hour, then immediately quenched in cold clean water. A cross-section of this pillar is also shown, and the martensitic case can be clearly seen. Because the molten salt is held at the upper critical temperature of mild steel, and the period of heating time is only one hour, no grain growth will occur; the rapid cooling will not only harden the case but will also give the mild steel core a fine grained and tough structure.

Pack-hardening

This process consists in surrounding the component with a carbonaceous material, usually a form of charcoal. The process is best suited for components that require a fairly deep case, say about 1 mm. The technique is illustrated in fig. 62, and it will be seen that a metal box is used. These boxes are made from heat-resisting alloy steel, for the

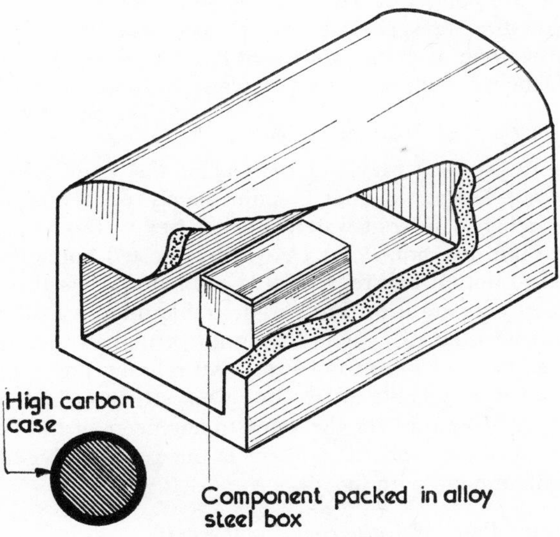

FIG. 62.—METHOD OF PACK-HARDENING.

carburising process involves heating to a temperature of between 900° and 950° C, and a plain carbon steel box would soon become unserviceable due to the severe scaling that would take place. In order to attain a depth of case of about 1 mm, the heating process will extend over a period of between six and eight hours, after which time the box is removed from the furnace and the component removed from the box.

The structure of the component is shown in fig. 62. We have in effect a component possessing two types of carbon steels. The outer layers will be about 0·9% carbon, whilst the remainder will be a mild steel of say 0·25% carbon. We have seen that the carburising process involved the heating of the steel to 950° C, over a period of 6 to 8 hours, followed by slow cooling of the component. These are the very conditions that produce a large weak grain structure, with a low resistance to impact.

Refining the Core

The component must be heated to the upper critical temperature for mild steel and then quenched in oil. Reference back to the diagram shown in fig. 60 enables us to locate this temperature as point R, which will be equivalent to about 870° C.

Hardening the Case

The case will consist of 0·9% carbon steel, and will require heating to just below the upper critical for 0·9% carbon steel. This is point H on the iron-carbon diagram, equivalent to a temperature of 780° C, the component being plunged in cold water from this temperature.

Necessity for the Two Heat Treatments

Perhaps the student may well wonder at this point why the component is not heated to 780° C immediately on removal from the box, and quenched in cold water. The answer to this is provided by the iron-carbon diagram. Point H, when projected horizontally across to the vertical dotted line representing mild steel, cuts this below the upper critical temperature; thus the desirable minute austenitic structure will not be attained, much of the grain structure remaining coarse and weak, so that the omission of the vital refining process will result in a component very liable to fracture when struck a sudden blow.

This is a good example of the value to engineers of the iron-carbon equilibrium diagram, and the student is once again advised to study fig. 60 in conjunction with fig. 55.

Obtaining Soft Parts on Carburised Components

It is seldom that threads are hardened, and it may be necessary to produce a component case-hardened with the exception of the thread. If the component is to be superficially hardened in a cyanide bath, the thread can be copper-plated; this will prevent the addition of carbon to the metal comprising the thread. If the thread is internal, that is to say a tapped hole, then clay can be used to plug the hole. Components that are to be carburised by the pack-hardening process will have an additional allowance of metal for those parts that are required to be soft. On removal of the component from the carburising box, the component is returned to the machine shop, and this machining will remove the carburised metal. The technique is illustrated in fig. 63; the thread of 25 mm diameter is required to be soft, whilst the rest of the

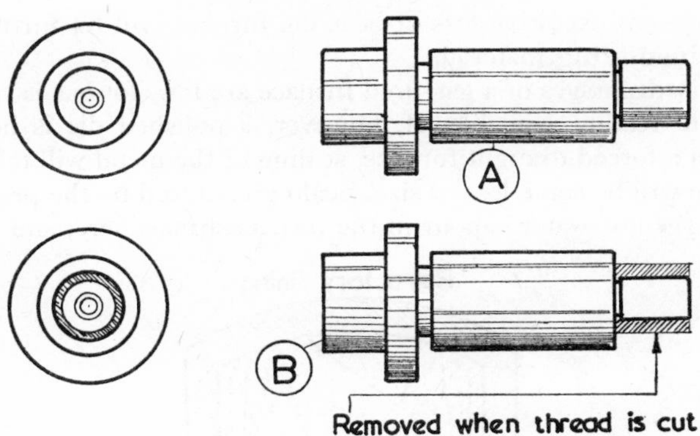

Fig. 63.—Method Adopted to obtain Soft Threads when Pack Hardening.

component is to be hard, and will be ground to final size. Note that the turned blank ready for carburising has no thread cut on it, and the diameter to be threaded is 30 mm. At A we see the blank after carburising, and at B the thread has been machined. The machining has removed the carburised metal, and after refining and hardening the blank will be set up for grinding. Note the use of the centre line as a datum, location being provided by the use of centres.

Principles of Heating

The heating of a component to the correct temperature is an essential part of heat treatment. We have seen in Volume I the use of the domed roof in both the puddling furnace and the open hearth furnace, the object being to concentrate the heat on to the metal. Much the same technique is adopted for the furnaces used to carry out the heat treatments described above.

Gas-fired Furnaces

A section through a simple gas-fired furnace is shown in fig. 64. The burners are similar in principle to the well-known Bunsen burner, and this means that the furnace is known as a **natural draught furnace.** If rapid heating is required, air may be supplied under pressure, and such a furnace is known as a **forced draught furnace.** In both cases it is the hot gases or products of combustion that heat the component, and the diagram shows how the domed roof reflects the hot gases on to the work. Thus a **refractory** material will be used as the inside lining of the furnace. Some heat is bound to get through the refractory lining, and to prevent excessive loss of heat the furnace will be further lined with an **insulating** material.

The disadvantages of a gas-fired furnace are few, for gas is relatively cheap and readily available. If, however, a polished die is heated to 900° C in a forced draught furnace, scaling of the metal will take place, and there will be some loss of size. Scaling is caused by the presence of either oxygen or water vapour in the furnace atmosphere, and as water

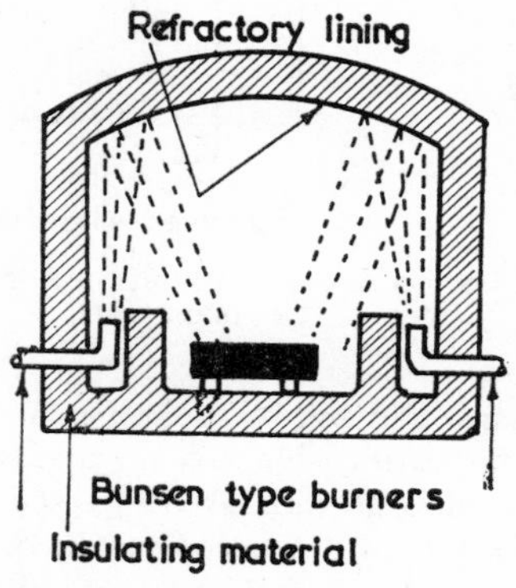

FIG. 64.—SECTION OF A SIMPLE GAS-FIRED NATURAL DRAUGHT FURNACE.

vapour or H_2O is a product of combustion, scaling is inevitable in the furnace shown in fig. 64.

Gas-fired Muffle Furnace

The muffle furnace, as the name suggests, protects the work from the products of combustion. The hot gases surround and heat a separate chamber, and in this way scaling is reduced. It is possible to introduce an inert gas into the muffle, and such a furnace would be known as a **controlled atmosphere furnace.** A muffle furnace is shown in fig. 65.

Temperatures up to 1000° C are readily obtained with gas-fired furnaces, and it is an essential condition that the waste gases be vented outside the heat treatment shop.

Electric Furnaces

The simplest electric furnace uses resistance elements to provide a source of heat. Temperatures up to 1000° C are easily reached provided the cubic capacity of the furnace is not excessive.

An electric furnace possesses many advantages over a gas-fired furnace; there are no products of combustion, and installation is simple as there are no pipes or ducts required. It lends itself readily to automatic control, and temperatures up to 1000° C are easily attainable. Reference to fig. 66 shows that the principle of construction is similar to that of a gas-fired furnace.

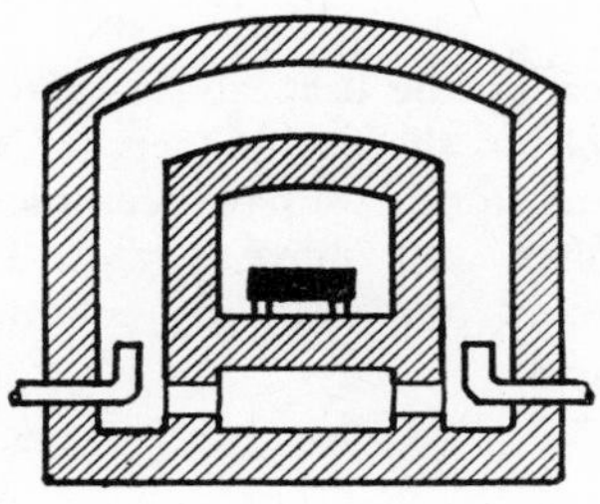

FIG. 65.—SECTION OF A GAS-FIRED MUFFLE FURNACE.

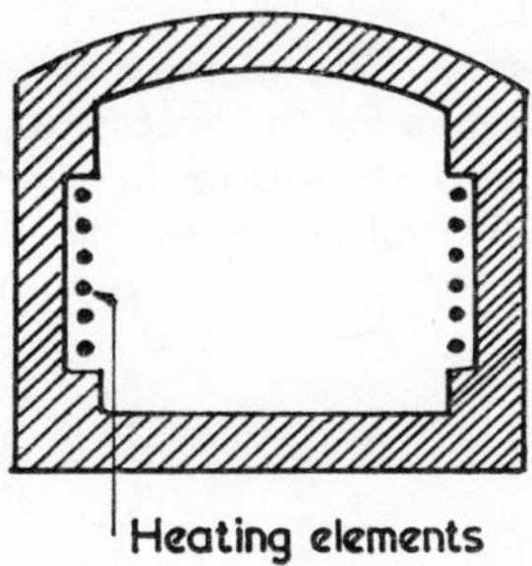

FIG. 66.—SECTION OF A SIMPLE ELECTRIC FURNACE.

Furnace Fuels

The following table gives some indication of the types of fuels, together with approximate temperatures.

Fuel	*Principle of Combustion*	*Temperature*
Coal gas plus atmosphere	Natural draught with Bunsen-type burners	1000° C
Coal gas plus atmosphere	Forced draught with Bunsen-type burners	1300° C with small volume furnace
Coke plus atmosphere	Fuel in contact with work, or products of combustion reflected on to work	1000° C (with regenerative principle)
Fuel oil plus atmosphere	Products of combustion (hot gases) blown into furnace	Up to 1200° C

Temperature Control

No furnace will be of practical value unless an efficient and accurate method of determining the temperature of the furnace is available.

There are many instances when the temperature of a steel tool must be held to within plus or minus 5 degrees Celsius, and this means that an accurate **pyrometer** is an essential feature in the correct heat treatment of metals.

Mercury Thermometers

Mercury boils at 357° C, and thus cannot be used above this temperature. This places a severe limitation on the use of mercury thermometers for the heat treatment of metal, for as we have seen most of our heat treatments involve temperatures well above 357° C. It is, however, possible to use the pressure of an expanding column of mercury to operate a pressure gauge. This gauge will be calibrated in degrees Celsius, and the principle of such an instrument is shown in fig. 67. There are some heat treatment processes which are carried out below 357° C, such as tempering, tinning, and galvanising, and a mercury pressure thermometer would be quite suitable for these operations.

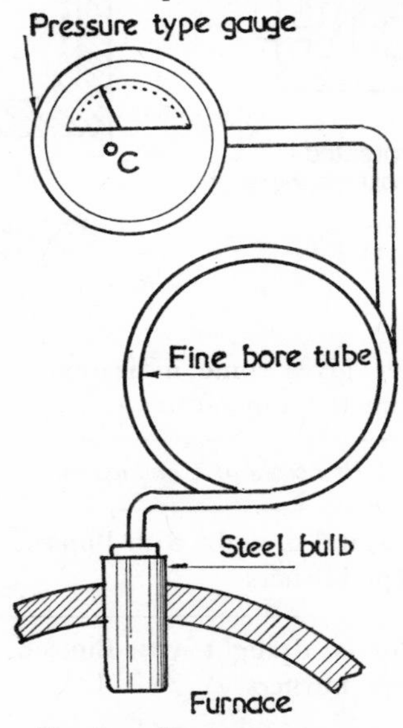

FIG. 67.—PRINCIPLE OF THE MERCURY PRESSURE THERMOMETER.

Electrical Resistance Thermometers

These thermometers operate on the fact that the resistance to the passage of an electric current increases as the temperature of a metal conductor rises. Pure metals are used, either nickel or platinum, and the principle is shown in fig. 68. The electrical resistance thermometer is most suitable for adaptation as a recording device, and in this way a permanent record of a furnace temperature is obtained.

Thermo-electric Pyrometers

These are widely used in the determination of furnace temperatures, and their popularity is due to the simplicity and reliability of the principle involved. If two dissimilar metals are joined together, with a galvanometer placed in closed circuit at the open ends, a rise in temperature of the joined ends produces an electric current which will be

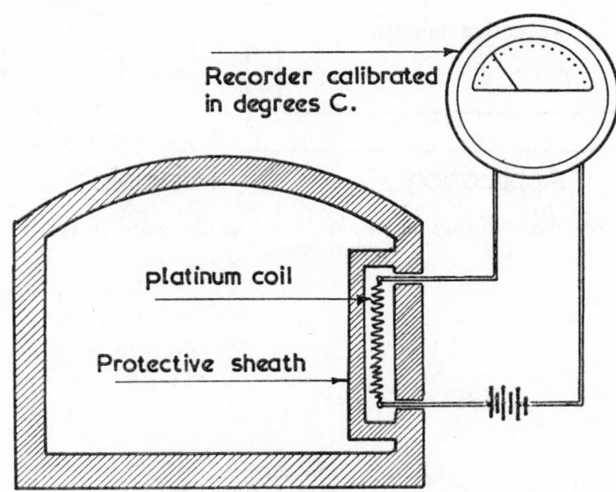

FIG. 68.—PRINCIPLE OF THE ELECTRICAL RESISTANCE THERMOMETER.

recorded by the galvanometer. The principle is shown in fig. 69, together with a typical application. Note that a direct reading in millivolts is obtained, but the millivoltmeter will be calibrated in degrees Celsius. Temperatures up to 1100° C are accurately recorded by the thermo-couple inserted in the furnace, and this simple device is in wide use as a furnace pyrometer.

Segar Cones

These are useful as a temporary expedient, as when, owing to the breakdown of the permanent pyrometer, a temporary means of temperature determination must be employed. The cones are pyramidal in shape, made of silicate or wax, each cone melting at a predetermined

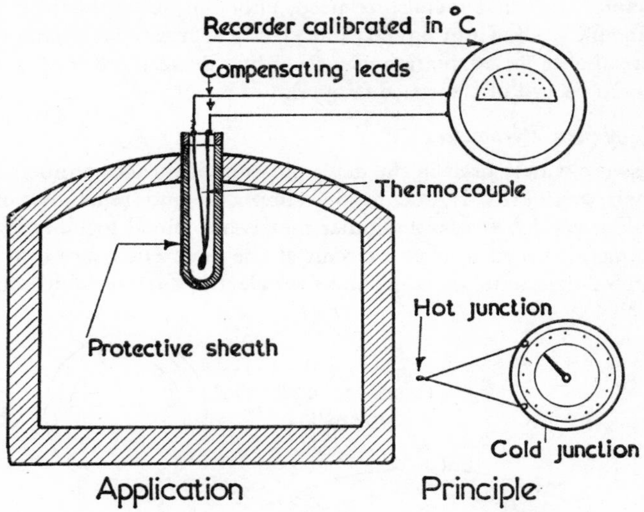

FIG. 69.—PRINCIPLE OF THE THERMO-COUPLE AND ITS APPLICATION.

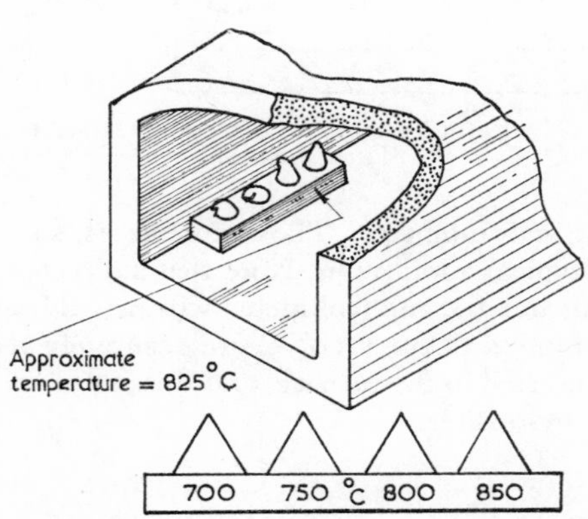

FIG. 70.—FURNACE TEMPERATURE CONTROL USING SEGAR CONES.

temperature. The technique is shown in fig. 70, and for the conditions shown the temperature of the furnace can be taken as 825° C.

Summary

Heat treatments are carried out to improve or modify the structure of metals. It may be necessary to improve the physical properties of a metal, thus making it more able to stand up to the stresses it will receive in service. It may also be necessary to modify the structure of a metal in order that it may be more easily cold or hot worked.

The changes in the structure of slowly heated carbon steels are clearly seen in the iron-carbon equilibrium diagram, and this diagram is of great value to engineers, for it enables them to determine accurately the correct temperatures at which to heat treat steels of different carbon content.

Furnaces are used to bring the steel to the correct temperature, and several different types are in use. They all, however, operate on the same principle; namely the efficient and economical heating of the component within the furnace, with every effort made to prevent loss of heat.

Finally, the temperature at which heat treatments are carried out must be controlled to within small limits, and this is only possible if the furnace is equipped with an efficient and accurate pyrometer. The type of pyrometer used will depend on the size and temperature of the furnaces used, and the use of pyrometers provides an excellent example of the close link between scientific principles and applied workshop techniques.

QUESTIONS ON CHAPTER FOUR

1. Explain why a die cast aluminium alloy component will possess a greater tensile strength than a similar component produced by sand casting.
2. What is meant by "stress relieving"? Illustrate your answer with a component requiring this process.
3. What is the difference between normalising and refining?
4. A mild steel component was found to be brittle following a brazing operation. Give possible reasons for this defect.
5. Explain why a deep-drawing operation cannot be carried out using bright mild sheet steel. What is the essential heat treatment required? Give reasons.
6. Make a neat sketch of that part of the iron-carbon diagram relevant to the heat treatment of carbon steel. Show, by means of a simple example, the practical use of this diagram.
7. Sketch an engineering component requiring superficial hardening, and describe briefly the method adopted.
8. Write down the disadvantages of the carburising process known as pack-hardening.
9. Make a neat sketch showing the essential principles involved in the construction of a gas-fired furnace.
10. By means of sketches, illustrate the principle of a pyrometer to be used to determine the temperature of a gas-fired carburising furnace.

5 Measurement

MEASUREMENT is the key to all manufacturing processes. The rolling, casting, forging, and machining of metal all involve the important fact that the finished product must be within the dimensions laid down. We have seen in Volume I that all engineering components will possess the following items of measurement:

(i) linear dimensions,
(ii) angular dimensions,
(iii) non-linear functions.

The methods adopted to determine these items will depend on the degree of accuracy required, and the greater the accuracy, the more costly will be the equipment needed, not only to produce the surfaces, but also to determine whether they possess the necessary dimensional accuracy.

Dimensioning of Engineering Components

All engineering components are produced from drawings or blueprints. A machinist has no alternative but to follow the drawing, and the method or sequence of machining is governed by the faces or points from which the dimensions are made. It follows, then, that draughtsmen or designers have a great responsibility in this matter, and the work of the machinist is assisted if the component is dimensioned so that full use can be made of the geometric movements inherent in the machine tools utilised to produce the component.

Let us consider the component shown in fig. 71. It is certain that a machinist, faced with a drawing as badly dimensioned as this, would be sorely tempted to march up to the drawing office and suggest to the draughtsman concerned that he machines the component himself. We will find on close examination of this drawing that there is some justification for his despair on this occasion.

The Datum or Location Faces

It is evident that faces X and Y have been chosen as the location or datum faces from which the measurements have been made. This

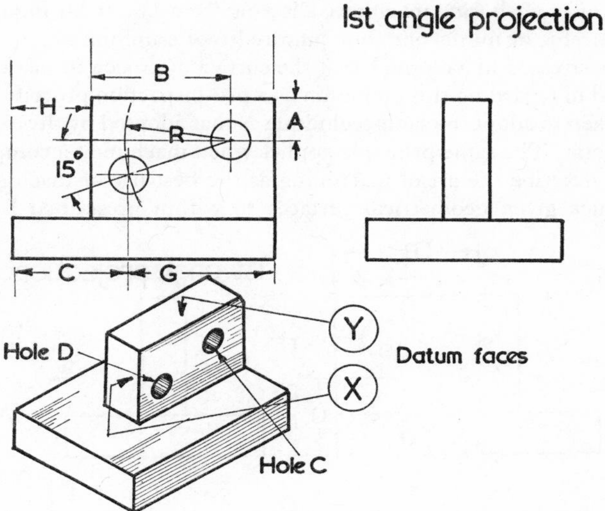

FIG. 71.—POORLY DIMENSIONED ENGINEERING COMPONENT.

means that the machinist, if he is to produce the component to within the limits, must locate from these faces. This is going to be a difficult matter, for these faces are small, and it is unlikely that the resultant set-up will possess the necessary rigidity.

Location of the Holes

Note that the location of hole D with respect to hole C is determined by a radius and an angle. This is an example of the use of **polar co-ordinates.** It is going to be a difficult proposition for the machinist to mark out these hole centres to any reasonable degree of accuracy.

In short, this component is going to demand a difficult machining operation, resulting in increased machining time and a higher cost of manufacture. The probability of scrapping the component is also increased, and we see now the importance of careful and logical dimensioning of engineering components.

Fig. 72 shows the same component redimensioned. Note that the new datum faces X and Y will permit simplified and more rigid setting of the component.

Note also that the positions of the two holes are governed by the linear dimensions A and B from the datum face X, together with the linear dimensions C and D from the datum face Y. This system of hole positioning is known as **rectangular co-ordinates**, and is widely used on most jig-boring machines, allowing the accurate boring of holes to within plus or minus one four-hundredth of a millimetre.

It was stressed in Volume I that the correct approach to marking out consisted in regarding this operation as a pre-inspection procedure, care being taken to adopt the same technique as that adopted by the examiner or inspector. The same principle applies when machining a component. We can describe the art of machining as the best use of machine tools to produce given geometrical surfaces to within prescribed limits of

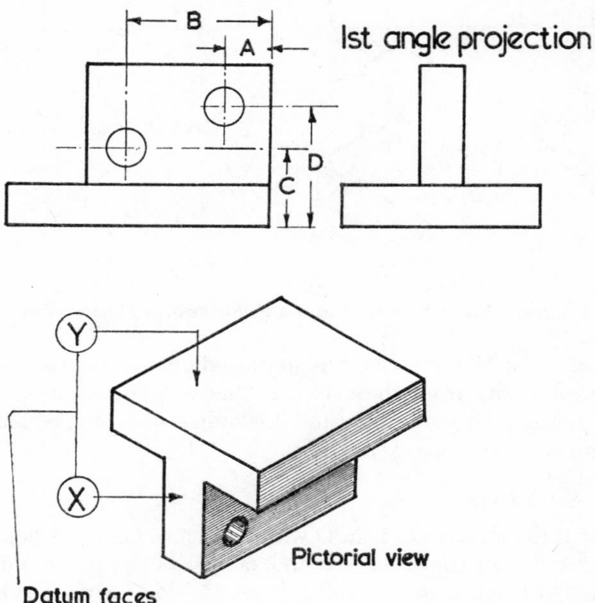

FIG. 72.—COMPONENT HAVING CORRECT DATUM FACES.

accuracy. As previously stated, these limits will involve linear, angular, or non-linear functions, and the purpose of measurement is to determine whether the component has been produced to within the limits laid down in the drawing.

The Use of Flat Surfaces

The famous engineer Sir Joseph Whitworth pointed out many years ago that all precision measurements start from flat surfaces. The surface plate or surface table is an essential feature of all measurement, and the type of surface plate used will depend on the accuracy required. Three grades of accuracy are available, namely A, B, and C, and fig. 73

illustrates the essential requirements of a surface plate measuring 1 metre across the diagonals. A recent British Standard acknowledges only grades A and B, but grade C will continue to be used in industry for some time yet.

It will be seen that the four edges of a surface plate are machined to close limits, and this means that these faces can be used for purposes of measuring. The accuracy of the flat surface is determined by the

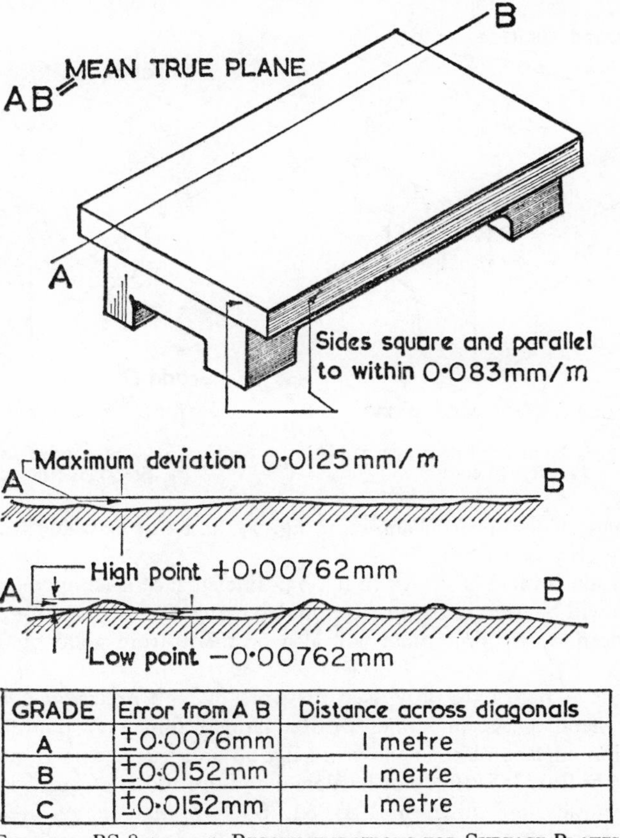

GRADE	Error from A B	Distance across diagonals
A	±0·0076mm	1 metre
B	±0·0152 mm	1 metre
C	±0·0152mm	1 metre

FIG. 73.—BS 817: 1957 RECOMMENDATIONS FOR SURFACE PLATES.

amount of variation of the surface from the **mean true plane.** The principle is shown in fig. 73; thus for a grade A surface plate the maximum distance of a high or low point must not exceed plus or minus seven-thousandths of a millimetre. This accuracy applies to the whole bearing surface of the plate, and it is also necessary that no area of the plate shall depart from the mean true plane by more than plus or minus one-hundredth of a millimetre per metre. Full details of the specifications for surface plates are given in British Standard No. 817 1957.

Because of the high degree of accuracy possessed by surface plates it is essential that the correct plate be used in the correct place. Grade C plates are often used in the workshops; they possess a finished planed surface, a broad nosed or finishing tool being used during the final cut.

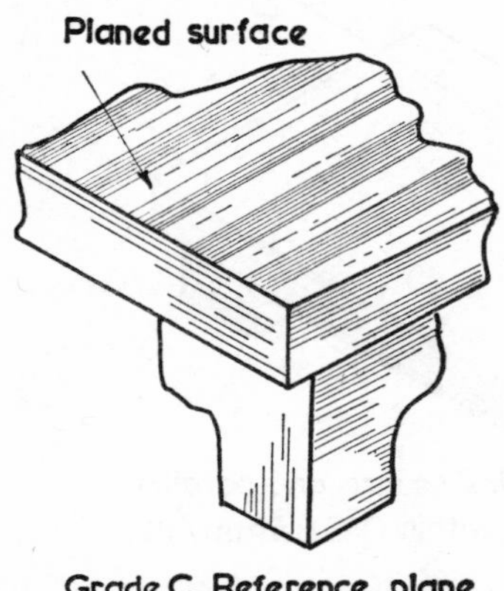

FIG. 74.—SURFACE PLATE WITH PLANED FINISH.

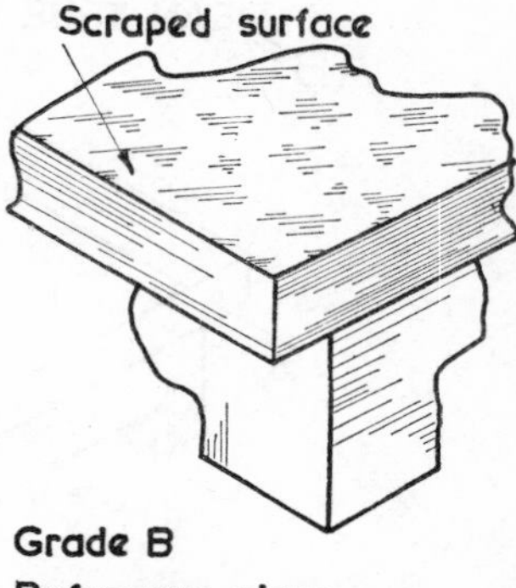

FIG. 75.—SURFACE PLATE WITH SCRAPED FINISH.

The plate will appear as shown in fig. 74, and will be made from good quality grey cast iron.

A grade B plate is shown in fig. 75, The surface is scraped, and such a plate will be used in the inspection department or perhaps for accurate tool-room work. This plate will also be made from good quality cast iron.

Grade A plates are only used for work of high precision. They may be of metal, glass, or stone, with a lapped finish. A popular small precision surface plate is shown in fig. 76 and this is known as a **toolmaker's flat.** It is made of hardened and ground alloy steel, lapped to the accuracy laid down in BS 869. Such a plate is of great value when precision measurement involving the use of end standards or slip gauges is required.

Linear Dimensions using Surface Plates

We mentioned in Volume I that an engineers' steel rule is a **line standard.** The accuracy possible using a steel rule is greatly increased

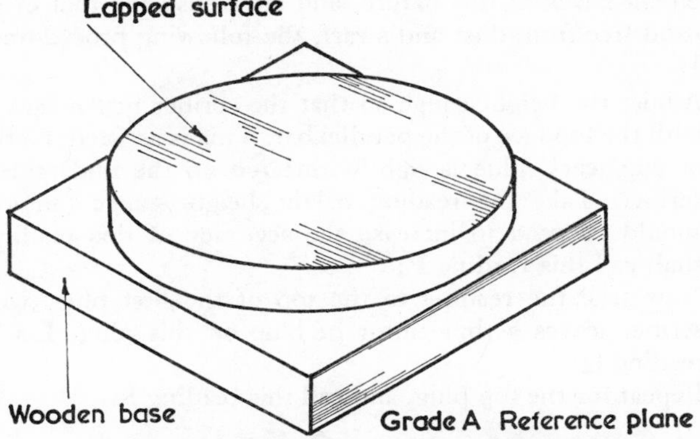

FIG. 76.—SURFACE PLATE WITH LAPPED FINISH.

when a vernier device is fitted, and vernier height gauges are much used for determining linear dimensions using a surface plate. Fig. 77 shows a typical example: the use of a vernier height gauge in determining the distances C and D. These are the linear dimensions of the hole

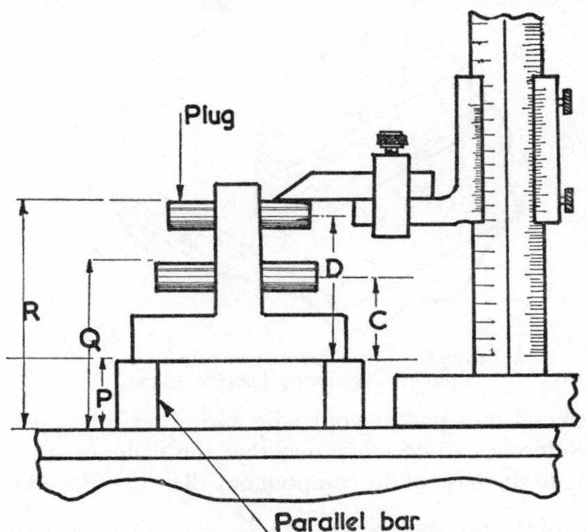

FIG. 77.—USE OF A VERNIER HEIGHT GAUGE TO DETERMINE LINEAR DIMENSIONS.

centres from the base of the component shown in fig. 72. Note the use of precision parallel bars, and the insertion of well-fitting plugs in the holes.

It is wise to follow a neat and logical procedure when carrying out a measurement check of this nature, and after ensuring that everything is clean and free from dust and swarf, the following procedure can be adopted:

(i) Adjust the height gauge so that the scriber just makes contact with the top face of the parallel bar. This is assisted if a thin film of engineers' blue is lightly smeared on the underside of the scriber. Take the reading of the height gauge (an eye-glass should be used to increase the accuracy of this reading). We shall call this reading P;

(ii) Now take the reading to the top of the first plug, when the scriber leaves a thin smear of blue on this plug. Let this be reading Q;

(iii) Repeat for the top plug, and call this reading R.

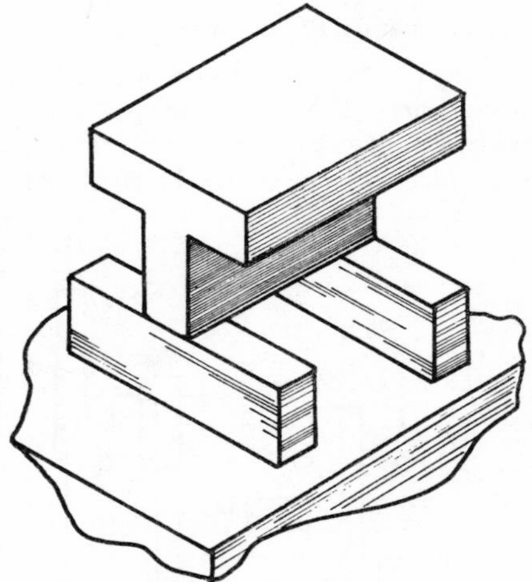

FIG. 78.—POOR LOCATION DUE TO INCORRECT CHOICE OF DATUM FACES.

Keep a pencil and pad at your side and enter the readings as they are made. Reference to fig. 77 shows that the distance from the top of the first plug to the base of the component will be $Q-P$, and the distance to the centre of the hole will be $Q-P-\frac{D}{2}$, when D is the diameter of the plug.

In the same way, the centre line of the top hole will be $R-P-\frac{D}{2}$. The same procedure will now be repeated for the hole dimensions from the face X, and it will now be evident (fig. 78) that had the component been dimensioned as shown in fig. 71, the problem of location would have been much more complicated. We see now the importance of locating from the largest surface area, and dimensioning from this surface area or datum face; the machinist is thus able to ensure not only maximum rigidity, but also maximum accuracy, especially with regard to the important non-linear function of alignment.

With regard to the accuracy obtained using the vernier height gauge, two points may be mentioned. The reading is obtained by the comparison of lines, and as lines possess thickness it is difficult to obtain precise readings. There is also the question of **feel.** This refers to the resistance offered to the scriber surface by the surface of the plug, and the combination of these two factors places a limitation on the accuracy possible using a vernier height gauge to determine linear dimensions.

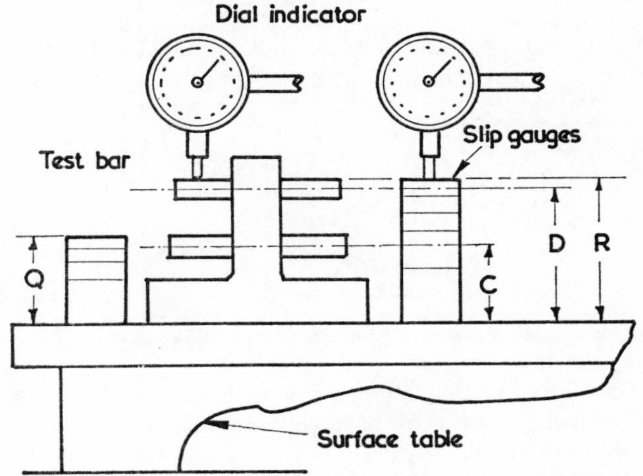

FIG. 79.—USE OF SLIP GAUGES AND DIAL INDICATOR TO DETERMINE LINEAR DIMENSIONS.

The Use of End Standards

The use of end standards makes possible an accuracy far greater than the accuracy possible when using a line standard. The principle was illustrated in Volume I, and we shall now recheck the height of the centre distances of the holes using end standards, or **slip gauges** as they are more commonly called. The set-up is shown in fig. 79; note that the principle involved is common to all measuring problems, namely the comparison of an unknown value against a known value. Note also that the set-up is identical to that employed when using a vernier height gauge, but whilst a grade C surface plate would be quite suitable when a height gauge is used, it is a better plan to use a grade B or even a grade A surface plate in conjunction with slip gauges.

Reference to fig. 79 shows that the technique is relatively simple. Let us assume that distance C is 55·355 mm and the diameter of the hole is 13 mm. This means that the height from the base to the top of a well-fitting plug will be 61·855 mm. Slip gauges are now built up to this height and a dial indicator set at zero, as shown in fig. 79. This dial indicator must read to one thousandth of a mm, with the pointer making about one revolution of the dial before setting to zero. The dial indicator

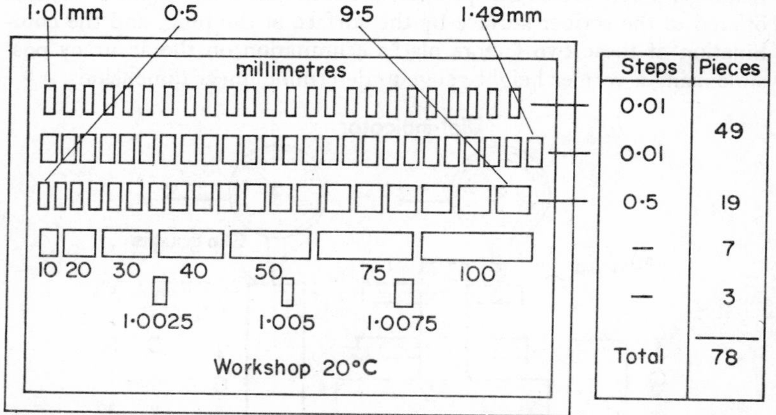

FIG. 80.—PLAN VIEW OF A 78-PIECE SET OF WORKSHOP SLIP GAUGES.

is now transferred to the plug and the reading noted; any deviation of the pointer will give the error of the hole centre from the base in thousandths of a millimetre.

This simple example of the use of slip gauges will serve clearly to show the great advantages that end standards offer when used to determine accurate linear dimensions. Firstly, the problem of working to lines is removed and, secondly, the problem of feel is also removed. It is essential, however, that slip gauges be properly used and cared for, and the following notes will give an indication of the essential procedure to be followed.

Use and Care of Slip Gauges

Fig. 80 shows a plan view of a typical set of slip gauges comprising 78 pieces. The table at the side of the diagram gives the incremental step, and the number of pieces for each step. When building up a height of slip gauges select the smallest increment first, or in other words eliminate the last decimal place. We will use the height given in fig. 79 to show the correct technique.

Height required = 61·855 mm.

Select smallest increment	1·005
Select next increment	1·05
Select next increment	1·3
Select next increment	8·5
Select next increment	50
Total	61·855

A total of five slip gauges will be required. It is a rule when using slip gauges that the **minimum** number of slips be used, and we must now reconsider the problem to find out whether it is possible to reduce this number. Let us retabulate in the manner shown below.

Method	*Slip Chosen*	*Total*	*Remainder*
Remove smallest decimal	1·005	1·005	60·850
Remove smallest decimal and leave 0·5	1·35	2·355	59·5
Remove decimals	9·5	11·855	50
Complete	50	61·855	0

It will be seen that by using the method shown above the number of slip gauges required has been reduced to four. This has been achieved by selecting the 1·35 slip, leaving 59·5. It is then a rule, when using a 78-piece set, that the remaining $\frac{1}{10}$ be reduced to 0 or 5, and this simple rule will permit the completion of the dimension using the slips having the $\frac{5}{10}$ increments.

Wringing Slip Gauges

Before wringing slip gauges together, each slip must be checked individually. Although the slip size is indicated on the case opposite each slip it is possible that the slips have been incorrectly replaced by the previous user. It is a wise plan to tabulate as shown above and then check each slip against the calculated value. Wringing proceeds as shown in fig. 81; note that two distinct stages are involved. The two slips are first placed at right angles as shown at A, then the top slip is slid across and rotated through 90 degrees. This technique ensures that there is no dust or foreign matter between the slip faces, and a tight adhesive contact will result. It is also essential that a similar technique be adopted to break the slips apart, and this is done by rotating the top slip through 90 degrees before breaking apart.

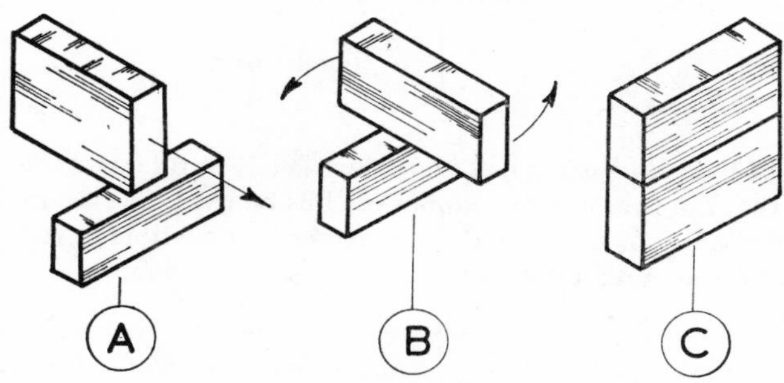

Fig. 81.—Method of Wringing Slip Gauges.

Slip gauges are measuring devices and must be treated as such. As soon as the correct slips have been chosen, the lid of the box must be closed, thus preventing any dust or swarf from entering the box. Before wringing, the measuring faces may be gently wiped with a clean piece of soft cloth; after use the surfaces must again be wiped carefully and a thin smear of vaseline applied. Especial care is needed if the slip gauges are to be used near a grinding machine, for the dust produced by the grinding operation is exceedingly abrasive, causing rapid and excessive wear of the measuring surfaces. This is also true if slip gauges are used to check the accuracy of a component during a lapping operation. Once again the lapping compound is highly abrasive, and every care must be taken to ensure that none of this compound gets on to the measuring faces of the slip gauges.

Slip Gauge Sets

Sets of slip gauges are available having different grades of accuracy. We have already stated that the method or equipment adopted to determine an engineering measurement will depend upon the degree of accuracy required. Surface plates, and many other measuring devices, are available in three grades of quality, namely A, B, and C. The same principle is adopted when slip gauges are used to determine linear dimensions, and the three types of sets in general use are listed below, together with their applications.

Workshop Set

This set, as the name suggests, is used in the workshop. The accuracy of these slips is very high; within two hundred and fifty millionths of a mm for all slips up to 25 mm length, and within two hundred and fifty millionths of a mm per 25 mm length thereafter. We see now the necessity for keeping the number of slips to a minimum, for the greater the number of slips used, the greater will be the variation from the true length caused by the summation of the slip tolerances.

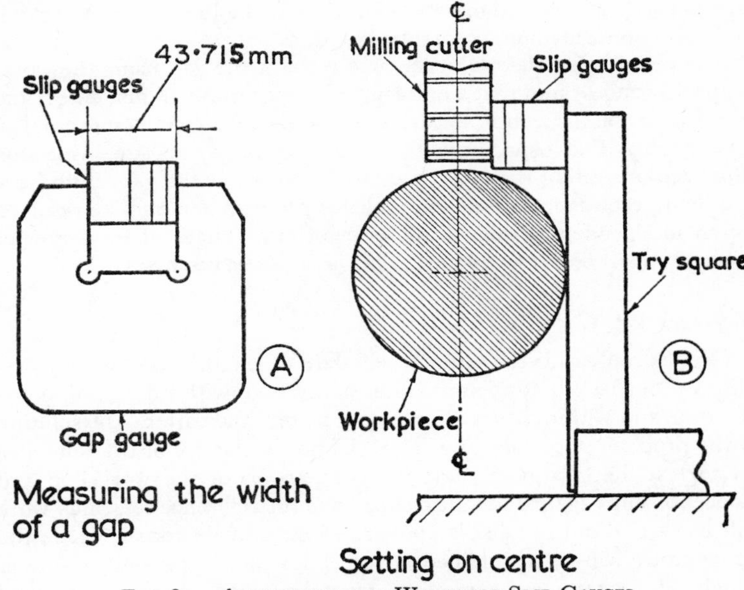

FIG. 82.—APPLICATIONS OF WORKSHOP SLIP GAUGES.

There are many uses for the workshop set of slip gauges. They are of great value in testing the accuracy of external and internal micrometers; they may be used to determine the width of slots; and they can be used to facilitate the setting-up of a precise machining operation. Fig. 82 illustrates two typical workshop applications, and it will be evident that the slip gauges, if not used with care, will be subject to wear or damage. It is certain that both the gap gauge and the milled slot shown in fig. 82 will be further tested by an inspector, and it is necessary that he be provided with his own personal set to be used only for inspection purposes.

Inspection Set

The slip gauges in this set will be accurate to within one hundred millionths of a millimetre up to a length of 25 mm, and within one hundred millionths of a millimetre per 25 mm thereafter. With accuracies such as these, it is essential that they are well treated, and one can be sure that the inspection department will not permit this set to be subjected to the more rigorous conditions existing in the workshops. Let us assume that the gap gauge shown in fig. 82A has been completed to the toolmaker's satisfaction and passed on to the inspector for final checking. Let us assume also that the gap gauge is later returned to the toolmaker, together with an inspection note informing the toolmaker that the gap is undersize and thus not acceptable.

It is certain that the toolmaker will recheck the gap using the workshop slip gauges; find that a build-up of 43·715 mm will just enter; and march into the inspection department armed with convincing proof of his accuracy. The inspector will now check the gap using the inspection slips, demonstrating that 43·715 mm will not enter the gap. Both have excellent grounds for argument, and this problem can only be resolved by an independent check, using a set of slip gauges of even greater accuracy than the inspection set. This is the **reference set.**

Reference Set

This set represents the ultimate standard of length within the factory. Slips up to a length of 25 mm will be accurate to within fifty millionths of a mm, and within fifty millionths per 25 mm thereafter. The solution of the problem posed above will consist not in the use of the reference set to test the gap gauge, but the comparison of the workshop and inspection slips against identical slips from the reference set. Such work will be carried out in what is known as a **standards room**, where the temperature will be maintained at 20° C, for this is the temperature at which all accurate measurements must be taken. A well-conducted standards room can do much to prevent the sort of argument described above, thus increasing the efficiency of production and the quality of the finished product. All sets of slip gauges used within the factory should be periodically checked, with inaccuracies tabulated and enclosed within the box. This system should also be adopted for all other measuring devices used, such a micrometers, plug and gap gauges and the like.

Slip Gauge Accessories

The use of slip gauge accessories is essential if full use is to be made of a set of slip gauges. Slip gauges should not be handled for longer than is necessary, or heat will be absorbed, leading to a measurable increase in length. The best plan is to insert the slips into a suitable nest, as shown in fig. 83A. Note the use of the two special end slips possessing a radiused surface, thus permitting the measurement of an internal diameter. The external diameter may also be determined using the inside faces of the end slips. Fig. 83B shows the use of accessories allowing slip gauges to be used for purposes of precision marking out. Whilst this method permits very accurate scribing of lines, it must be remembered that the lines scribed in this way will themselves possess thickness, dependent on the pressure used; thus we have the unusual circumstance of end standards used to produce a line.

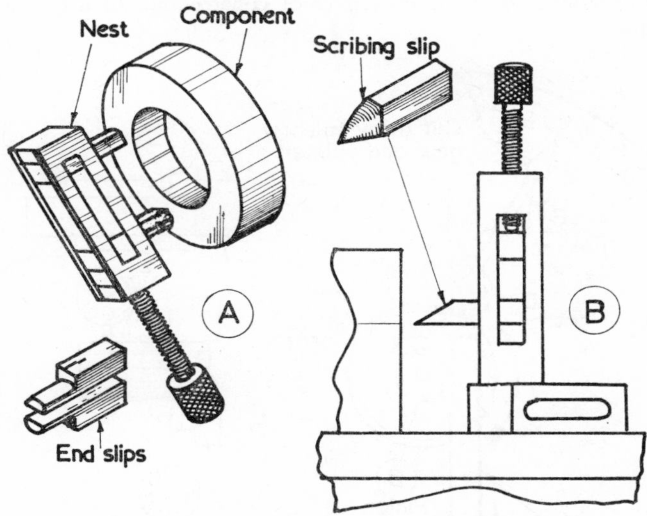

FIG. 83.—APPLICATIONS OF SLIP GAUGE ACCESSORIES.

The Problem of Feel

If slip gauges are used as shown in fig. 83A to determine the internal diameter of a component, the accuracy will be affected by the amount of force or pressure used. This is known as **feel**, and presents a serious problem when making accurate measurements. Mention was made in Volume I of the method to be adopted when setting an 0–25 mm external micrometer to zero, and perhaps it may now be appreciated that the use of the ratchet device eliminates the problem of feel when an external micrometer is properly used. When slip gauges are used the problem of feel is removed by the use of a **dial indicator.**

The Dial Indicator

We have already dealt with the use of a dial indicator when determining precise linear dimensions from a datum face, as shown in fig. 79. It must be appreciated that a dial indicator is essentially a **comparator**, allowing a visual comparison of the difference in height between an unknown value and a known value. The main quality of a dial indicator is that it **magnifies** the actual linear displacement of the plunger, and this magnification is brought about by mechanical devices. Fig. 84 shows in simple form the principles of construction of a typical dial indicator.

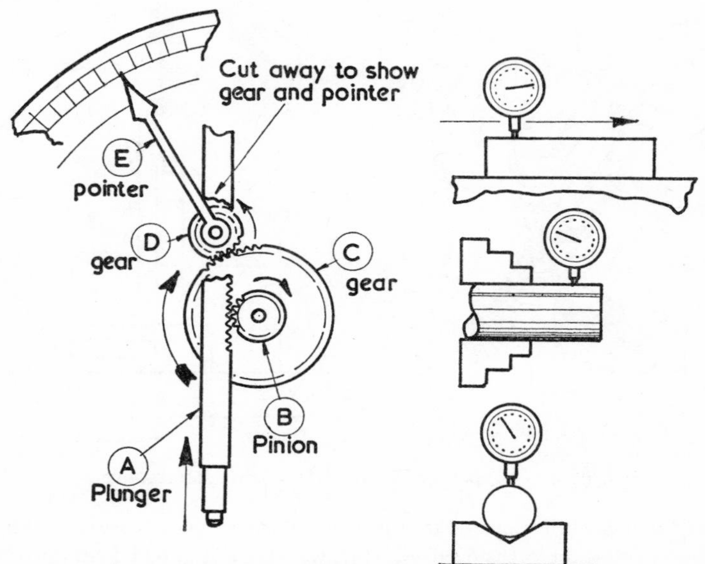

FIG. 84.—PRINCIPLES AND APPLICATIONS OF A DIAL INDICATOR.

Movement of the plunger A causes rotation of the small pinion B, which meshes with the rack machined on the plunger body. A hair or helical spring keeps the pinion in close contact with the rack. Rotation of pinion B causes a greater rotation of the larger pinion C which meshes with the gear D, which carries the pointer E on its spindle. Thus with a suitable gearing arrangement relatively large angular movements of the pointer are achieved for small linear displacements of the plunger.

The advantages of a visual indication of height differences, together with a constant feel, which is achieved by a spring, are very great. The difficult non-linear functions of concentricity, parallelism, flatness, and alignment are readily determined using a dial indicator. Fig. 84 also illustrates some typical workshop applications.

All dial indicators must be handled with care. Although they are of fairly robust construction, they will not stand up to ill-treatment, and sticking of the plunger is a sure indication that a dial indicator has not received the treatment this delicate and precise instrument warrants.

Straight-edges

Although a dial indicator provides a visual indication of the variations in height of a surface under test, it suffers from the disadvantage that

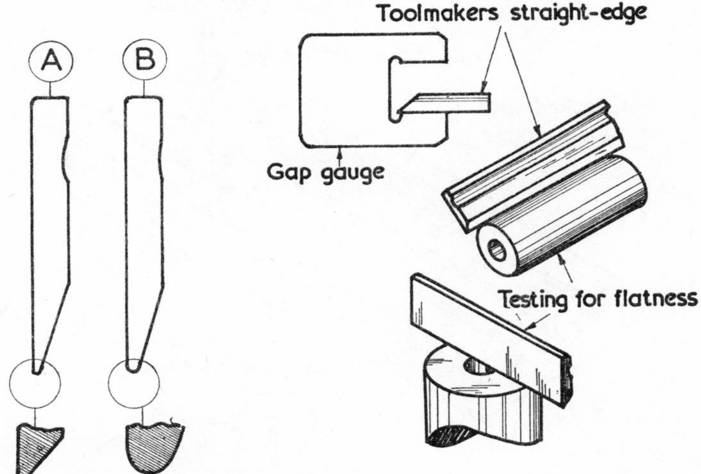

FIG. 85.—TYPES AND USES OF TOOLMAKER'S STRAIGHT-EDGES.

the readings are obtained with movement of the dial indicator or work, and a complete picture of error is not possible at one glance. This is precisely what straight-edges can achieve, and for this reason they are often used to determine the flatness of relatively small surfaces. A further advantage of the use of a straight-edge consists in the fact that flatness can be tested in any particular direction.

A straight-edge may be considered as a surface plate of narrow width. The accuracy of straight-edges is very similar to the accuracy of surface plates, and full details are given in BS 818:1963. The length of a straight-edge may vary from 100 mm to 5 metres; small straight-edges are usually available in sets of three or four and will have the section in fig. 85. Note the reduced bearing surface of the straight-edge shown at A; this type is often referred to as knife-edge, whilst the straight-edge shown at B has a radiused edge permitting line contact with the work under test, and thus allowing a very accurate assessment of the surface flatness. These small straight-edges are known as toolmaker's straight-edges, made from high-quality tool steel, hardened and tempered, and covered by BS 852:1939. Some typical applications of toolmaker's straight-edges are also shown in fig. 85, and it is essential that a strong source of white light be available behind or below the surface under test. White light cannot penetrate a gap of less than one four-hundredth of a millimetre; the thin film of air which must exist between the surface under test and the straight-edge acts as a refractive

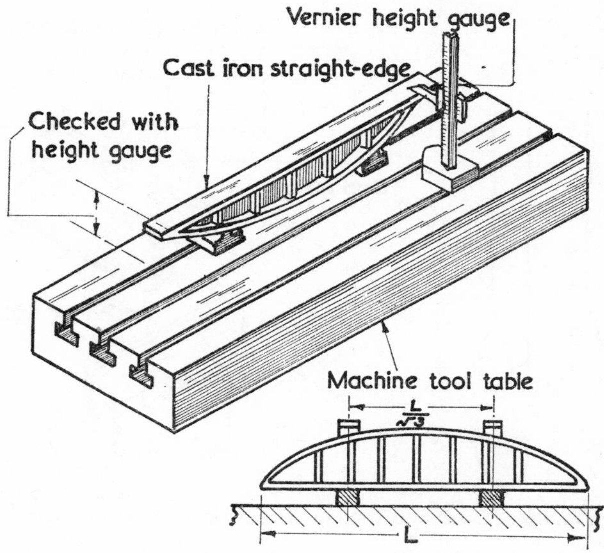

FIG. 86.—LARGE CAST IRON STRAIGHT-EDGE USED TO DETERMINE THE FLATNESS OF A MILLING MACHINE TABLE.

medium, separating white light into its component colours. Careful observation will reveal quite a variety of colours, and if no white light is visible, the surface tested is within four-hundredth of a millimetre of true flatness. If a slip gauge is tested with a toolmaker's straight-edge, no colours will be seen, unless the slip has been scored or scratched through misuse.

Large-type straight-edges are made from good-quality cast iron, and they must be supported on the points provided, if deflection of the straight-edge is to be kept to a minimum. Fig. 86 shows a large-type straight-edge; note the use of a vernier height gauge to check the flatness of the machine table under test.

Angular Dimensions

We have seen in Volume I that a vernier protractor can be used to determine the relative inclination of two surfaces to within plus or minus five minutes of arc. Because the vernier protractor is a line standard, considerable skill is required when determining the vernier reading, and much greater accuracy can be achieved if a **sine bar** is used.

The Sine Bar

A sine bar can be considered as a straight-edge having two rollers or plugs of equal diameter with centre distances of either 100 or 200 mm.

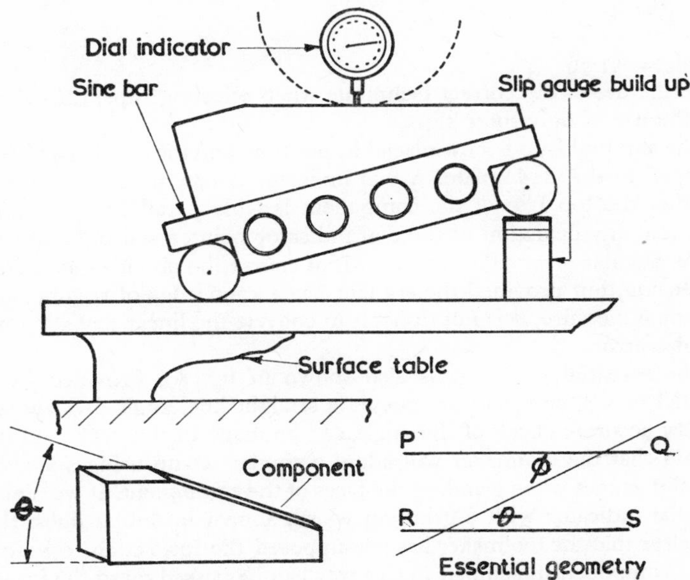

FIG. 87.—PRINCIPLE AND APPLICATION OF A SINE BAR.

It is essential that the working face of the sine bar be parallel to the centre line of the plugs. The use of a sine bar is best shown by reference to the determination of the inclination of two surfaces of an engineering component. Fig. 87 shows an insert for a forming die. It is required to check the angle θ. The technique, together with the essential geometry, is also illustrated in fig. 87. Note the use of a surface plate to provide a reference plane or datum face.

We will assume that a 200 mm sine bar is available, together with a good-quality angle plate and clamps. The sine bar is to be clamped against the angle plate with the working surface at an angle of 15° to the datum or reference face. This means that the linear height must be equivalent to 200 × sin 15°. More simply, look up the sine of 15° and multiply by 200.

$$\sin 15^\circ = 0{\cdot}2588$$
$$200 \times \sin 15^\circ = 51{\cdot}76$$

This linear dimension of 51·76 mm is readily obtained by wringing together the following slip gauges from a 78-piece set:

(i) 1·26 (eliminate the six hundredths, leave five tenths)
(ii) 5·5 (eliminate tenths)
(iii) 45

Total = 51·76

Note the use of the correct technique when selecting slips, thus allowing the use of only three slips.

The slip build-up is now placed in position, and the sine bar carefully clamped to the angle plate. A dial indicator is now used to determine whether the top face of the component is truly parallel to the datum face, and any deviation of the dial indicator pointer will be a measure of the angular error. This error will, of course, be obtained as a linear dimension, but provided the student has a knowledge of trigonometry or radian measure, it is not difficult to convert the linear deviation into angular error.

The essential geometry is also shown in fig. 87. Provided PQ is parallel to RS, and both are cut by a straight line, angle ϕ = angle θ. A very accurate check of the angle can be made in this way, and it is certain that the toolmaker will adopt a similar set-up using a sine bar and slip gauges when grinding the faces of the component. If we replace the dial indicator with a grinding wheel, shown in dotted lines, then it is clear that the toolmaker has presupposed the inspection technique, and a component machined in this way can be passed on to the inspection department with every confidence with respect to the accuracy of the angle.

This example of machining and measurement will also serve to remind the student of the necessity for the different grades of slip gauge sets.

The Spirit Level

Spirit levels are available in a wide range of sizes and accuracies. It may not be appreciated that the first measuring device capable of determining a linear error of twenty-five millionths of a millimetre consisted of a precision spirit level mounted on a circular table. Whilst it is true to state that even workshop levels are capable of determining linear dimensions to a remarkable degree of accuracy, they are seldom used for this purpose. They are, however, of great value when installing equipment such as machine tools, and also for testing the alignment of lathes and drilling machines.

The principle of a spirit level is shown in fig. 88. Note that the glass vial possesses a curvature, allowing a bubble of air to remain in its

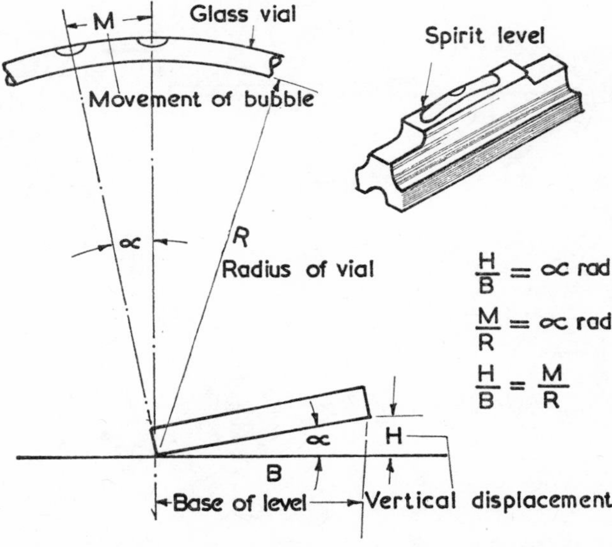

FIG. 88.—SPIRIT LEVEL PRINCIPLES AND CALCULATIONS.

highest position. The radius producing the curvature of the vial is shown as R, and the greater this radius, the more sensitive will the level be. The base of the level is shown as B; and a small displacement at H will produce an apparent movement of the bubble, M. For small displacements at H the calculations shown in fig. 88 can be used; thus it is possible to determine the radius of, say, a simple workshop level, and with the radius known the level may be used as a simple comparator. For best results the base of the level must be kept small, thus increasing its sensitivity, and the level can be mounted on slip gauges.

The Combination Set

Fig. 89 shows the component parts of a typical combination set. Much useful non-precision work can be carried out with the aid of such a set, and the small spirit level integral with the protractor attachment can be used for the simple determination of angles.

Fig. 89 shows two typical applications. At A the table of a pedestal off-hand grinder is to be adjusted so that a clearance angle of 20° can be ground on a lathe tool. Set the protractor so that the bubble lies central. Note the reading; if this is not 0°, the grinder is not properly installed.

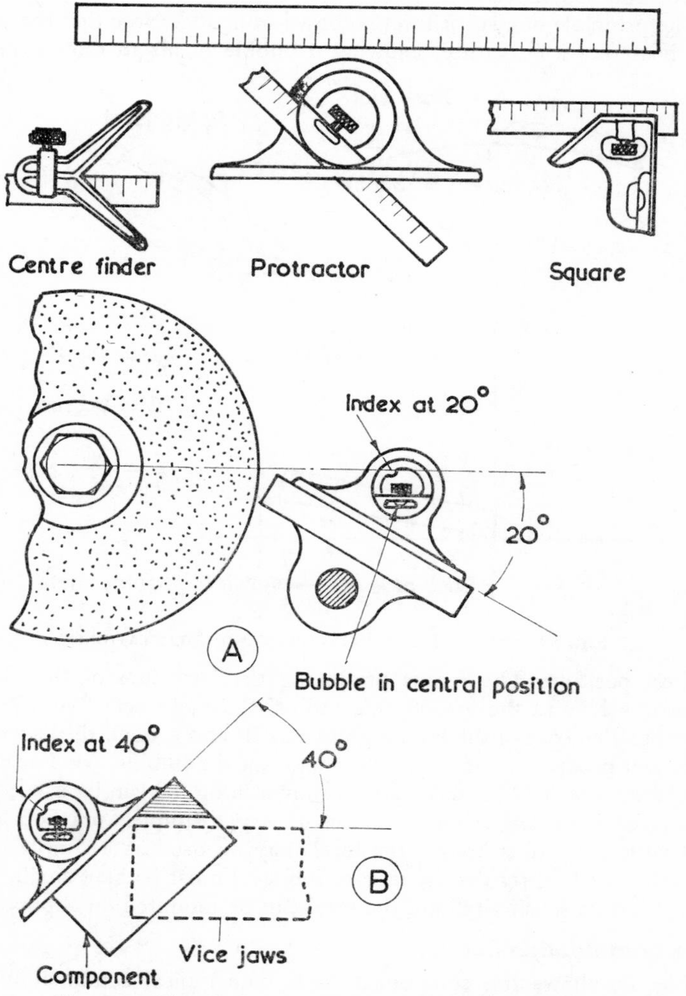

FIG. 89.—THE COMBINATION SET AND ITS APPLICATIONS.

Add 20° to the reading and lock the protractor in this position; place on the work table of the grinder and adjust until the bubble lies central; lock the table at this position. The table will now be at 20° to the centre line of the grinding wheel as shown in fig. 89A.

Much the same technique can be adopted to determine the angle of the component shown in fig. 89B. In this case we wish to rough-mill an angle of 40°, and the procedure is similar to the one just described. Check the level of the milling machine table with the protractor set at 0°. Index the protractor through 40°, and with the protractor resting on the work, tighten the vice with the bubble in the central position. If the necessary care is taken, very good accuracy can be obtained in this way, and the technique would be quite suitable for roughing operations, where the removal of metal takes precedence over the degree of accuracy.

Summary

It is an axiom of measurement that the instruments or techniques adopted will be in accordance with the degree of accuracy required.

It is wasteful of both time and equipment if precision measuring devices are used to determine non-precision dimensions. We have seen that measurements relating to engineering components will comprise linear, angular, and non-linear functions. The principle of measurement is the same; the comparison of an unknown value against a known value. The flat surface is the basis of all engineering measurements, and the use of a surface plate as a reference plane is an essential part of measurement. If engineering components are to be produced economically, using machine tools to produce the desired geometrical surfaces, it is essential that the dimensioning proceeds from the surfaces of greatest area, thus permitting maximum rigidity during the marking-off and machining operations.

Line standards, such as engineers' steel rules and vernier devices, are quite suitable provided the accuracy required is within the capabilities of the instrument used, but for precise measurement end standards such as slip gauges are to be preferred. The use of a dial indicator removes the troublesome aspect of feel, and it should be noted that the dial indicator is essentially a magnifying device operating on mechanical principles. The use of a sine bar provides an interesting example of the essential link between mathematics and measurement, and this is also true for the use of the spirit level. The real use of mathematics to the practical engineer lies in its use as a tool, allowing the positive and accurate check of an angle to be obtained by converting an angular dimension into a linear dimension; thus allowing the use of end standards or slip gauges. In the same way, holes having their centres in terms of angular relationships, or polar co-ordinates, can readily be redimensioned and the hole centres checked in terms of linear or rectangular co-ordinates.

It must always be remembered that there is little point in having a well-equipped, efficient inspection department if indifferent machining techniques are in use in the workshops. It is a wise machinist who anticipates the inspection technique or procedure, and sets up for the machining operation working from the same datum faces as those used by the inspector. The equipment used in workshops may be Grade C, whilst the inspector will have more accurate equipment, but there is much that an efficient standards room can do to ensure that no disagreement arises owing to the wear and tear of the equipment used.

It is also a general rule in engineering measurement, that in order to measure a given dimension, the measuring device used must possess an accuracy of ten times the tolerance given on the dimension. For example, if a diameter has a tolerance of plus and minus one hundredth of a millimetre, then the measuring device used to determine the diameter must be capable of reading to one thousandth of a millimetre. In this way the inspector should be capable of assessing the diameter to the fourth decimal place.

QUESTIONS ON CHAPTER FIVE

PART A

1. Explain why the largest surface areas of a casting are chosen as datum faces.
2. What are the production advantages gained when the position of hole centres is given by rectangular co-ordinates, as opposed to polar co-ordinates?
3. In what respects does a toolmaker's straight-edge differ from a Grade A plate glass surface plate?
4. With neat sketches illustrate **two** typical applications of a set of toolmaker's straight-edges.
5. Describe the essential technique to be adopted when wringing slip gauges; why is this technique necessary?
6. Show with neat sketches **two** applications of slip gauges used in a machining set-up. Why would the workshop set be used?
7. Describe how a bored hole 116·13 mm, with a tolerance of plus and minus one hundredth of a mm, would be checked using slip gauges and accessories.
8. Make a neat diagram illustrating the principle of magnification inherent in a dial indicator. Give **three** workshop applications of this instrument.
9. With an engineering component of your own choice, illustrate the use of a sine bar to determine the accuracy of two angular faces; include the necessary calculations.
10. What are the factors that determine the accuracy or sensitivity of an engineer's spirit level? Give two typical workshop uses for this instrument.

PART B

1. (*a*) Explain the essential difference between the use of a Line Standard and an End Standard when determining a linear dimension.

(*b*) Write brief notes on each of the following topics:

(i) Method of wringing the End Standards known as slip gauges.
(ii) Use of Workshop, Inspection, and Calibration sets of slip gauges.
(iii) Two typical uses of Workshop slip gauges.

W. J. E. C. (1963)

6 Inspection

THE inspection of engineering components is an essential and necessary part of engineering manufacture. It is important to appreciate the difference between inspection and measurement, and the following remarks will help, not only to illustrate the difference, but also to show the need for the inspection of engineering components.

Measurement

We have seen in the previous chapter that the measurement of either linear or angular dimensions involves the use of expensive and delicate equipment according to the degree of accuracy required. In all cases a definite assessment of the required dimension must result, and it is true to state that accuracy can be reckoned in terms of cost, time, patience, and skill. Exact results are not possible when measuring engineering components; to measure, say, a diameter to within plus or minus fifty millionths of a millimetre would require equipment costing somewhere around £1000. If we consider the countless millions of components produced each year by the engineering industry, it is evident that it is quite impracticable to measure all of them. In many cases the cost of measurement would considerably exceed the cost of manufacture.

Fig. 90 shows a gear cluster blank, an essential part of the gear box of a motor car. This gear cluster blank is automatically handled and completely externally machined ready for gear cutting in the remarkable time of forty-five seconds. Fig. 90 shows also a typical forged valve used in a motor car engine. This valve must have its stem ground to very close dimensional limits, and this precision machining operation is carried out on a centreless grinding machine. The production rates for this job are 720 finish ground valve stems every hour. This means that the time taken to machine a single valve stem is five seconds.

Both components can be considered as good examples of precision machining, and to measure each single component produced would be a most expensive and time-consuming project. Yet if the finished motor car is to have a long and useful life, it is vital that components similar to those shown in fig. 90 should be within the limits laid down in the drawing or blue-print.

Inspection

The purpose of engineering inspection, then, is to ensure that components are within the limits laid down. From the production figures given above, it will be clear that inspection plays a vital role in all engineering manufacture, for a high rate of production may well involve a high rate of scrap, if strict control is not maintained on the quality of

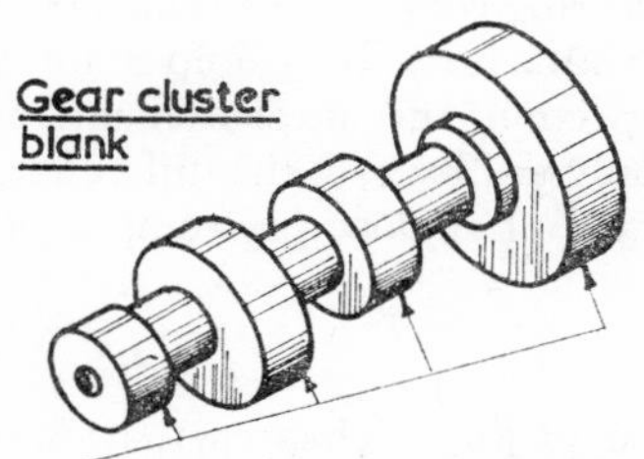

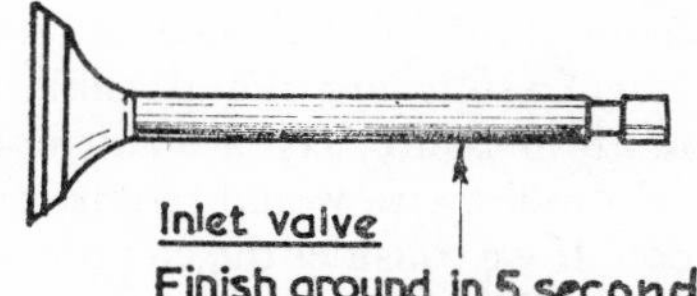

FIG. 90.—EXAMPLES OF PRECISION COMPONENTS PRODUCED IN LARGE NUMBERS.

the machined component. If the cost of the product is to be kept to a minimum, such inspection must be carried out as cheaply as possible.

Limits

We have already stated that exactness is not possible with respect to the determination of either linear or angular dimensions. This is also true for the machining of these dimensions, and for this reason most engineering dimensions will carry certain limits.

Let us consider a simple but important engineering assembly, namely the fitting of a valve guide in the cylinder block of a motor car engine, and the fitting of the valve in the valve guide. A sectional view of this assembly is shown in fig. 91. We can be sure that both valves and valve guides will be produced at high production rates, and this will

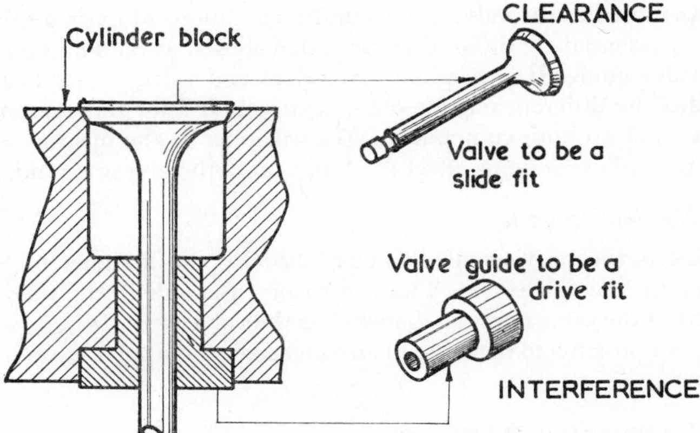

FIG. 91.—MASS PRODUCED ENGINEERING ASSEMBLY INVOLVING TWO SEPARATE TYPES OF FITS.

also be true for the machining of the cylinder block. Another important feature is that the component parts must be capable of rapid assembly; it is also essential that they be readily interchangeable, as this will permit an efficient and economical spare part service.

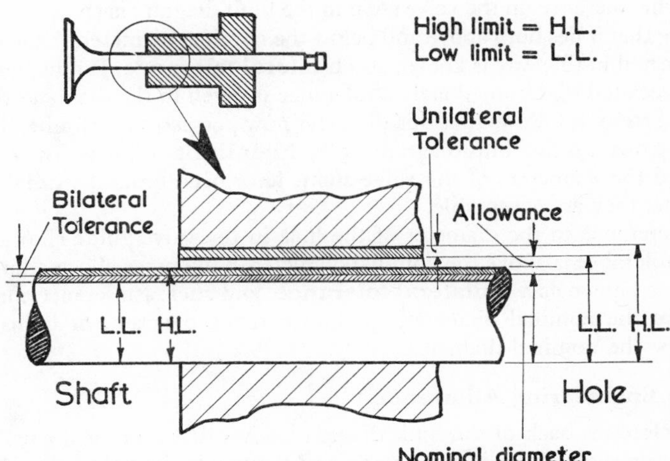

FIG. 92.—ESSENTIAL CONDITIONS FOR A CLEARANCE FIT.

Limit Diagram

Fig. 92 shows in diagrammatic form the conditions existing between the valve and valve guide when assembled. If the valves are to be assembled to the valve guides under conditions of mass production, it is an essential condition that any valve chosen at random must enter any valve guide. It is possible that valves and valve guides have been supplied by different outside manufacturers, and for this reason limits will be put on both components. We will refer to the diagram and see how the following items affect the limits on both valve and guide.

The Nominal Diameter

This is the provisional diameter fixed by the designer of the car engine for the valve stem. Thus, in theory, the hole in the valve guide will be of the same nominal diameter as the valve stem. It is, as we have seen, not possible to machine to an exact size, and a **tolerance** must be allowed.

The Engineering Tolerance

We can define tolerance as the amount of deviation allowed from the nominal size. This is very necessary because of the imperfections of both machine tools and operators. It is a general rule that tolerances are kept as large as possible; small tolerances involve expensive machine tools, together with the possibility of increased scrap due to the difficulty of keeping within the tolerances.

The tolerance on the valve stem in the limit diagram is shown shaded. Note that it lies both above and below the nominal diameter. A tolerance allocated in this way is known as a **bilateral tolerance.** It must now be appreciated that immediately a tolerance is given to the diameter of the valve stem, it follows that this diameter now possesses two limits. These are shown on the limit diagram as the **high limit** and **low limit**. Provided the diameters of the valve stems have been ground within these limits, they are acceptable.

Reference to the diameter of the hole in the valve guide shows that the tolerance is above the nominal diameter; a tolerance allocated in this way is known as a **unilateral tolerance**, and such a tolerance may be above the nominal diameter, as shown in the diagram, or it may be below the nominal diameter.

The Engineering Allowance

Reference back to the limit diagram shows that there is a small gap between the high limit of the valve and the low limit of the valve guide. This amount is known as the **allowance**; the amount of the allowance determines the quality of fit. In the example shown the allowance will be very small, probably no more than one eightieth of a millimetre. Note carefully that this allowance ensures that any valve will enter a valve guide, because it is the difference between a valve on high limit and a valve guide hole on low limit. In this way, provided all the valves and valve guides are machined so that their respective diameters are between the high and low limits, they will all assemble and permit rapid and efficient engine assembly.

Types of Fit

Fig. 92 shows a typical **clearance fit.** This means that provided the parts are machined to within their respective limits, a valve will always enter the hole in the valve guide. We may now consider the assembly of the valve guide to the cylinder block, and this is shown in diagrammatic form in fig. 93.

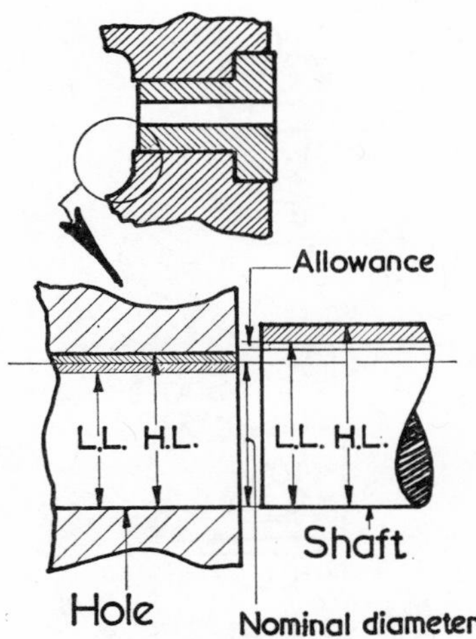

FIG. 93.—ESSENTIAL CONDITIONS FOR AN INTERFERENCE FIT.

Interference Fit

This assembly is a good example of an **interference fit.** We are now concerned with the outside diameter of the valve guide, and the diameter of the hole machined in the cylinder block. The valve guide is joined to the cylinder block by means of a press or force fit; this is a cheap and efficient method of joining two metal parts together. The quality or efficiency of the joint thus produced will depend on the accuracy of the machined diameters, and the degree of interference is determined by the amount of allowance. Note that the limit diagram is similar in all respects to fig. 92. Tolerances are given to both the valve guide and the bored hole in the cylinder block. Note that bilateral tolerances are given to the valve guide, whilst the bored hole has unilateral tolerances.

It must be appreciated at this stage that the quality of the fit obtained will be affected to some extent by the actual sizes or diameters of the components. For example, if the valve guide has been machined to the high limit and the bored hole is on the low limit, then greater force will be required to assemble the parts. On the other hand, if the valve guide is on low limit and the bored hole on high limit then less force will be required for assembly. In actual practice, however, most components are machined somewhere around middle limit, but the possibility of a variation in quality of fit will always exist.

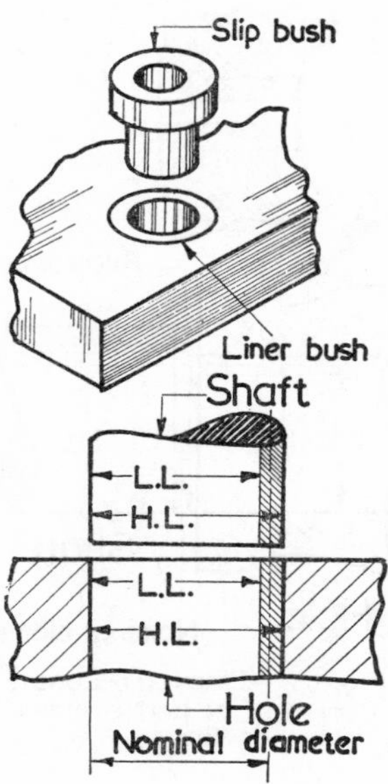

FIG. 94.—ESSENTIAL CONDITIONS FOR A TRANSITION FIT.

Transition Fit

Fig. 94 shows the essential conditions by which transition fits may be produced. It is now possible to have slight interference or slight clearance, according to whether the shaft or hole are on their high or low limits respectively. Thus if the shaft is on low limit and the hole on high limit the fit will be clearance; whilst a high limit shaft and a low limit hole will result in an interference fit. A typical practical example of such a fit is also shown in fig. 94. We see a slip bush, much used in drilling fixtures, and this bush may just enter the liner bush freely, or may require a slight push by the drilling machine operator.

A word of warning is now necessary with regard to the three limit diagrams used as illustrations in the above text. These are in the truest sense diagrammatic, and the tolerances and allowances are shown greatly enlarged. It must be clearly understood that the diagrams represent a much simplified picture of the conditions existing when two machined components are to be assembled together in order that a desired type of fit will result.

Interchangeability

The modern motor car provides an excellent example of the importance of interchangeable manufacture. There are several thousand separate items joined together in one way or another; yet every single item not only has been mass-produced, but also may be replaced with every confidence in its ability to mate accurately.

This problem of accurate mating is, perhaps, one of the most difficult that engineers have to face. A motor car engine is very similar to a machine tool, inasmuch as the useful life of the completed article will depend on the amount of wear taking place at the sliding or bearing surfaces. The greater the precision with which the component parts can be machined and then mated, the longer and more accurate will be the life of the completed assembly. Prior to the advent of mass-production techniques, a very great deal of costly and time-consuming hand or bench work was necessary for the production of components such as steam engines, pumps, and other mechanical devices. We need go back no further than the year 1776, when Matthew Boulton, a leading Midland manufacturing engineer, expressed great delight at the accuracy of the diameter of a 50 in bore steam cylinder, machined at the works of another famous engineer, John Wilkinson. The bore of this cylinder, said the delighted Boulton, "doth not err the thickness of an old shilling in no part".

In those days, accuracy was expressed in such terms as a "full thirty-second" or a "bare sixteenth". For the achievement of greater accuracy, the engineering industry owes a great debt to Sir Joseph Whitworth. The son of a schoolmaster, and an excellent practical engineer, he was probably the first to manufacture machine tools and offer them for sale. He also maintained that it was easier to work to one thousandth of an inch by his methods, than to work to one hundredth of an inch by the older methods. Any student who has guessed a cut when working on a centre lathe, instead of using the indexing dial, will appreciate the truth of this.

With the accurate machine tools now available, together with the precision available in measuring instruments, interchangeable manufacture is now the accepted method of producing a very wide range of engineering components, but it is necessary that a system of different types of fits be standardised. This is achieved by the use of **limit systems.**

Limit Systems

We have seen that the types of fits usually employed in engineering manufacture are either clearance, interference, or transition. The quality of the fit will be determined by the amount of allowance, and

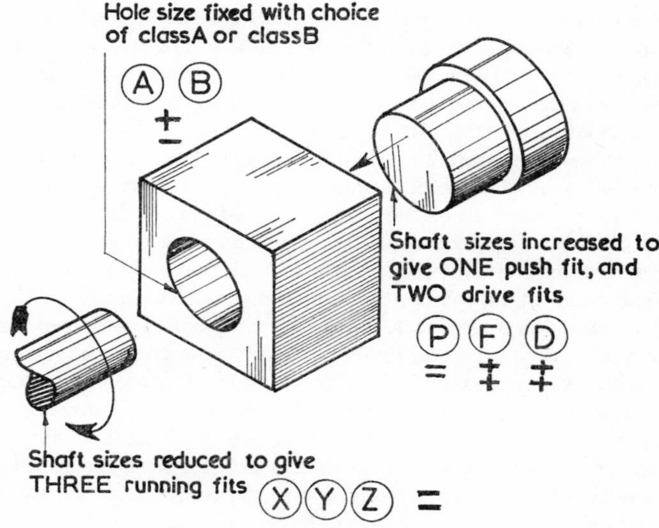

FIG. 95.—SIMPLIFIED PROVISIONS OF THE NEWALL LIMIT SYSTEM.

also by the amount of tolerance. The purpose of a limit system is to lay down standard values, so that any particular type of fit will be universal within the industries using the limit system.

The Newall System

This has been a popular system for a great number of years. It is simple to use, as all the necessary information is available in tabular form; no calculations are required. It operates on a hole basis; that is to say the hole sizes are constant, and various types of fits are obtained by including an allowance on the shaft. This principle is illustrated in fig. 95.

Newall Holes

Two classes of holes are provided, Class A and Class B; the tolerances on Class A holes are smaller than those for Class B, so that Class A holes are adopted for good quality machine tool work. All hole tolerances are bilateral, and the amount of tolerance is determined by the diameter of the hole, and obtained directly from tables.

Newall Shafts

Newall shafts fall into three categories, and these are listed below.

Clearance Fits

A typical clearance fit is shown on the left of the hole in fig. 95. Note that the shaft is to revolve in the hole, and this type of fit is always referred to as a **running fit.** The three grades of running fits are known as Class X, Class Y, and Class Z, the quality of the fit increasing in the order given. Thus a Class X fit will provide an easy running fit; Class Y would be used when a more precise fit is required; and Class Z is used for work of the highest quality.

Interference Fits

This is the second category of Newall shafts. Two grades are provided, Class F and Class D. Class F will be used when a force fit is required, and considerable pressure will be required to force the shaft or component into the hole. Alternatively, the hole may be heated, allowing expansion to take place, and the shaft inserted. This is known as a **shrink fit,** and we may consider this type of fit as permanent.

Class D denotes a **drive fit**, and this means that the component can be driven into position. A drive fit is always used when it may be necessary at a later date to remove the part for repair or replacement.

Transition Fits

The remaining fit provided by the Newall system is Class P, and this is known as a **push fit.** This is a transition fit, and the mating part can be pushed into the hole using hand pressure; slip bushes and dowels are good examples of the use of push fits in engineering manufacture. A push fit must never be used if rotation is to take place.

Note that the tolerances on all shafts are unilateral, plus plus for Classes F and D, and minus minus for Classes P, X, Y, and Z, whilst the hole tolerances are bilateral. The use of the hole basis for a limit system allows considerable economy and ease of manufacture. It is much more difficult to machine holes than it is to machine external diameters, and the production of holes to small tolerances will involve the use of a large number of reamers of different sizes. If the holes are of large size, expanding or adjustable reamers may be used, but it is a much better proposition to make use of the accurate indexing dials provided on machine tools, and control the linear dimensions of the shafts.

Perhaps the greatest disadvantage of the Newall system is that there are not enough types of fits to meet the ever-increasing needs of precision manufacture. Another disadvantage is that the quality of the fits is the same for all classes of work; thus a Class D fit used for the construction of, say, a tractor engine would have the same quality or accuracy as a Class D fit used in a modern jet aircraft engine. Clearly we need not only different types of fits, but also different qualities of fits, and the British Standards Institution recommend the use of BS 4500:1969, thus making the Newall system obsolete.

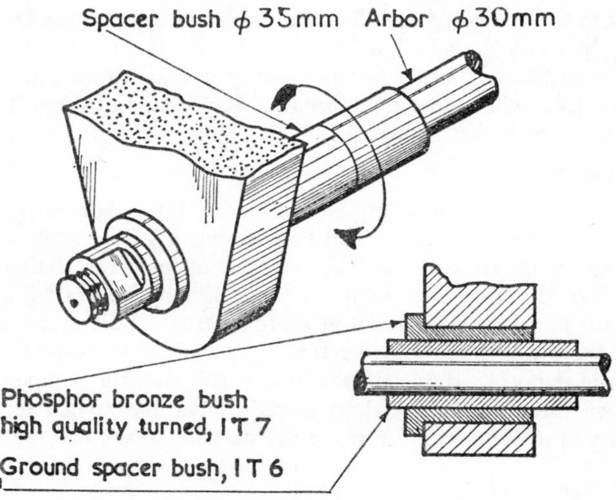

Fig. 96.—Details of Milling Arbor and Bush.

BS 4500:1969. ISO Limits and Fits

This is a very comprehensive limit system, and because of this it is not an easy system to follow. It is meant primarily for designers, and for this reason the following information may only be of value to those who are engaged, or likely to be engaged, in the design office. We will take as an example the fit obtained between the arbor of a horizontal milling machine and the phosphor bronze bush, shown in fig. 96. This is a good example of a running fit requiring a reasonable degree of accuracy. Fig. 97 shows a limit diagram for this fit, and we will refer to this diagram in order to show the essential working of BS 4500.

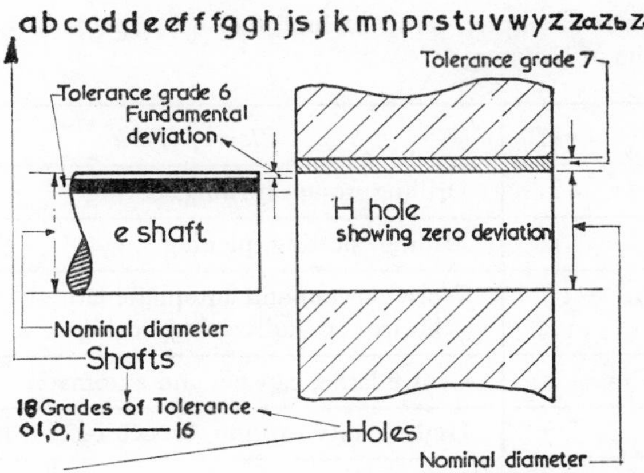

FIG. 97.—LIMIT DIAGRAM SHOWING ESSENTIAL CONDITIONS FOR A RUNNING FIT USING BS 4500.

The Nominal Diameter

The system covers work with sizes from below 3 mm up to 3150 mm. Let us assume that the arbor is 30 mm diameter, thus making the spacer bush 35 mm diameter, for we are concerned with the fit of the steel spacer bush in the phosphor bronze bush. The range from below 3 mm to 3150 mm is divided into separate sections or bands, in which the tolerances remain constant. The diameter of our spacer bush falls within the band 30 mm to 50 mm, and thus we are only concerned with the tolerances available within this particular dimensional band.

The Tolerance of the Phosphor Bronze Bush Hole

Eighteen grades of tolerance are provided, known as International Tolerances, or IT. This means that we may choose any one of these eighteen tolerances for the hole in the phosphor bronze bush. The actual tolerance chosen must depend on the quality of fit required, and suitable recommendations are laid down in this system. Thus the IT grade number will be chosen according to the class of work involved in the production of the component parts, and fig. 98 shows the tolerance grades most likely to be used in the typical engineering workshop. It is very important that the correct machine tool be chosen for the job in hand, because much scrap and reject work will result if precision work is attempted on a machine tool not capable of working to close limits of accuracy.

IT	*Class of Work*
11	Drilling, rough turning, boring
10	Milling, slotting, planing
9	Worn capstan and automatic lathe, horizontal and vertical boring
8	Centre lathe, capstan and automatic
7	High quality turning, broaching and honing
6	Grinding

FIG. 98. TOLERANCE GRADES.

We have chosen to machine the hole in the bush using a high quality centre lathe, thus, using the table at fig. 98, the tolerance grade for the hole will be IT 7.

This allocation of tolerance is shown diagrammatically in fig. 97, and such a tolerance will be unilateral.

Tolerance of the Spacer Bush

The choice of the tolerance for the spacer bush will proceed in exactly the same way; this bush will be ground, therefore we may choose an IT of 6. Reference back to fig. 97 shows that there must be an allowance between the spacer bush and the phosphor bronze bush if a clearance or running fit is to be obtained. This amount is known as the **fundamental deviation**, and determines the type of fit obtained. BS 4500 provides twenty-seven sets of tolerance zones, each with its deviation from nominal size, and this allows a wide choice of deviation to give the required quality of fit.

Designation of Holes and Shafts

Let us now attempt to sum up this somewhat complicated system. Twenty-seven different types of fits are available, with eighteen grades of tolerance.

Holes are designated by the following capital letters:

A B C CD D E EF F FG G H JS J K M N P R S T U V X Y Z Za Zb Zc.

Shafts are designated by the following small letters:

a b c cd d e ef f fg g h js j k m n p r s t u v w y z za zb zc.

Tolerance grade is indicated by the numbers from

01 0 1 2 3 4 5 6 7 8 9 10 11 12 13 14 15 16.

Example of the Use of BS 4500

Fig. 99 shows a typical pillar and bush assembly used in press tool work. We will consider only the fitting of the bush to the pillar, and this

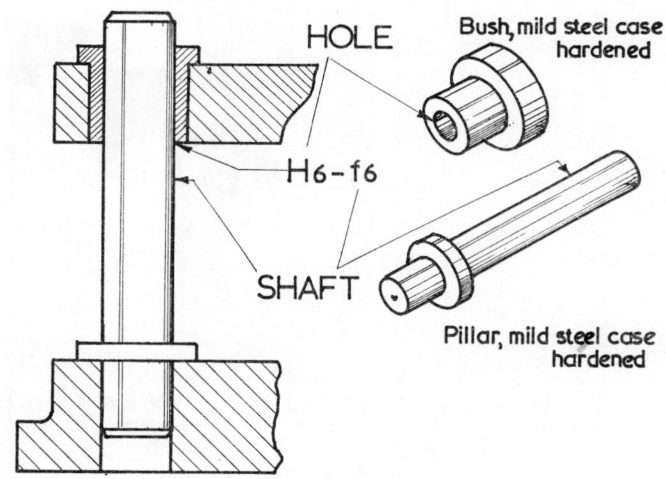

FIG. 99.—ASSEMBLY OF PILLAR AND BUSH TO OBTAIN PRECISE LOCATION OF A PRESS TOOL.

will be a clearance fit. The designer will designate the hole as H6, and the diameter of the pillar as f6. Because both pillar and bush will be produced by grinding, small tolerances are possible. Fig. 100 shows the tolerance zones from BS 4500 from which the designer has chosen the grade of tolerance.

The size of the hole diameter will appear on the drawing as

$50^{+0\cdot019}_{+0}$, and the diameter of the pillar will appear as

$50^{-0\cdot05}_{-0\cdot031}$

Provided both pillar and bush are ground to these limits, a good sliding fit will result, with the parts being completely interchangeable. Let us

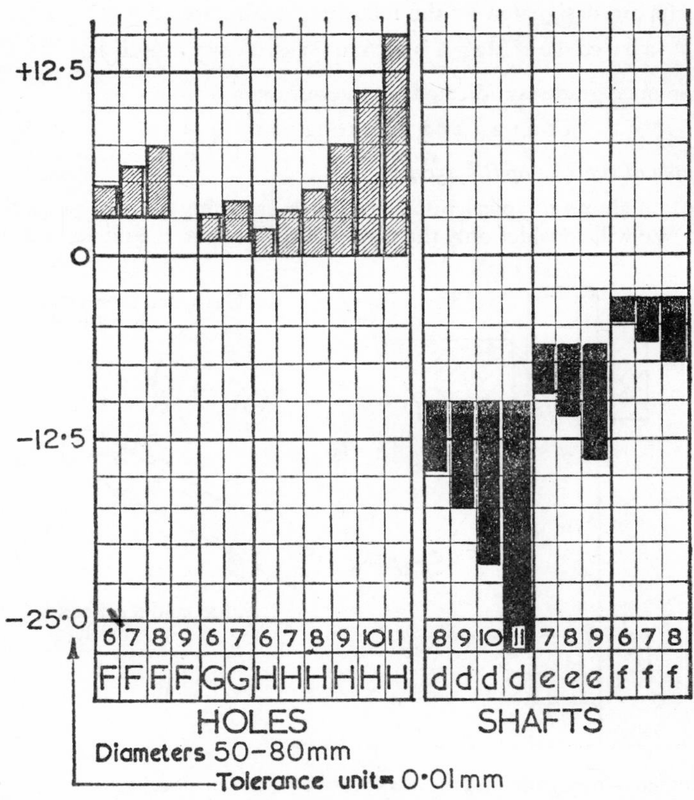

FIG. 100.—BS 4500 TOLERANCE ZONES FOR HOLES AND SHAFTS.

look into the results of assembling a high-limit pillar to a low-limit hole;

Low-limit hole	50
High-limit pillar	49·968
Clearance	0·032

Alternatively it is possible that the opposite condition may arise:

High-limit hole	50·019
Low-limit pillar	49·95
Clearance	0·069

As previously stated, however, the majority of the components will be somewhere around the middle limit, but even allowing for the above possibilities, clearance fits will always result.

With regard to the use of BS 4500 it must be clearly understood that the designation H6/f6 will not appear on the blue-print or drawing, and it is the draughtsman who converts these symbols into decimal tolerances; nevertheless it is hoped that the above examples will provide some indication of the working of BS 4500.

Limit Gauges

Limit gauges are used to avoid the costly and lengthy process of individual measurement of each component produced. Thus the purpose of a limit gauge is to ensure that the dimensions are within the limits laid down, and this permits very economical checking as skilled personnel are not essential for this work.

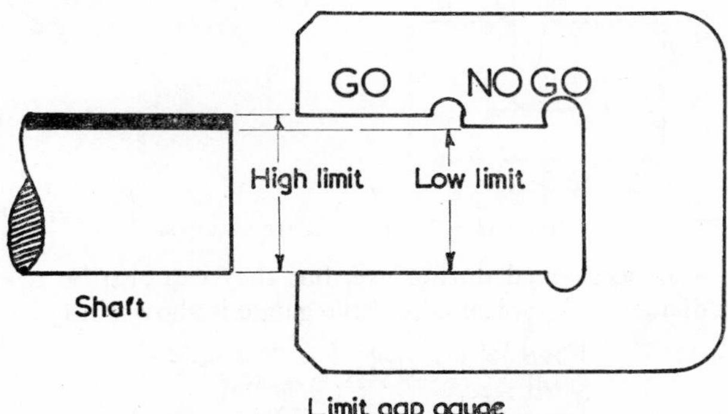

FIG. 101.—PRINCIPLE OF LIMIT GAUGING.

The principle of limit gauging is shown in fig. 101 with respect to the gauging of an external diameter. Such a gauge is known as a **gap gauge**, and the type shown is single-ended. If the **go** section passes over the work and the **no go** end does not pass over the work, then the work is acceptable. Note that we have not measured the diameter, but merely inspected the work to ensure it is within the limits laid down.

Some typical gauges are illustrated in fig. 102. These are all **fixed-size** gauges, and their manufacture calls for considerable skill. It must also be appreciated that precise measurement is involved during the manufacture of these fixed-size gauges, and the working faces of the gauges must be hardened and tempered to resist the wear that must take place over a period of use.

Adjustable Gauges

These gauges are very suitable for the checking of external diameters, and have the advantage that not only are they capable of adjustment to

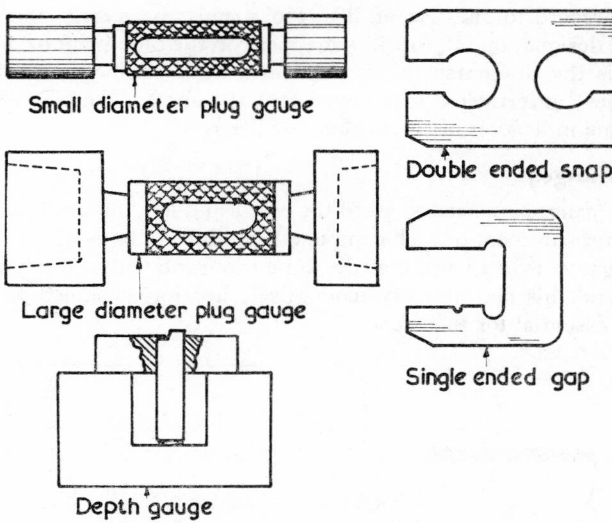

FIG. 102.—TYPICAL LIMIT GAUGES.

take up wear occasioned during use, but they can also be reset for a different diameter. A typical adjustable gauge is shown in fig. 103, and

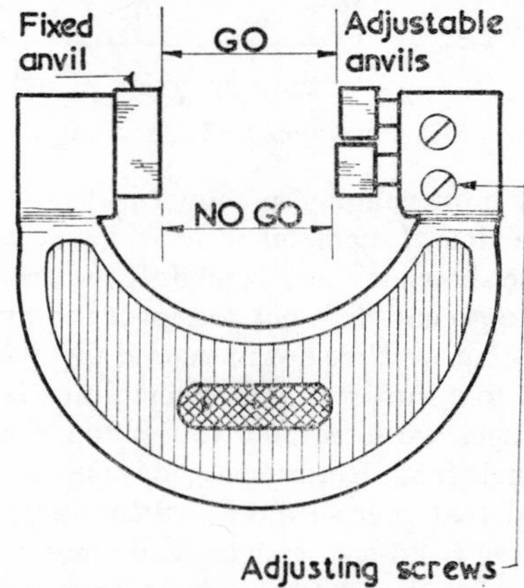

FIG. 103.—ADJUSTABLE GAP GAUGE.

such gauges are available in a range of sizes. They are readily set to the required **go** and **no go** dimensions, using slip gauges. This will be the work of the inspection department or standards room, and the use of these adjustable gauges offers considerable economy when compared to the costly manufacture and relatively short life of the gap gauges produced in the toolroom.

Summary

We have seen that the work of inspection is an essential part of all engineering manufacture. Essentially the inspection of a component consists in ensuring that the dimensions are within the limits laid down. These limits are the result of the placing of a tolerance on a machined dimension, producing a high limit and a low limit. When parts are required to be joined together, then the type of fit resulting will be determined by the amount of allowance, and if different parts are to be manufactured in various parts of the country, limit systems must be used to ensure that they will assemble correctly. The limit system now recommended is BS 4500:1969, and the H hole will be much used in all machine shop work. Finally the use of gauges is the means by which rapid and economic inspection can be carried out, although gap, plug, and other similar gauges are not suitable for very close tolerances. The use of the gauges mentioned above involves the vexed problem of feel, and for precision work increasing use is now made of the visual type of comparator, operated by mechanical, optical, or even pneumatic methods.

The introduction of interchangeable manufacture has enabled a wide range of precision products to be available to the mass of the population at prices within the reach of all; and both measurement and inspection play a vital part in this technique. Measurement ensures that the press tools, jigs, fixtures, and gauges possess the necessary accuracy, whilst inspection ensures that the components produced are within the desired limits.

QUESTIONS ON CHAPTER SIX

1. Explain the essential difference between engineering measurement and inspection.
2. Why is it necessary to give a tolerance on an engineering dimension? Give an example of both a bilateral tolerance and a unilateral tolerance.
3. Make a neat limit diagram showing the essential conditions for a clearance fit.
4. What is meant by a transition fit? Illustrate your answer with a simple limit diagram.
5. Explain the effect of the engineering allowance on the different types of fit required in engineering manufacture.
6. What is the importance of interchangeability with respect to an engineering assembly such as a motor cycle?
7. Describe the function of a limit system, and give brief details of a limit system of your own choice.
8. What are the advantages offered by the use of limit gauges in engineering manufacture?
9. Make a neat sketch of a limit gauge to be used for checking the diameter of a drilled hole, having the following dimensions: 64·72 ± 0·08 mm.
10. Describe the advantages of adjustable gap gauges. How can such gauges be set to within plus or minus two thousandths of a millimetre?

7 Cutting Tool Theory and Practice

MACHINE tools such as lathes, milling machines, shapers, slotters, and planers all remove metal in order to produce a desired surface. Whilst the purpose of a machine tool is to make possible the essential geometrical movements of work and tool, the actual removal of the metal is brought about by the **cutting tool** used.

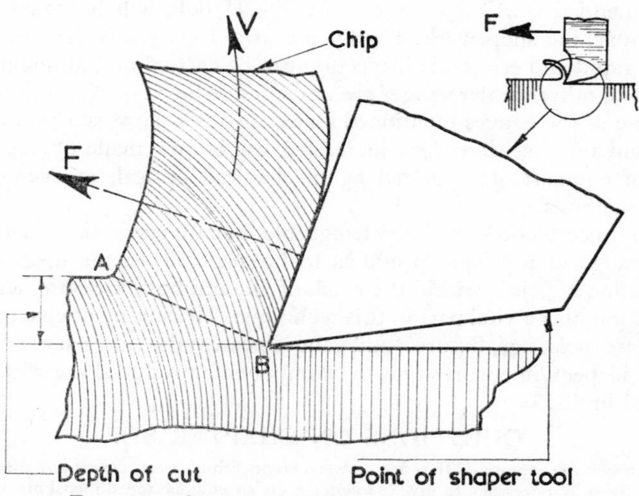

FIG. 104.—CUTTING ACTION OF A SHAPER TOOL ON DUCTILE METAL.

We have seen in Volume I that cutting tools may be either single- or multi-point; a single-point tool having a wedge-like action, whilst a multi-point tool will be made up of a number of wedge-like points.

Let us take a closer look at the shearing action of a single-point tool, for we will do well to remember that the efficiency of an expensive shaping machine can be measured in terms of the amount of metal removed in a given time. This, of course, is true for all machine tools, and because of this it is essential that the correct cutting tool conditions exist if maximum efficiency is to be obtained.

Fig. 104 illustrates the cutting action of a tool during the shaping of a plane or flat surface. We have in effect stopped the cutting action for a brief moment of time, and are now able to examine the cutting action in some detail.

Forces Acting at the Tool Point

The ram of the shaping machine will move forward during the cutting stroke with a certain force, and the magnitude of this force will depend mainly on the horse power of the driving motor. This force is shown as F in the diagram, and as the cutting tool is rigidly fixed to the head slide during the cutting stroke, the force exerted by the cutting tool will also

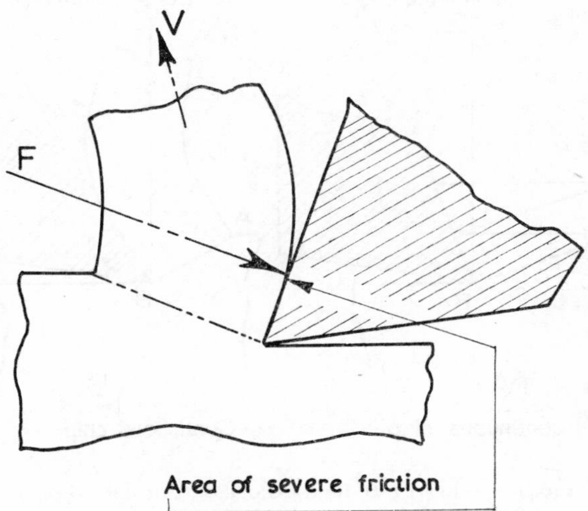

FIG. 105.—CHIP FORCES ON TOOL POINT.

have the value F. This force sets up a **shear plane** across AB; if the metal is ductile, considerable plastic flow will take place, as shown by the deformation of the vertical lines. A continuous **chip** will be produced and will move upwards in the direction indicated by the arrow V. It must now be appreciated that as the chip moves up the face of the tool, there will be an opposite and equal reaction to the force F, resulting in an area of severe friction. This is further shown in fig. 105; remember that the diagram shows the cutting operation static or stopped. In actual practice the tool will be moving at considerable speed, as will the chip, and it will be evident that severe frictional forces will be set up between the tool face and the moving chip as it is sheared from the parent metal.

If the removal of metal is to be as efficient as possible, the work done to overcome this frictional force must be kept to a minimum, and this means that the value of force F must be at a minimum.

Effect of Rake Angle on the Shearing Force

We can consider F as the force required to shear or deform the metal, and, as we pointed out in Volume I, the **rake angle** has a profound effect on the amount of force required to bring about shear or deformation of the metal.

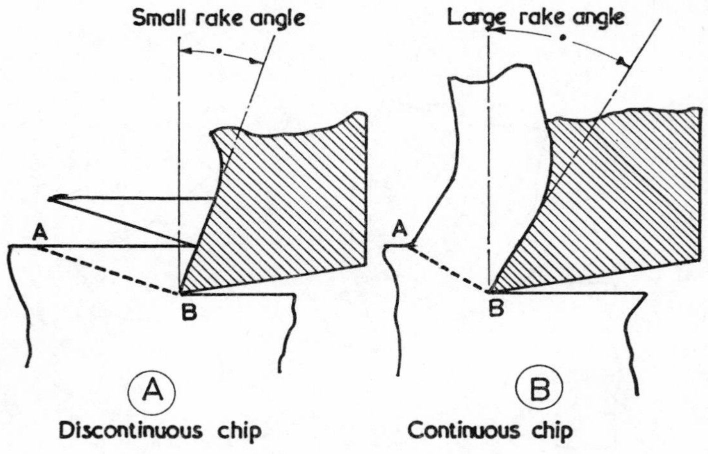

FIG. 106.—EFFECT OF RAKE ANGLE ON SHEARING FORCE.

Fig. 106 shows two shaper tools, both taking an identical cut; in other words both tools are doing the same amount of work, or removing the same amount of metal in the same time. The tool shown at A has a small rake angle, and this means that the shear plane extends from A to B. This shear plane will be at approximately 90° to the breast of the tool; the breast is formed by the rake angle, and it is this surface which takes the opposite and equal reaction force to F. It will be clear from fig. 106 that the smaller the rake angle, the greater will be the shear plane, shown as AB, and thus a greater force F will be required to shear the metal.

Not only will a small rake angle require a greater shearing force, but also the useful life of the tool will be considerably reduced. The breast of the tool will be subject to severe frictional forces set up by the increased force F and the speed or velocity of the chip as it moves up the breast of the tool. The useful life of a cutting tool is governed by the ability of the breast of the tool to stand up to the frictional forces caused by the pressure and velocity of the moving chip. These must result in severe abrasion of the breast of the tool, and as the physical property of hardness is that which resists abrasion or indentation, we can be sure that a high degree of hardness is an essential quality of all cutting tools.

Although fig. 106 shows only the forces acting on a shaping tool, it is important to remember that a similar condition exists whenever the

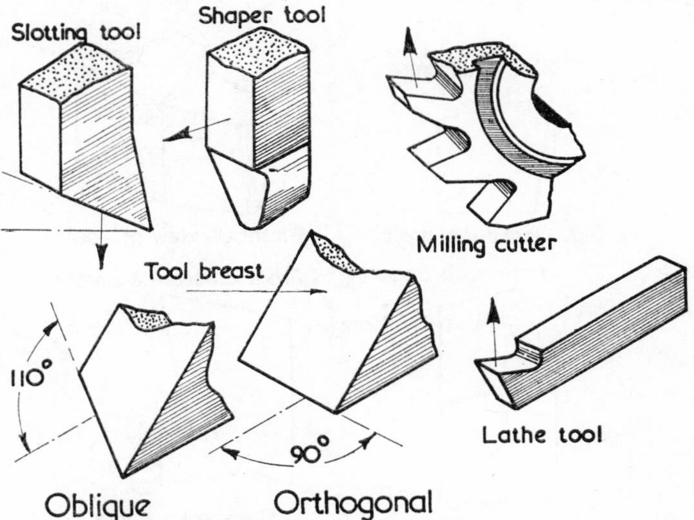

FIG. 107.—THE WEDGE PRINCIPLE.

wedge principle is used. This is clearly illustrated in fig. 107. Four tools are shown: a milling cutter, lathe tool, shaper tool, and a slotting tool. Of these four tools, only the milling cutter is a multi-point tool, having a number of teeth, and rotation of this milling cutter presents successive wedge-like points to the work. Note that the wedge principle is common to all the cutting tools shown, and all the remarks made in connection with our discussion on the shaper tool, using figs. 104, 105, and 106, apply to the cutting conditions encountered when any of the tools illustrated in fig. 107 are used.

Note also that both the **orthogonal** and **oblique** cutting actions are shown in fig. 107, together with the cutting conditions that are applicable in each case. It will be seen that orthogonal cutting takes place when the breast or cutting face of the tool is at 90° to the line of action or path of the tool. If, however, the cutting face is inclined or at an angle to the path of the tool, the cutting action is known as oblique.

Lathe Tools

Some confusion has always existed with regard to the names of the different parts of a cutting tool; for example, terms such as Top Rake, True Rake, Side Rake, and Back Rake are in popular use. The best plan is to refer to British Standard 1886 : 1952 for single-point cutting tools. Fig. 108 shows the correct nomenclature to be used when describing single-point cutting tools.

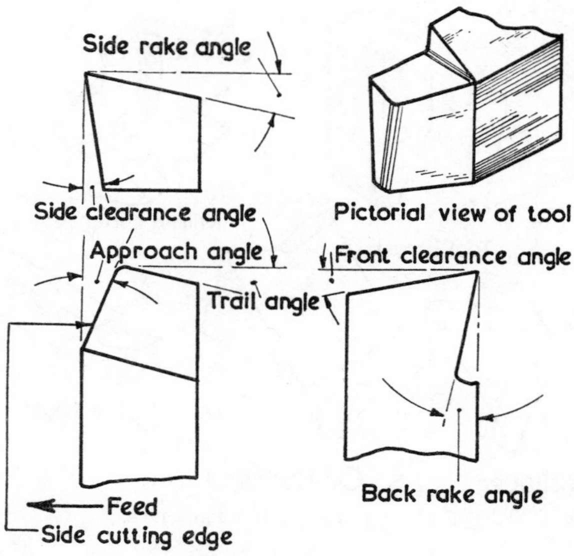

FIG. 108.—LATHE TOOL NOMENCLATURE.

Importance of Correct Tool-setting

Not only is it important that the correct rake and clearance angles be ground on a lathe tool, but it is also essential that the tool be accurately and rigidly supported in the tool post. In most turning work, the lathe tool is mounted **radially**. This means that the point of the tool must lie on a line equivalent to an extension of the centre line of the work. This principle is shown in fig. 109, and it will be seen that provided the tool point is on the centre line of the rotating bar, any radial line can be used. Centre lathes, of course, use the position shown at A, the use of a four-way tool post permitting four tools to be presented to the work.

A capstan lathe will have an additional tool position, shown at B, and this allows speedy parting-off of the work without changing the direction of rotation.

Automatic lathes may have several tool positions, shown in the diagram as C, D, E, and F; in this way it is possible to carry out a considerable amount of machining, the movement of the tools being controlled by cams. In all cases it is essential that the points of the tools are truly on the centre line of the work, if the effective rake angle is to be maintained.

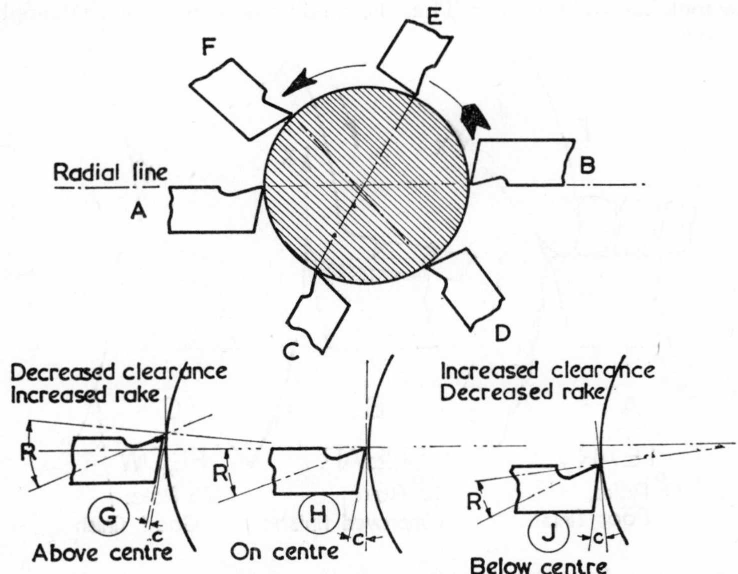

FIG. 109.—THE RADIAL CUTTING ACTION.

If the tool is set **above** centre, as shown at G, then the net result is an **increase** of the rake angle, with a **decrease** of the clearance angle. Similarly, setting the tool **below** the centre line results in a **decrease** of the rake angle and an **increase** of the clearance angle. These conditions are clearly shown in fig. 109; the correct setting is shown at H. Provided the tool is correctly set as shown, then the rake angle ground on the tool will be the rake angle applied to the work, and we can now consider the type of chip produced by the rake angle.

Effect of Rake Angle on Type of Chip and Work Finish

We have already seen that the amount of rake angle determines the energy required to shear or deform the metal being removed from the workpiece. A large rake angle reduces the force necessary to shear the metal, and reduces also the frictional forces set up as the sheared chip moves across the tool face. There is, however, another important advantage to be obtained when the correct rake angle is used, and this concerns the finish of the machined surface.

The type of chip produced by differing rake angles, together with the effect on the surface finish, is illustrated in fig. 110, and we must remember that although the examples shown refer to the use of a single point tool used on a centre lathe, the principle is equally applicable to the tools shown in fig. 107. Thus the conditions shown in fig. 110 apply

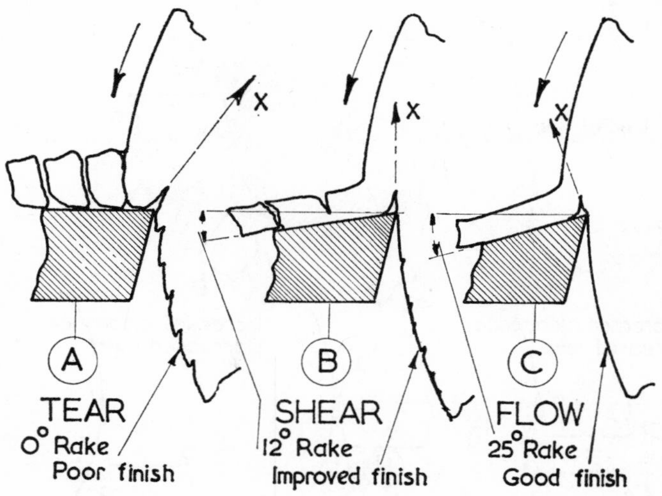

FIG. 110.—EFFECT OF RAKE ANGLE ON TYPE OF CHIP AND WORK FINISH.

to a milling cutter tooth, a shaping, slotting, or planing tool, and indeed to any tool that removes metal by the wedge principle. It should be noted that the metal being removed in fig. 110 is a ductile one, for engineers make much use of ductile metals; we must never forget that engineers are concerned with making things, and hard brittle metals have a very limited use in engineering manufacture.

Tear

This condition is shown in fig. 110A. Note that the rake angle of the tool is 0°; this is known as a **negative rake**. The force component of the torque of the revolving work will now act vertically downwards, and will be opposed by an equal and opposite force acting upwards. Reference to the diagram will show that there is a tendency for the work to split in the direction of arrow X; whilst the chip produced will be broken or discontinuous, and will soon discolour due to the very high frictional forces generating heat. Note carefully that the point of the tool does **not** make contact with the work, and a poor finish must result.

It should be clear that this is a most inefficient method of removing metal, yet this is the sort of cutting condition that will arise if, say, a facing tool is used to take a sliding cut on a centre lathe. If Volume I is at hand the student is advised to refer to fig. 228. This shows a typical shaping tool, and if this tool is allowed to cut in both directions, feeding the table in the direction of arrow B will result in the cutting conditions known as **tear**, and would represent very poor machining technique.

Shear

Fig. 110B shows the conditions producing a shear type chip. Note that the rake angle is now increased to 12°, and we see that the split has moved to the left, or towards the chip. Because the shear plane is at approximately 90° to the cutting face, the metal shears more readily and the resultant chip will be longer and less likely to discolour. Note also that the point of the tool may at times clean up the surface of the work, producing a better finish. It is evident that this type of cutting condition represents better machining technique than that producing a tear type of chip.

Flow

We may regard the conditions producing a flow type of chip as ideal. These conditions are shown in fig. 110C. The rake angle is now 25°. We see from the diagram that the work turned is mild steel, and a rake angle of 25° is ideal for this metal. Both shear plane and split are now well to the left; much deformation of the metal takes place as shown in fig. 104, and a long continuous chip results. Note also that because the metal tends to split with the shear plane, the point of the tool now removes a small amount of metal or cleans up the work and a good finish results. Energy requirements are low due to the small shear plane area, and this means that the reduced forces will cause less distortion and vibration of the work.

We see now the importance of using the correct rake angle for the metal to be machined; the importance of accurate setting of the cutting tool, and the effect of cutting conditions on the type of chip produced. When the chip leaves the parent metal in a long continuous ribbon, we can be sure that cutting conditions are about right, especially if a good finish is present on the work.

Chip Breaking

Whilst there may be a certain amount of pleasure and fascination in watching a long ribbon of swarf turned off a bar, such swarf represents a source of danger as well as a problem when its removal is required. For purposes of safety and convenience it is better that the swarf or chip be broken into short lengths, and in many cases this is achieved through the small radius ground at the end of the tool breast. Fig. 111

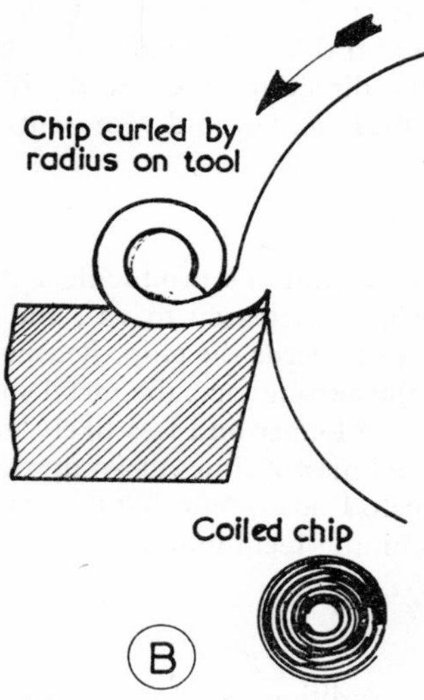

FIG. 111.—CHIP BREAKING.

shows how this radius tends to turn the chip, causing it to bend back on to the rotating bar and break off. The operation shown would be a parting-off operation, and very often the chips are produced in close tight-packed spiral coils; a typical coil is shown in fig. 111B.

Effect of Back Rake and Approach Angle on Chip

Both the back rake and approach angle have an important effect on the type of chip produced by the cutting action of a single-point tool. We have stated several times that a machine tool such as a lathe is only of value when metal is actually being removed, and the greater the volume of metal removed in a given time, the more efficient is the machine tool.

A centre lathe when properly used is capable of producing a considerable volume of swarf or metal chips in the course of a day's work, and the presence of this swarf in the vicinity of the revolving work represents both a nuisance and a danger to the operator of the lathe. Long continuous lengths of swarf are exceedingly dangerous; not only are they capable of being caught up by the rotating work, but also they invariably possess sharp edges and can cause severe injury.

This type of swarf is very likely to result when a good cut, at high speed, is taken with a knife-edge tool as shown in fig. 112A. This is orthogonal cutting. Note that the cutting tool shown at A has no back

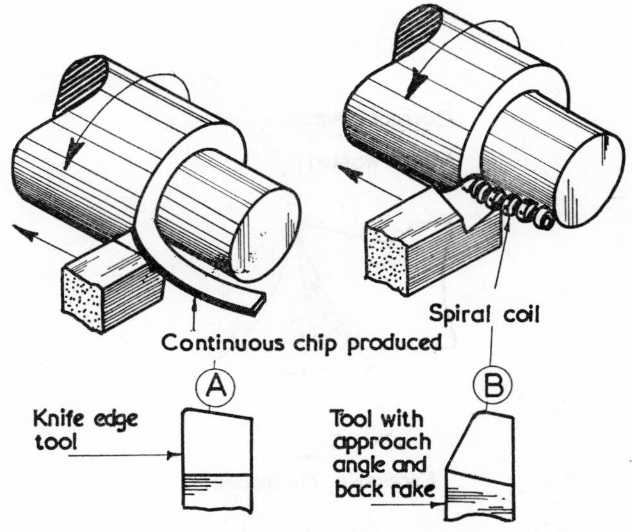

FIG. 112.—EFFECT OF BACK RAKE AND APPROACH ANGLE ON CHIP.

rake and no approach angle. If now the tool is ground as shown in fig. 112B, with an approach angle and a back rake angle, the chip will tend to form a spiral coil as it moves across the tool face, and this type of chip or swarf is much easier to control than the straight chip.

Because of the tendency for the back rake angle to produce a spiral chip, it is in much favour with centre lathe turners; the approach angle is also popular for the same reason, and this is especially so if large cuts are to be taken. Thus fig. 112B shows a typical **roughing tool**, and is of course a good example of the oblique cutting action.

Clearance Angles

Clearance angles take no part in the cutting process. Their purpose is to prevent rubbing of the tool against the work, and it is a general rule that clearance angles are always kept to a minimum. For external machining, a value of 10° is seldom exceeded, and to grind an excessive clearance angle on, say, a lathe tool is a serious fault. This is shown in fig. 113, the tool illustrated being a simple parting-off tool. The correct clearance angle is shown by the dotted lines, and the shaded area represents the excess metal that has been needlessly ground away if the clearance angle has the value C. Not only have both time and tool material been wasted, but also the tool point is seriously weakened, and will rapidly break down under the strong frictional force of the moving chip.

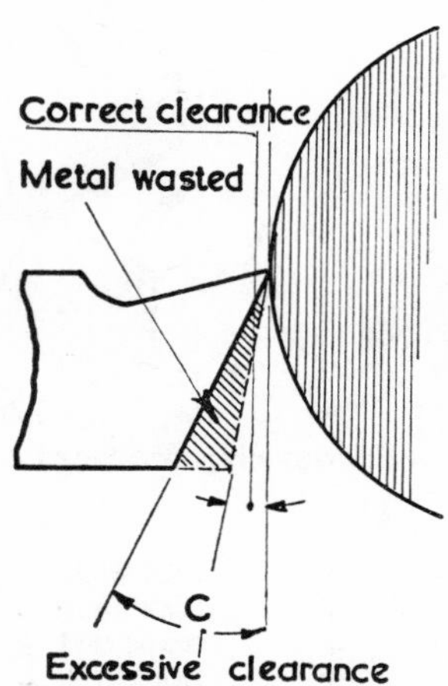

FIG. 113.—IMPORTANCE OF CORRECT CLEARANCE ANGLE.

The reduction of metal at the tool point also reduces the ability of the tool to conduct away the heat generated by friction, so that rapid overheating of the tool point is certain to take place. The sum of all this is that the life of the tool is greatly reduced; in a very short while it must be removed from the lathe and reground. It is not difficult to imagine the considerable wastage of tools that would take place if all machine operators were allowed to grind and sharpen their own tools. There is perhaps no greater wastage of expensive material in engineering manufacture than that which takes place when machine tool operators are allowed to sharpen their own tools.

Secondary Clearance Angles

To conserve tool material, secondary clearance angles may be ground on a cutting tool. Fig. 114 shows a tool bit inserted in a boring bar, a typical set-up used for the boring of internal diameters. If the bore is of relatively small diameter, a clearance angle of 10° will not be sufficient to prevent the base of the tool from rubbing the work, and this means that the clearance angle must be increased. Grinding the tool as shown in fig. 114A would represent bad practice, for the point of the tool would be seriously weakened as shown in the diagram, and such a tool would have a very short life.

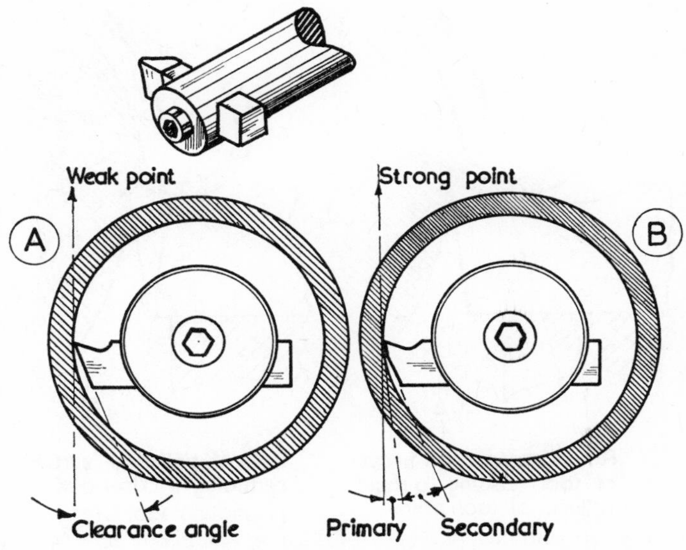

FIG 114.—PRIMARY AND SECONDARY CLEARANCE ANGLES.

Better results are obtained when the tool is ground as shown in fig. 114B. Note that a primary clearance angle of 10° has been ground on the tool, followed by a secondary clearance angle. The purpose of the secondary clearance angle is to prevent rubbing of the tool, and no more metal than is necessary will be removed. Reference to fig. 114B shows clearly that a tool ground in this way with secondary clearance is much stronger than the tool shown in fig. 114A. Much the same principle is used when providing the clearance angles for the teeth of milling cutters.

Tool Wear

As previously stated, the life of a cutting tool will be determined by its ability to withstand the severe abrasion set up by the pressure and velocity of the chip as it moves across the tool face. If a cutting tool is to have a long life it is essential that this face be as smooth as possible, as this will reduce the frictional effect; this means that a fine or smooth wheel must always be used for the final grinding of the tool face. This principle is illustrated in fig. 115. At A we see a tool having a roughly ground face or breast. Clearly, due to the poor surface finish of the tool face shown at A, the frictional effect of the moving chip is severe, and rapid deterioration of the cutting face of the tool is inevitable.

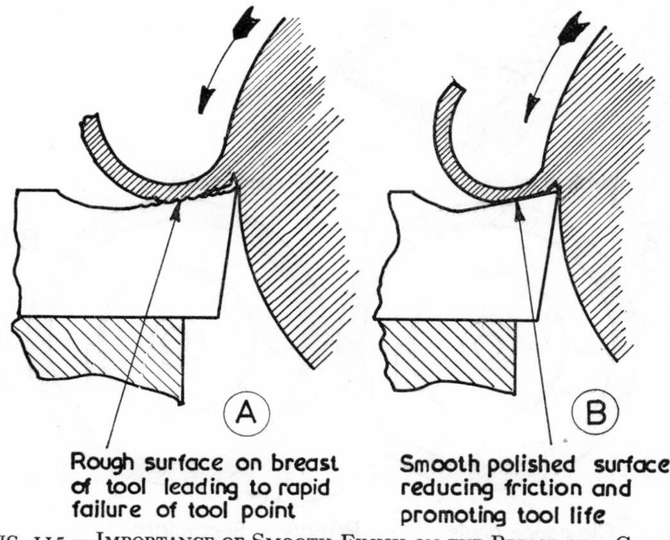

FIG. 115.—IMPORTANCE OF SMOOTH FINISH ON THE BREAST OF A CUTTING TOOL.

At B, we see a tool with a well-ground, smooth cutting face, and it is certain that this tool will last a great deal longer than the tool shown at A.

It is clear also that the use of suitable cutting fluids will do much in reducing the friction and heat generated during the cutting action, and thus increase the useful life of the tool.

Cutting Fluids

Although the main function of a cutting fluid is to dissipate heat, and provide some lubrication, several other functions are also performed. We may list the functions of a cutting fluid as follows:

(i) To conduct heat away from tool and work;
(ii) To reduce friction between chip and face of tool;
(iii) To improve surface finish;

(iv) To reduce energy requirements;
(v) To extend the life of the cutting tool;
(vi) To carry away swarf and chips from the cutting point.

For the efficient and rapid machining of most metals, a suitable cutting fluid is essential, and the type of cutting fluid chosen depends on the cutting action of the tool. We can divide cutting fluids into two main types:

(i) **coolants,**
(ii) **lubricants.**

Coolants

A coolant is used when the cutting action takes place at high speed. Considerable heat is generated, not only by the friction of the sheared chip as it moves over the tool face, but also by the cold working or plastic flow of the chip as it leaves the parent metal. Unless this heat is conducted away, the temperature of both the tool and the work will rapidly rise, leading to considerable expansion with the possibility of poor dimensional accuracy.

Water-soluble oils are widely used when the above conditions are applicable, and the word **suds** is often used in the workshops to describe a coolant which is, in effect, a water-soluble oil.

Water-soluble Oils

These are widely used to make a cheap and efficient coolant, suitable for the machining of most steel components. The cheapness of this coolant is due to the fact that the main constituent is water; the soluble oil is added at the rate of one part oil to twenty parts water. Soluble oils are usually mixtures of mineral or fatty oils, together with an emulsifier such as lime or soda soap. When these are added to water the familiar milky liquid results, and such a liquid will not corrode the work or the machine tool, neither is it harmful to the machine tool operator. Because of the high water content, the specific heat will be high, and provided an adequate flow of coolant is maintained on the cutting tool point, the greater part of the heat generated by the cutting action will be carried away by the coolant.

Lubricants

Water-based coolants, however, do not possess very good lubricating properties, and would not be suitable for a more complex machining operation such as gear-cutting or spline-milling. Operations such as these involve considerable metal removal in minimum time, and because of the precision of the parts produced, it is essential that the cutter wear be kept to a minimum. The use of a suitable **cutting oil** will do much to preserve, not only the useful life of the cutting tool, but also the quality of finish on the machined component.

Cutting Oils

Cutting oils consist of mixtures of mineral oils with fatty oils; small percentages of sulphur and chlorine may also be added to improve the surface finish of the machined part. The transparency of these oils is an additional advantage, allowing the machine tool operator to observe the cutting action, and provided there is an adequate flow of oil, both heat and swarf will be carried away from the tool point.

The specific heat of cutting oils is lower than that of the coolants made up of water and soluble oils, but cutting oils have very good lubricating properties, reducing the frictional effects between the chip and tool breast, and thus preserving the life of the tool.

Both coolants and cutting oils must be able to keep well, that is to say they must not deteriorate over a period of time, and become offensive in either appearance or smell. Cutting oils are always used when components are mass-produced on special-purpose machine tools such as automatic lathes or gear-cutting machines. As previously stated, the main purpose of their use is the preservation of the cutting tool faces, allowing long machining runs before tool changing is necessitated by the wear on the tool faces. On the other hand, the use of the water-soluble oils is generally confined to the less productive type of machining operation, and for this reason they are much used on centre lathes, milling machines, and drilling machines.

Cutting Tool Materials

The most important physical property required by a cutting tool material is **hardness.** At the same time the tool material must also be tough enough to withstand the pressures encountered during the cutting action. There are not many materials which possess both hardness and toughness, but the hardening properties of high carbon steel have been appreciated and put to good use for over two thousand years.

High Carbon Steel

High carbon steel is still in extensive use as a cutting tool material. Its use, however, is limited to cutting tools which are not likely to have an increase in temperature during the cutting operation, for as we have seen in Volume I, and also in the chapter on Heat Treatments in this volume, high carbon steel quickly loses its hardness when the temperature of the tool point reaches 250° C.

Such temperatures are easily reached when metal is removed using a lathe, drilling, or milling machine, and the use of high carbon steel tools on these machines means that both speeds and feeds must be kept low if a temperature rise of the tool point is to be avoided.

The use of a copious supply of coolant will permit the raising of the cutting speed, but the coolant supply must be both constant and reliable, with no possibility of failure. Thus the machining ability of the early machinists was limited by the high carbon steel tools used, and up to 1900 a 50 mm diameter bar would be turned at about 60 revolutions per minute. This is equivalent to a cutting speed of 0·157 metres per second (m/s).

In the year 1900, a new type of cutting steel, developed in America by F. W. Taylor and Maunsel White, was introduced at the Paris Exhibition. Single-point lathe tools made from this new steel were on public view, removing metal from 50 mm diameter bars rotating at the remarkable speed of 5 revolutions per second (rev/s). Equivalent to a cutting speed of 0·785 m/s, this was five times faster than the cutting speed possible with a high carbon steel tool.

Even more remarkable was the fact that the tools made from the new steel would still continue to remove metal even though the tool point was at red heat. In such a fashion did **high-speed steel** show its great superiority.

High-Speed Steel

High-speed steel is widely used as the material from which lathe tools, milling cutters, drills, and reamers are made. It is essentially an alloy steel, containing tungsten as the main alloying element together with a small percentage of chromium. The hardening of this steel is totally different from the hardening technique adopted for carbon steel. The high-speed steel tool to be hardened is first pre-heated to about 800° C, then rapidly heated to 1300° C. A special furnace will be used, and severe scaling can be prevented by immersing the tool in a bath of lead. When the tool has attained a temperature of 1300° C it is cooled in a blast of air; this considerably reduces the risk of cracking and distortion.

Re-heating to about 600° C will give a slight increase in hardness, and is very similar to the tempering process carried out on high carbon steel. A properly hardened high-speed steel tool will give a Brinell Hardness Number of 680, or about 63 on the Rockwell C scale.

Summary

Cutting tools play an important part in all engineering manufacture. Whilst it is true to state that the machining of metal represents, perhaps, the most expensive method of producing a desired surface, a very large number of products have machined surfaces, usually to very close limits of accuracy. Machine tools are expensive items of equipment, and they are only of value when they are actually removing metal; their efficiency also can be measured in terms of the amount of metal removed in a given time.

This is the work of the cutting tool used. The tool must stand up to the very considerable forces involved when metal is removed; for example when turning on a centre lathe, the pressure on the cutting tool exceeds 1500 N/mm^2. The tool must possess the correct rake and clearance angles; the setting must be correct; and the correct type of cutting fluid must be applied. High-speed steel is widely used as a cutting tool material; its property of **red hardness** means that the swarf or chip may leave the parent metal at red heat with no loss of hardness of the cutting tool point.

We shall see in later work that the main cause of tool failure is the **cratering** or breaking down of the tool face under the severe frictional forces set up by the pressure and velocity of the chip as it moves across the tool face.

We shall see also, in the chapters on Drilling and Milling, that the cutting tools used for these operations work on the same principles as those described in this chapter.

QUESTIONS ON CHAPTER SEVEN

1. Show, by means of a neat diagram, the forces acting on a shaping tool.
2. Explain the importance of the rake angle on a single-point cutting tool.
3. With the aid of simple diagrams, illustrate the principle of both the orthogonal and oblique cutting actions.
4. Incorrect setting of a lathe tool will affect the effective rake and clearance angles. With the aid of neat diagrams, show the effect of setting a lathe tool **above** centre.
5. Describe the **three** main types of chip produced using a single-point cutting tool, with special reference to the quality of finish produced.
6. Make a neat sketch of a lathe tool used for a roughing operation, showing clearly the following angles:
   (i) approach angle,
   (ii) side rake,
   (iii) back rake.
7. What is the purpose of clearance angles? Why must they be kept to a minimum? Describe the circumstances that would require a primary and secondary clearance angle.
8. Show by means of a diagram the frictional forces causing tool wear. How can this wear be reduced?
9. Give **three** reasons why a cutting fluid is essential when taking heavy cuts with a lathe tool. What are the main types of cutting fluids in general use?
10. Explain why high carbon steel is seldom used as a cutting tool material when a high rate of metal removal is required. What quality is possessed by high-speed steel that makes it ideal as a cutting tool material for milling cutters, drills, and other single-point cutting tools?

8 Drilling Machines

MANY types of drilling machines are used in engineering manufacture, and the choice of a particular drilling machine will depend on the diameter of the hole to be drilled, and whether the drilling operation is part of a mass-production process. Drilling machines used on a production line can be considered as special-purpose machines; although these machines are of complex design, possessing several spindles or drilling stations, they are set and tooled for repetition work. This means that the drilling machine operator takes no part in the setting or adjustment of the machine, but merely operates the controls that set the drilling action in operation.

If holes are to be drilled in single components, a considerable degree of skill and knowledge will be required, and generally speaking three types of drilling machines are used for this kind of work. These are:

(i) sensitive drilling machine,
(ii) pillar drilling machine,
(iii) radial drilling machine.

For each machine the essential geometry will be the same, namely that the centre line of the drilled hole be at 90° to the worktable of the machine, and we will find that the difference between the three types is mainly one of size or capacity.

The Sensitive Drilling Machine

This machine is dealt with in Volume I of this series. Perhaps the student will recall that a sensitive drilling machine was described as essentially a compact structure built arou nd a sleeve within which a spindle rotated. Changes in spindle speeds are effected by changing the position of the driving belt on the coned pulley whilst a self-centring chuck allows rapid drill changing. The feeding, or downward vertical movement, of the drill is motivated by hand, permitting a nice sense of touch or feel, very necessary when small-diameter holes are to be drilled; hence the name **sensitive** driller.

This type of machine is ideal for the drilling of small-diameter holes, and a relatively high range of spindle speeds is available. This means, that this type of drilling machine is unsuitable for the drilling of large-diameter holes, or for such operations as counterboring, spotfacing, or countersinking.

The Pillar Driller

We may consider the pillar driller as a stronger and more robust type of sensitive driller. A typical pillar driller is shown in fig. 116. Although provision is made for hand feed of the drill, it is usually possible to feed the drill using automatic feed, and a range of feeds will be provided. The spindle speeds will have lower values than those of a sensitive

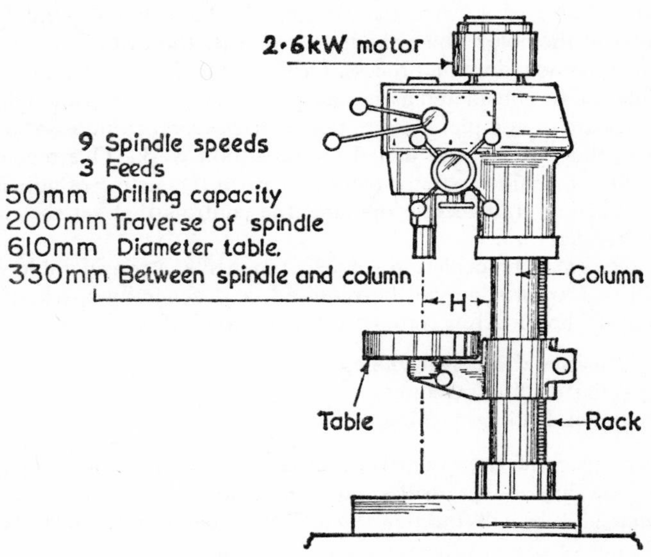

FIG. 116.—TYPICAL PILLAR DRILLING MACHINE.

driller, thus permitting the use of larger-diameter drills and of spot-facing or countersinking tools. A typical range would be from 50 to 1200 rev/min, with about six or eight speeds provided; this would permit the drilling of holes from 6 mm to 25 mm diameter. Automatic feeding of the drill is arranged through suitable gearing, with feeds ranging from 0·076 mm to 0·38 mm per revolution. The greatest of care must be exercised when using automatic feed on a pillar drilling machine. Absolute rigidity of the clamping of the work is essential, and it is a wise plan to use a smaller drill than finished size, opening out with larger-diameter drills under automatic feed, and reducing the feed per revolution as the diameter of the drills increases.

Work Holding

Not only does a pillar driller offer the advantage of automatic feed, together with the use of larger-diameter drills, but also the work holding capabilities are much greater. This means that a wider and more accurate range of drilling operations is possible on a pillar driller. Fig. 117 illustrates the available movements of the worktable. Note that the table itself is located on an arm attached to, and capable of movement both up and down, the column of the machine. This will allow for work

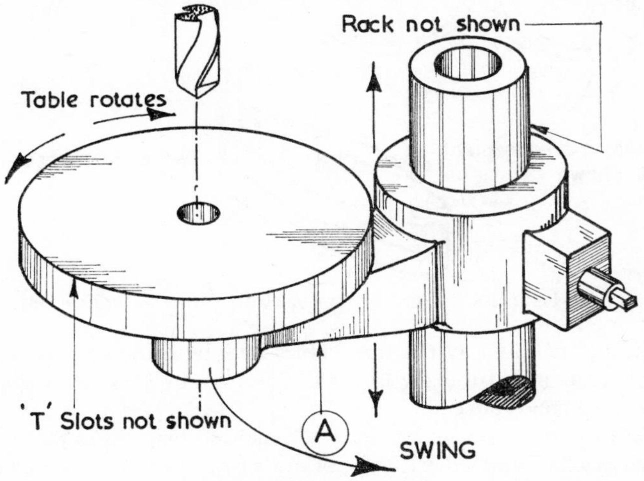

FIG. 117.—WORKTABLE MOVEMENTS OF A PILLAR DRILLING MACHINE.

of different heights, and the same principle is used on the sensitive driller.

The table proper, however, may be rotated through 360°, and can be locked in any suitable position. At the same time, the arm A can be swung through 180°, and also locked in any position. The combination of these movements allows a considerable amount of accurate setting with respect to drilling, reaming, counterboring or countersinking. Fig. 118 shows the principle involved, and represents a plan view of the components to be drilled, suitably clamped on the table of the pillar driller. At A we see the setting for the large hole in the two components to be drilled. When this hole is finish drilled the setting is changed by slight rotation of the table together with swinging of the table arm: this brings the hole marked Q on the centre line of the machine without disturbing the clamping arrangements and thus the alignment of the two component parts. The same technique is adopted for the drilling of the

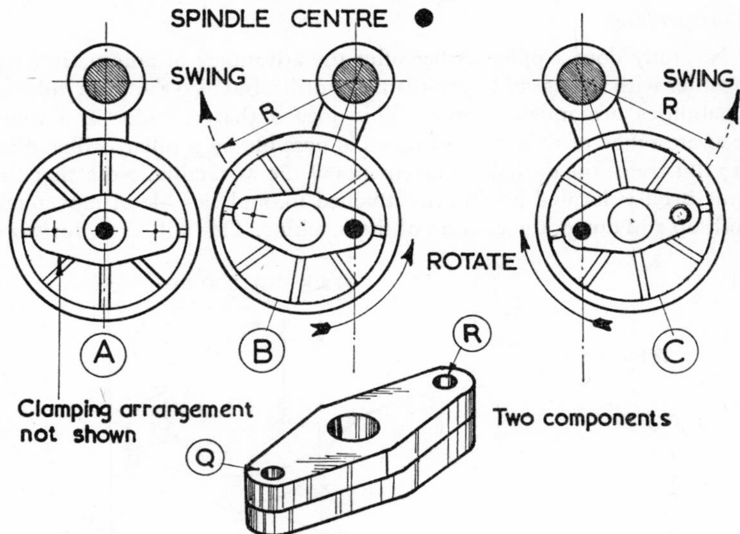

FIG. 118.—TECHNIQUE WHEN DRILLING HOLES USING A PILLAR DRILLER.

hole R, and in this way the three holes may be drilled in one setting, and it is certain that the alignment of the holes in the two components will be very good indeed.

Pillar drillers are invaluable for work such as this, and as the capacity of these machines includes the use of drills from 3 m to 25 mm diameter a wide range of drilling operations is possible. There is however, a limitation on the size of work that can be accommodated on these machines, and this is shown by the distance H in fig. 116, or the radius R in fig. 118. Because of this, large work cannot be drilled using a pillar driller, and there is also the undesirable feature of loading the worktable with heavy castings. It is, of course, possible to clamp a heavy casting to the base of the drilling machine, bringing down the drilling spindle, and this technique should always be adopted for heavy castings.

Let us assume that the large casting shown in fig. 119 requires the holes in the top face to be drilled. We see from the drawing that this is a large casting with overall dimensions of 1·800 m× 1·200 m× 1·200 m. Clearly even the largest-size pillar driller cannot cope with a casting of this size, because of the fixed nature of the distance between the spindle centre line and the pillar. If now this distance could be varied, the capability of a drilling machine would be greatly improved. This is shown in fig. 119; once again we see a plan view of the drilling operation for our large casting. Let *O* represent the centre line of the drilling spindle. If now we are able to vary this distance as shown in the diagram (where R1, R2, and R3 represent the different positions of the spindle centre line), then provided we are able to swing the spindle, the drilling of large castings will present little difficulty. It will be necessary to remove the need for a movable table, that is to say, a table which can be raised or

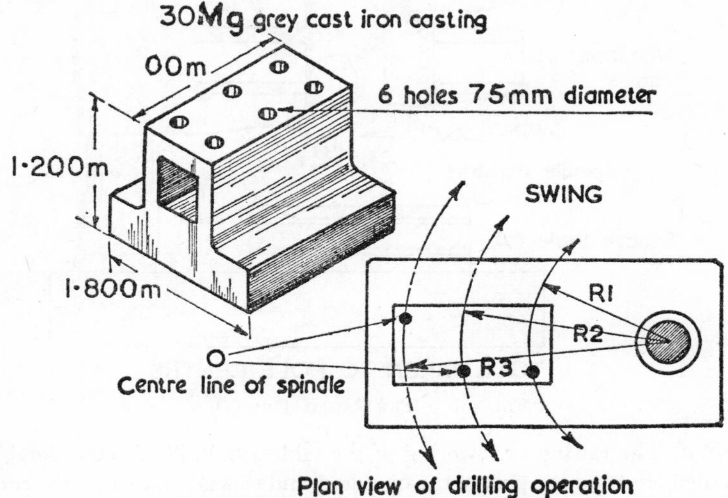

FIG. 119.—CASTING REQUIRING DRILLED HOLES.

lowered vertically, for it is not practical to raise or lower heavy castings. It is easier to raise or lower the drilling head.

The Radial Drilling Machine

A radial driller is capable of all the movements described above. This means that it is eminently suitable for drilling operations on large castings, and we may consider a radial driller as an improved version of a large-duty pillar driller. A typical radial driller is shown in fig. 120, together with the essential movements. Note the large area that can be covered by the drill spindle, as shown in the plan view. Note also that the base of the machine is the worktable, with T slots machined to provide for the clamping of the work to the base of the machine. The square table shown as A is an additional piece of equipment known as an **auxiliary table**, and smaller castings may be clamped on any surface of this square table.

The capacity of radial drillers is very great. A self-centring chuck, similar in type to those fitted on sensitive drillers, may be used on a radial driller, whilst a 50 mm diameter drill may also be used when re-

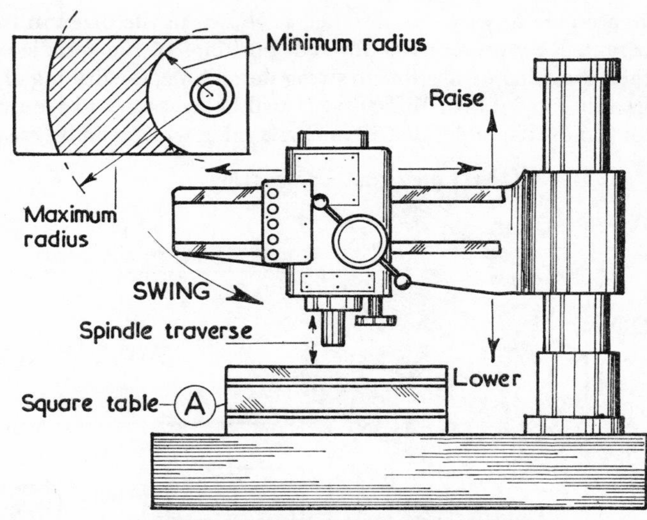

FIG. 120.—THE RADIAL DRILLER.

quired. The raising or lowering of the table would entail considerable manual effort on the part of the operator, and this is avoided by the provision of an automatic lifting and lowering device.

We see now that unlike both sensitive and pillar drillers, where the work is brought to the spindle centre line, the radial driller brings the spindle to the work.

Automatic feed is also provided for the downward movement of the spindle, with a range of spindle feeds and speeds. Once again, the greatest care must be exercised when drilling large-diameter holes using automatic feed. All locking handles must be securely tightened before any drilling commences, with the arm brought down to its lowest position; large-diameter holes must be opened out using smaller diameter drills, and the greatest of care must be taken to ensure that the casting or component is rigidly and firmly clamped to the work-table.

Types of Drills

Both spade drills and twist drills have been dealt with in Volume I, and it was stressed that the once-popular spade drill has now been replaced by the twist drill. Let us have another look at a cross-section of a twist drill, as shown in fig. 121. It will be clearly seen that a twist drill has a relatively small cross-sectional area, because of the metal removed in machining the flutes of the drill. If we also take into consideration the fact that drills are made from hardened steel, then the combination of a hard material with a small cross-sectional area means that it will not be difficult to break a twist drill should an excessive torque be applied.

These facts must be kept in mind when the automatic traverse for the spindle is used to drill holes with a pillar or radial driller, and considerable experience is necessary before confident use of feed traverse can be attained. A further defect of a two-fluted spiral drill is that should the vertical feed be excessive the drill, if it does not break, is certain to bend or deflect, leading to misalignment of the drilled hole.

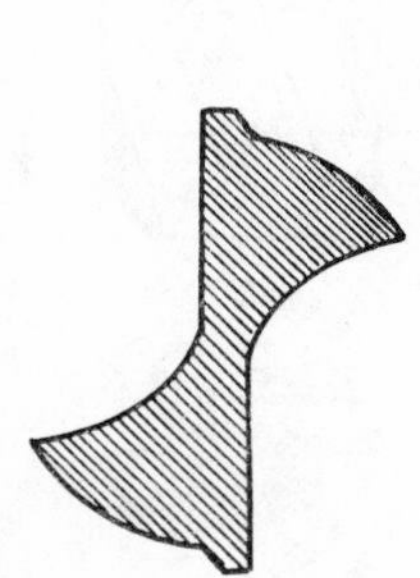

FIG. 121.—SECTION OF A TWO-FLUTED TWIST DRILL.

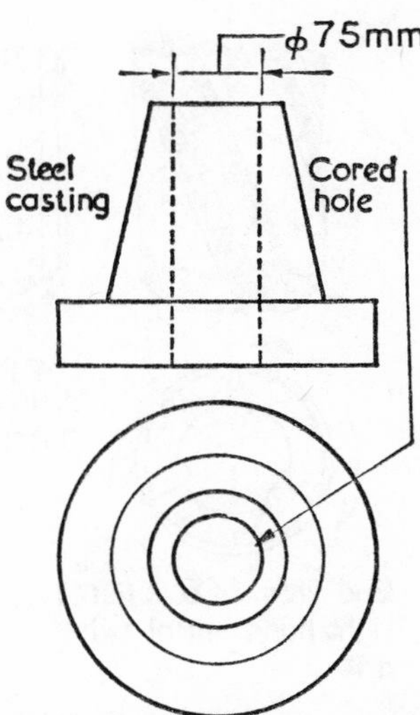

FIG. 122.—CASTING WITH A CORED HOLE.

If a drill is to be used to open out a large-diameter hole, there is no reason why a three-fluted or a four-fluted drill should not be used.

Three- or Four-fluted Drills

Fig. 122 shows a mild steel casting with a cored hole of approximately 75 mm diameter. If we wish to open out this hole, say prior to boring, we shall not choose a two-fluted drill. Apart from the tendency of a two-fluted drill to wander or deflect and possibly follow the alignment of an incorrectly cored hole, there is the further danger that because of the right-hand helix the drill will tend to snatch or screw itself into the cored hole. This is a dangerous state of affairs, with the risk of injury to the operator and damage to both workpiece and machine, with certain breakage of the drill.

The use of a three- or four-fluted drill will remove all these undesirable possibilities, and the reasons are shown in fig. 123. It is evident that a three-fluted drill has a greatly increased cross-sectional area, and it is much stronger as a result. The four-fluted drill is stronger still, and is most unlikely to wander or follow a badly cored hole. At the same

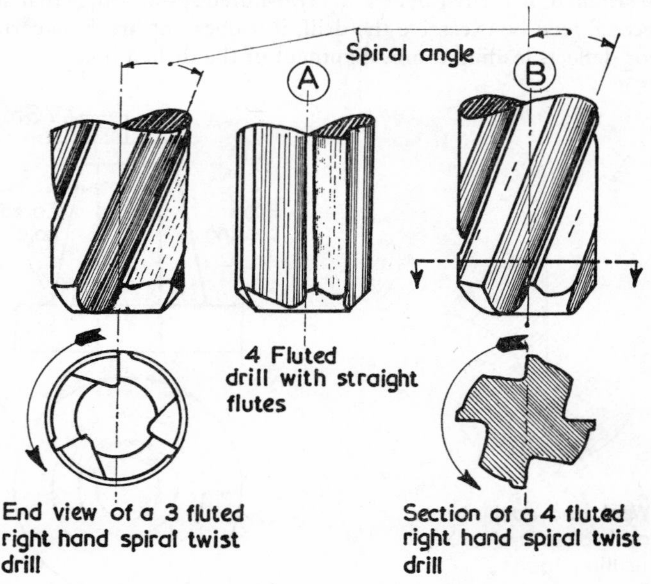

FIG. 123.—THREE- AND FOUR-FLUTED DRILLS.

time the use of these multi-spiral drills will permit a much higher rate of metal removal, thus increasing the efficiency of the drilling machine used.

Fig. 123 shows also that these drills are available with right-hand spiral flutes, or with straight flutes. The twist drill equivalent of a rake angle, as shown in Volume I, is the spiral or helix angle. The drill shown at A has straight flutes; thus the spiral angle is 0°, giving a negative rake. This drill will be very suitable for the drilling of grey cast iron.

At B the drill shown has a positive rake, and the softer the metal to be drilled, the greater will be the spiral angle. Perhaps the great disadvantage of three- or four-fluted drills is that they can only be used for the opening out of an existing hole. It is impossible for these drills to start a hole, for they cannot be sharpened to a point. This ability to drill its own hole from scratch is a very important feature of the ordinary two-fluted drill, but much care is needed in the sharpening of the drill point if the drill is to produce a hole of accurate size.

Sharpening of Large-diameter Drills

Under no circumstances should large-diameter drills be hand-sharpened at a pedestal off-hand grinder. It is virtually impossible to grind the correct angles, and incorrect grinding not only leads to over-size holes, but may also cause serious damage to the spindle bearings of the drilling machine. This is due to the fact that the badly sharpened drill will tend to rotate about its centre, and this will not be the centre of the drilling machine spindle. This principle is illustrated in Volume I, fig. 195. This means that a drill grinding device or jig is an essential feature of all well-equipped workshops.

Reamers

Reaming is an operation often carried out on a drilling machine, but the purpose of a reamer is not, as with a twist drill, to remove metal, but to produce a well-finished accurate hole. Metal will, of course, be removed in the process; but the amount of metal left for the reamer will be kept to a minimum. Reamers used on drilling machines are called **machine reamers**, and they must not be confused with **hand reamers.** Fig. 124 illustrates the difference between hand and machine reamers; note that the hand reamer is tapered and has a parallel shank, whilst a machine reamer has no taper on its cutting part, but has a tapered shank. Reamers are generally given either straight or left-hand spirals; a right-hand spiral reamer would have a most undesirable tendency to screw itself into the previously drilled hole, causing either rotation of the work or breakage of the reamer.

Reaming must always be carried out at a much lower speed than drilling, and efficient reaming is seldom possible using a sensitive drilling machine because of the high spindle speeds always found on these machines. It is permissible to ream at one-third the drilling speed, and a copious amount of cutting fluid must be supplied to the reamer. This will not only prolong the life of the reamer, though this is very important, but also promote a good surface finish to the reamed hole. It must, however, be remembered that a reamer will always follow a drilled hole; the use of a reamer will not rectify the error present in a badly aligned drilled hole.

Production Reamers

Reamers used on production work differ from the machine reamer shown in fig. 124. They are often called **chucking reamers**, and are of the shape shown in fig. 125. Note that the cutting length is much smaller, and these reamers may be of the **rose** or **fluted** type. The principles are also shown in fig. 125, and it will be seen that the rose type is end-cutting with slight clearance on the flutes. Metal removal is good with this type, but the finish will not be so good. They are useful

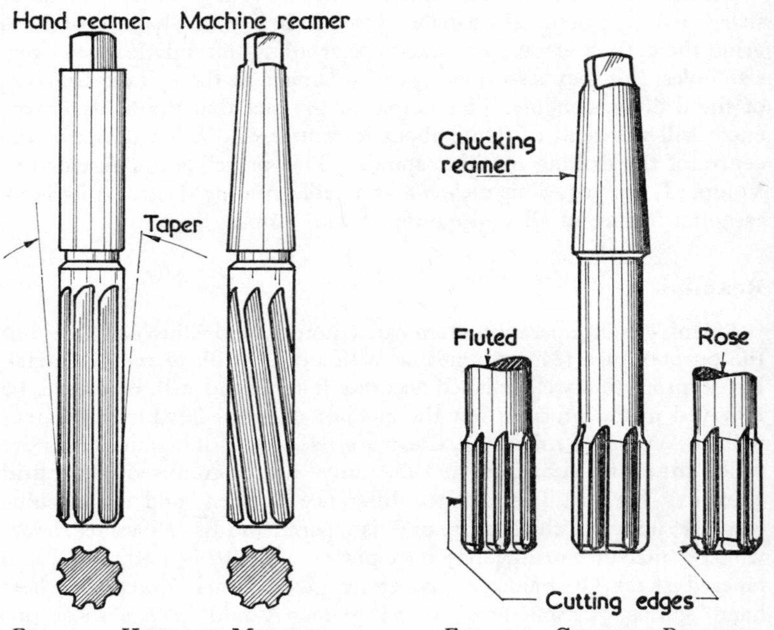

FIG. 124.—HAND AND MACHINE REAMERS.

FIG. 125.—CHUCKING REAMERS.

as a preliminary finishing operation, and are generally slightly below finished size, thus permitting the use of a fluted reamer; this reamer cuts on the flutes, producing a well-finished hole. **Floating reamers** are also used on production work; this means that the reamer is held in a special holder which allows it complete freedom to follow the drilled hole.

All the reamers so far described are of the fixed type. Any wear taking place must reduce the diameter of the hole produced, and this means that if accurate work is required these reamers will have a relatively short life, as no compensation for wear is possible.

Adjustable Reamers

These reamers are capable of slight adjustment. A popular type is illustrated in fig. 126. It will be seen that tapered slots are ground in the body of the reamer, with hardened cutting blades of the same taper fitting these slots. Adjustment of the screws A and B, allowing movement of the blades axially in the direction of arrow C, produces an increased diameter, and in this way the reamer can be reset for size after cutter-grinding.

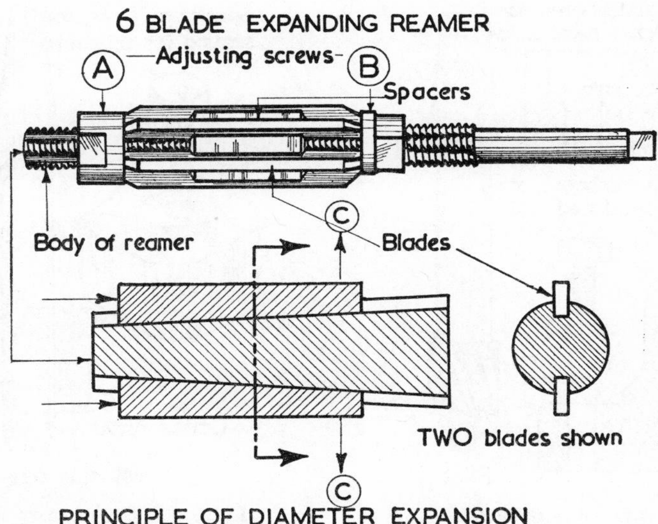

FIG. 126.—ADJUSTABLE REAMER.

Counterboring

This operation is often carried out on a drilling machine and consists in enlarging an existing hole, usually to accommodate a socket head screw. The counterbore must possess the non-linear function of concentricity if the head of the socket screw is to be a snug fit in the counterbore. Fig. 127 shows a typical counterboring tool used to produce a standard size counterbore. Note the pilot at the cutting end, which must be a slight clearance fit in the drilled hole.

Spotfacing

Spotfacing is essentially a counterboring operation, the only difference being that the amount of metal removed by the tool is relatively small.

A typical spotfacing operation is illustrated in fig. 128, together with the spotfacing tool used. Note that the purpose of the spotfacing operation is to provide a flat seating for the tightening bolt shown at A. The spotfacing cutter illustrated in fig. 128 consists of a cutter bar, tapered at the top to provide location in the drilling machine spindle, with a pilot at the bottom end. Note that a loose cutter is used; this cutter or blade is easily removed and a set of blades is available producing counterbores of varying diameters.

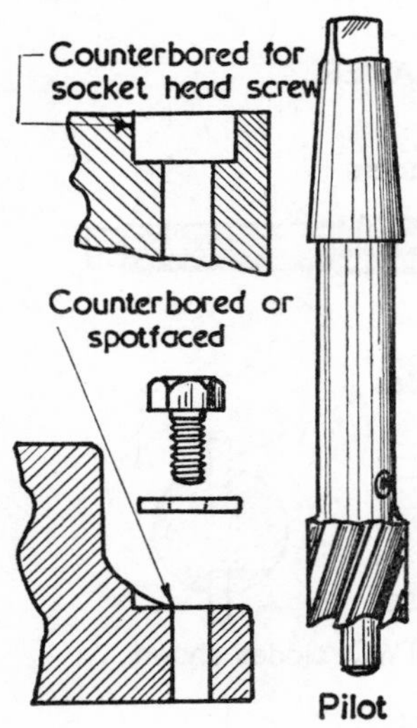

FIG. 127.—COUNTERBORING TOOL WITH TYPICAL APPLICATIONS.

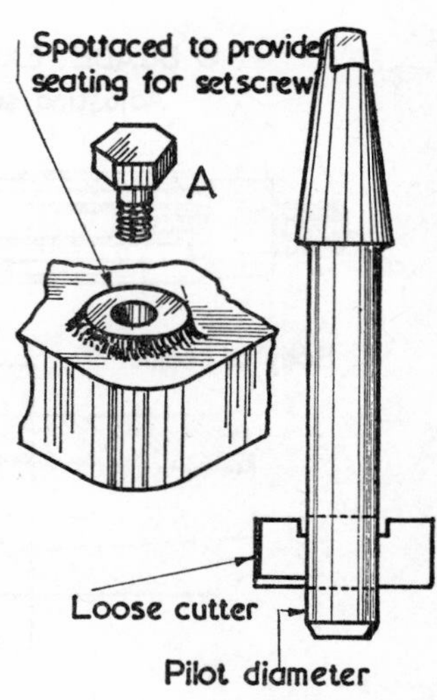

FIG. 128.—SPOTFACING TOOL WITH TYPICAL APPLICATION.

Countersinking

This is another operation often carried out on a drilling machine. A countersinking tool is used, and may have an included angle of 90° or 60°. A typical countersinking tool, together with its application, is shown in fig. 129. Remember that this tool, in common with a counterboring tool, presents a large contact area to the work, and the condition known as **chatter** is likely to occur if the spindle speed is too high. This causes an extremely poor finish to appear on the work, and a certain remedy is to reduce the spindle speed. Adequate supplies of coolant should always be provided for the operations of counterboring and countersinking, and the finish is further improved if the tool is allowed to dwell for a few seconds at the end of the cut.

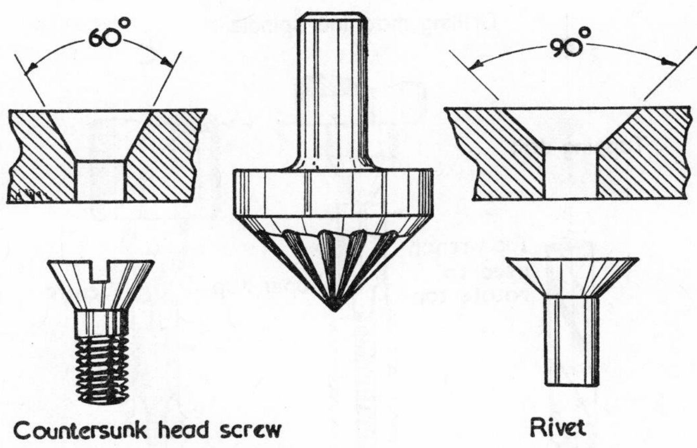

FIG. 129.—COUNTERSINKING TOOL WITH APPLICATIONS.

It is important, also, to make full use of the stop provided on most drilling machines. This applies to the depth of both counterbores and countersinks, and if several counterbores are to be machined, say on the top bolster of a press tool, it is a good plan to ensure that they are all of the same depth, resulting in a neat and workmanlike job.

Tapping

A drilling machine may be used to promote accuracy when cutting an internal thread. This operation should be carried out immediately after the drilling of the hole, with the work still securely clamped. It is not necessary to thread the hole for the full depth, but the taper tap should be taken to full depth. This technique ensures that the axis of the tap is truly at 90° to the face of the work, and the threads produced by the taper tap can be finished off at the bench. The technique is illustrated in fig. 130, and is most suitable for taps of fairly large diameter, say from 9 mm upwards.

Taps of this size will have a small countersink or centre at the top of the shank; a 60° centre inserted in the tapered sleeve of the drilling machine spindle will locate in the centre in the tap, thus providing vertical alignment of the tap. The tap is rotated in the usual way with a tap wrench, and care must be taken to ensure that the spindle is fed downwards as the tap enters the work. A heavy weight suspended on the feed handle would be quite suitable.

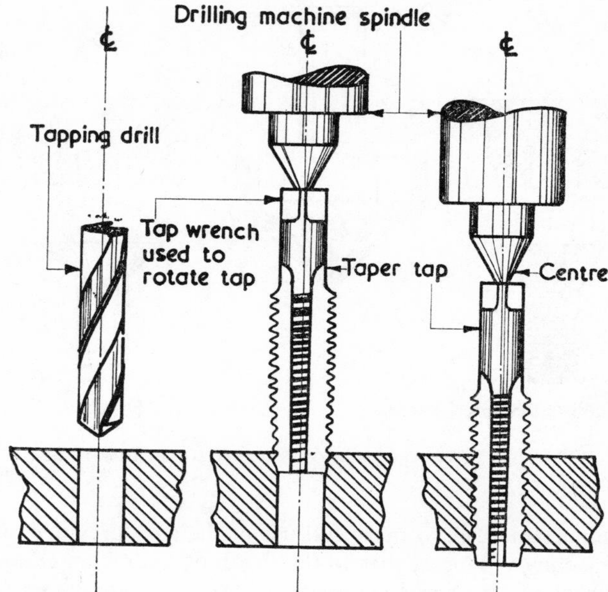

FIG. 130.—METHOD OF OBTAINING TAP ALIGNMENT USING A DRILLING MACHINE.

Tapping Heads

These are special attachments used on production work. Threads produced in this way are considered as machine tapped, and drilling machines are often fitted with tapping heads. These tapping heads fit into the taper in the spindle of the drilling machine, and contain a frictional device which transmits the necessary torque to the tap. At the end of the tapping stroke, the tapping head automatically reverses, usually at an increased speed, and the tap is withdrawn from the work. The depth of stroke is adjustable, and the frictional drive is so arranged that the reverse mechanism comes into action should the hole be blind or flat-bottomed or should the tap meet with an obstruction.

Standard hand taps may be used, although best results are obtained with the special machine taps designed for this purpose. Once again a copious supply of cutting fluid is essential if a good finish and prolonged tool life are to result.

Drilling Techniques

The drilling of holes to accurate linear dimensions with respect to the diameters of the holes and their centre distances is a most difficult task.

If the accuracy required is less than two hundredths of a millimetre a jig boring machine must be used. Although **compound tables** are available on pillar drillers, accurate centre distances are still difficult to achieve. The use of a compound table, however, will permit reasonably accurate work, and we will consider the machining of the holes shown in the components illustrated in fig. 131. The three parts shown

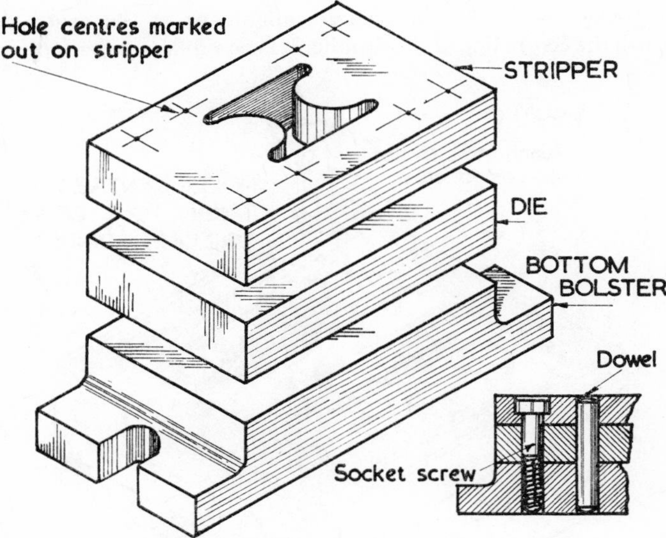

FIG. 131.—ASSEMBLY REQUIRING DRILLED AND REAMED HOLES.

represent the stripper plate, die, and bottom bolster of a press tool; this tool is illustrated in fig. 59, Volume I. We are concerned here with the drilling of the four holes, together with counterboring and tapping, and also the drilling and reaming of the four dowel holes. The alignment of these three parts will be achieved by the insertion of the punch, and it is necessary to drill, counterbore, ream, and tap, thus ensuring that the parts will always re-align accurately every time they are stripped and reassembled.

The Use of the Compound Table

A compound table permits movement of work clamped to the table face. This is achieved by providing sliding faces or guideways at 90°, and adjustable stops are fitted to prevent excessive movement of the table. With the punch in position the three plates are mounted on parallel bars and rigidly clamped to the table of the drilling machine.

Fig. 132 shows the essential set-up, together with the principle of the compound table. If the positions of the holes have been marked out, and this can be done very accurately using a vernier height gauge, the essential technique is to bring each hole centre to the centre line of the spindle. It is wise to proceed first with the drilling and reaming of the dowel holes.

Perhaps the most difficult problem associated with the use of the drilling machine is that of accurate alignment of the centre-dotted hole with the centre line of the spindle. It is possible to use a toolmaker's

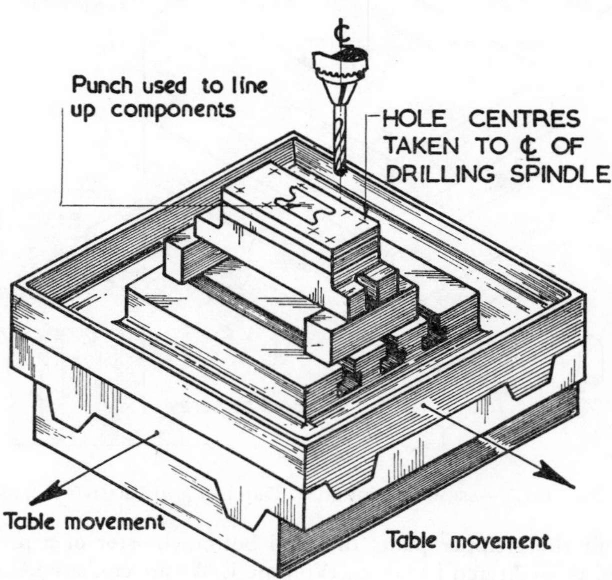

FIG. 132.—SET-UP FOR DRILLING AND REAMING ON A COMPOUND TABLE.

drill chuck; this is equipped with an optical device by which the intersection of the scribed lines can be observed and adjusted until it is seen to lie in the centre of the field of vision. Another method is to insert a test bar in the chuck of the drilling machine, and adjust the work until the tapered point of the test piece truly enters the centre dot. The work is now securely clamped and a **centre drill** used to open out the centre dot. Both techniques are illustrated in fig. 133.

The hole is now drilled to within about 0·2 mm of finished size, a reamer inserted instead of the drill chuck, and the hole reamed at a lower spindle speed. It is quite permissible to insert a dowel in the reamed hole at this stage. The table lock is now slackened, the other dowel hole brought under the drilling spindle, and the sequence of operations repeated, including the insertion of the second dowel. Note that once we have established the position of the centre dot in line with the drill spindle, all the machining is carried out on the hole with no further change or alteration of the setting until the machining is completed. This is a most important feature of drilling, and the same technique is adopted with respect to the remaining holes. This sequence of

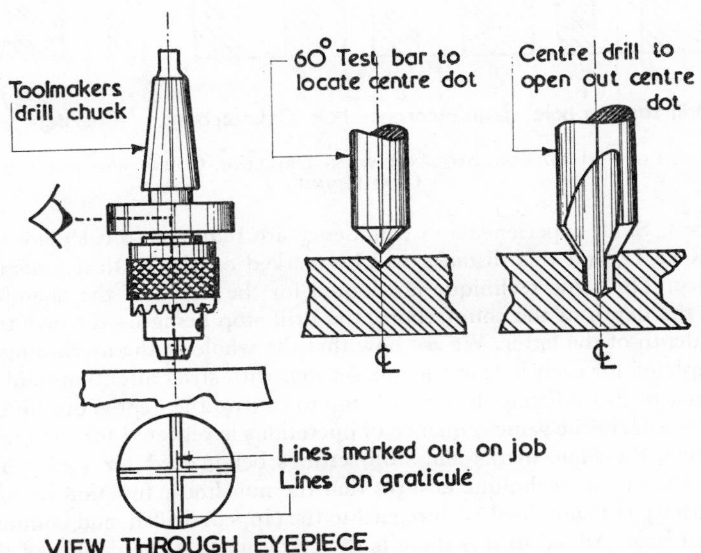

FIG. 133.—CENTRE-FINDING TECHNIQUES.

machining in the one setting is shown in fig. 134, and may be summarised as follows:

(i) hole centre drilled, and drilled in stages to tapping size,
(ii) hole drilled to clearance size in stripper and die,
(iii) hole counterbored in stripper,
(iv) counterbore chamfered using a countersinking tool,
(v) taper tap inserted, centred as shown in fig. 130, and thread started.

Note in operation (ii) that the clearance drill has been allowed to drill a depth of about one or two threads in the bottom bolster; this will prevent the taper tap from throwing up a burr when the thread is

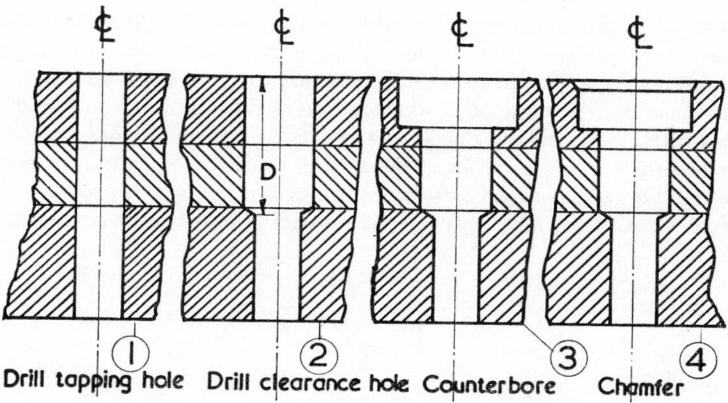

FIG. 134.—MACHINING SEQUENCE WHEN DRILLING, COUNTERBORING AND CHAMFERING.

tapped. Skill, experience and confidence are required to calculate the distance D, and this distance will be marked on the vertical indexing device. The same technique is adopted for the depth of the chamfer, and the depth of the counterbore, the drill stop being used to control the depth of the latter. We see now that the whole of the machining is completed for each hole at the one setting, with strict attention paid to the use of the indexing device and stop to control the depths machined.

Once again the same sequence of operations is repeated for each hole in turn, the same marks and stop settings being used for each hole. The use of this technique ensures that the non-linear function of concentricity is maintained with regard to the tapped, drilled, and counterbored hole. Added to this there is the certainty that the depths of the counterbores and chamfers are the same, and this must result in a neat, workmanlike job. Because we first dowelled the holes, the alignment of the three parts of this press tool is ensured, and accurate and rapid reassembly is certain each time the press tool is stripped for regrinding of the die.

It must not be forgotten that the circular table in fig. 117 can also be considered as a compound table, and is quite suitable for the drilling technique described above. Note that the essential technique involved when using the pillar driller is to bring the centre of the hole in line with the centre of the spindle of the drilling machine. This as we have seen is no easy matter, and represents a serious limitation in the ability of a drilling machine to drill holes having their centre distances to close dimensional accuracy. We have seen in Chapter 5 (fig. 72) that the best method of dimensioning holes is to proceed from two datum faces at

90° to each other. In this way the positions of the hole centres are determined by linear dimensions, and if holes are to be drilled having centre distances with small tolerances, then clearly drilling machines are not able to provide the necessary accuracy with respect to control of table movement. Because of this jig boring machines must be used, and much use will be made of end standards and dial indicators to obtain the necessary accuracy of linear movement of the table.

Summary

Although the geometrical requirements for a drilled hole are relatively simple, namely that the axis of the hole be at 90° to the surface of the worktable of the drilling machine, the production of drilled holes is always a somewhat difficult task. Holes are essentially internal cylindrical surfaces, and twist drills are used to generate these surfaces. A twist drill, because of its weak cross-sectional area, is very liable to deflect, wander, or even fracture if excessive forces are brought to bear on the drill. Small-diameter drills require small-capacity drilling machines, possessing a nice sense of feel or touch, if excessive breakage of these small-diameter drills is to be avoided. Larger-diameter drills can be used in larger-capacity drilling machines, and both pillar and radial types are available in a range of sizes. Pillar drilling machines require the centre of the drilled hole to be brought to the spindle centre line, whilst radial drilling machines take the spindle to the hole centres. A very large area can be covered by the spindle of a radial driller, and this means that large castings can readily be drilled.

The value of a drilling machine is much increased if proper use is made of additional tools such as reamers, counterbores, spotfacers, and countersinking tools. These tools should always be used at **one** setting of the work, and the use of quick-change chucks reduces the time taken for tool changing; when we have brought the centre of the hole on the centre line of the spindle, it is vital that the work be securely clamped in this position, and all machining carried out before the setting is disturbed. Every possible use must be made of the stop or indexing device fitted to the drill spindle, and advantage must be taken of the range of speeds provided. The larger the drill, the slower the speed, and this is also true for tools such as counterbores and countersinks which have a large work-tool contact area.

Remember also that the drilling machine is a prolific source of accidents, and secure and rigid clamping of the work is an essential factor in any drilling operation. Much use is made of angle plates, both fixed and adjustable, to facilitate the drilling of holes at various angles, whilst V blocks are used for the location of cylindrical work. Holes required on mass-produced components will demand special-purpose multi-spindle drilling machines, or the use of drilling jigs. The drilling of holes having their centre distances held to small tolerances is a most difficult matter, and outside the range of work possible with an average drilling machine.

QUESTIONS ON CHAPTER EIGHT

PART A

1. Name the three main types of drilling machines used in engineering workshops. Describe briefly the class of work carried out at each machine.
2. Make a neat sketch of the worktable of a pillar drilling machine, showing clearly how the table can be adjusted to bring the centre line of the required hole in line with the centre line of the drilling spindle.
3. Explain the difference in technique when drilling holes using
   (i) a pillar driller,
   (ii) a radial driller.
4. Make a neat plan view of a radial drilling machine, showing clearly the essentia movements of the arm and drilling head.
5. Explain and sketch the operations of countersinking, spotfacing, and counter-boring.
6. Make neat sketches of **three** different types of reamers, giving a typical application of each.
7. Describe a typical drilling operation for which a three-fluted drill would be preferred to the standard two-fluted drill. What are the limitations of a two-fluted drill?
8. Why is it essential to sharpen large-diameter drills using a drill-grinding device?
9. Describe briefly how a drilling machine may be utilised to ensure correct alignment of a tapped hole.
10. Explain why a hole is drilled, counterbored. spotfaced, and tapped in **one** setting of the work, assuming that a radial driller is used.

PART B

1. (*a*) List the main causes of accidents arising in the use of drilling machines.
   (*b*) Explain any procedure for machine-tapping a screwed hole using a drilling machine; give details of any special equipment needed.

C. & G. (1962)

9 The Centre Lathe

The centre lathe is a machine tool designed primarily to produce both external and cylindrical surfaces. Provision also exists for the machining of conical surfaces or tapers. It was stressed in Volume I that the art of machining consists in the production of as many surfaces as possible in **one setting** of the workpiece, and a typical example of good turning technique was illustrated in fig. 155 of that volume. In this way the non-linear function of concentricity is assured, the degree of accuracy being dependent on the quality and condition of the lathe, together with the correct and efficient use of well-sharpened cutting tools.

The linear accuracy of the machined diameters depends on the skill and experience of the lathe turner, and a skilled, highly paid craftsman is required. There is much time taken up in tool setting and tool changing, together with work holding. This means that centre lathes are most unsuitable for use on production work, where the accent is on rapid and efficient metal removal in the minimum of time, with accurate, well-finished work produced.

We must remember, then, that centre lathes are to be found only in toolrooms, maintenance shops, and in prototype or development shops; and they are used only when single components are required, or perhaps a limited number of complicated turned components. It should be remembered also that the efficient use of these machines is the work of a craftsman, and not, strictly speaking, the province of the technician. It may well be, however, that a technician is concerned with the planning, or perhaps the estimating and rate-fixing, of work produced on centre lathes, and for this reason it is essential that the technician be familiar with the technique underlying the art of turning.

Two-setting Jobs

A component requiring two settings on a centre lathe poses a difficult problem to the turner. As we have seen, provided all the machining is carried out in one setting of the work, concentricity is guaranteed irrespective of the number of different diameters turned. If, however, after machining say on a three-jaw chuck, the component is removed from the chuck and then reversed and chucked again, it is certain that the second setting will differ slightly from the first. In other words the second setting will have a different line of action for the work, and as a centre lathe generates a cylindrical surface by the combined effect of the line of action of the work and that of the tool, the surfaces produced during the two settings will not be concentric.

This principle is illustrated in fig. 135. At A we see the first setting, with diameters P and Q turned down to size. At B the component is reversed and rechucked, with diameter R turned at this setting. A three-jaw chuck that will rechuck a component exactly on the same centre line as the first chucking has not yet been manufactured, and the

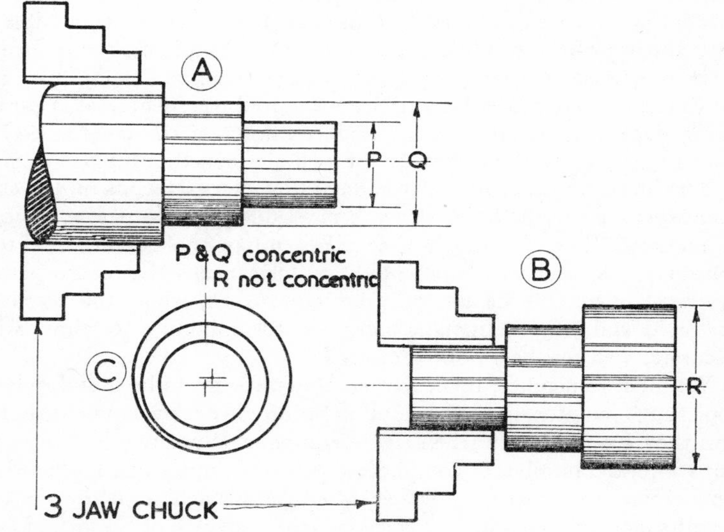

Fig. 135.—Effect of Second Setting on Concentricity.

inaccuracy will depend on the amount of wear or misuse to which the chuck has been subjected. The effect of the two different lines of action is shown at C, much exaggerated. With the two diameters on different centre lines a condition of non-concentricity or eccentricity exists.

This problem of errors arising from the resetting of a job is of course common to all machining operations, and it is a general rule, as explained in Chapter 5 (figs. 71 and 72), that the largest surface is used as a datum or location face for the first setting. This will provide more accurate and positive location for the second setting, together with increased rigidity in the holding of the work.

Let us consider the machining of the component shown in fig. 136; one component only to be produced, and a centre lathe of good quality available. It is not possible to machine this component in one setting; at one end there is a small internal tapered diameter, whilst the other end is recessed. Note the external thread behind the external taper. The correct functioning of this component will depend on the concentricity of all the machined surfaces with respect to the centre line of the component. We will outline the essential stages to be adopted in the machining of this component, and perhaps in this way the student technician may appreciate the considerable skill and experience required by the craftsman if this component is not only to be produced in the minimum time, but also to prove satisfactory when put into service.

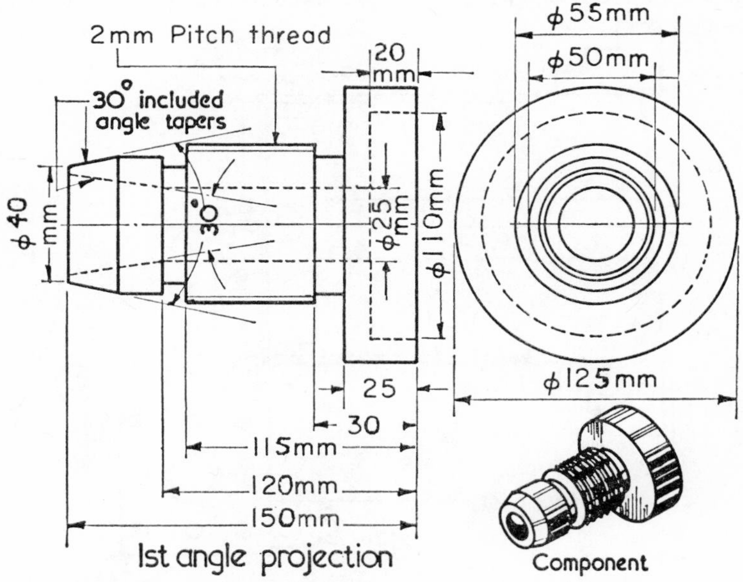

FIG. 136.—COMPONENT TO BE PRODUCED ON A CENTRE LATHE.

First Setting

The primary object of the first setting is to provide a datum face which will allow a good location for the second setting, thus reducing the possibility of error. The work may be held in a three-jaw chuck, or a four-jaw chuck can be used if a more powerful gripping action is preferred. This setting is shown in fig. 137, and the sequence of operations is outlined below:

(i) face end and centre,
(ii) rough down diameter A,
(iii) drill hole C to within 1 mm of finished size,
(iv) rough out recess D.

This completes the roughing for the first setting, and the object here is maximum metal removal in the minimum of time, with less regard for

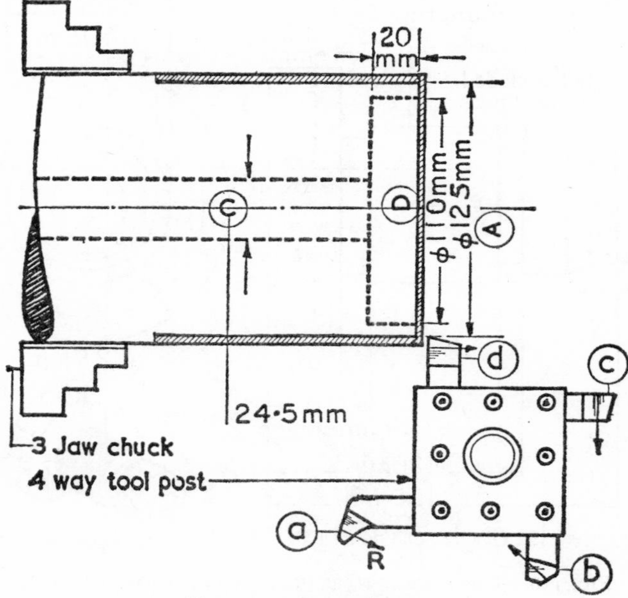

FIG. 137.—FIRST SETTING.

the quality of the finish of the machined surfaces. The experienced turner will make full use of the four-way tool box, and will now index the tool box presenting a finishing tool to the work. Fig. 137 shows also a plan view of a four-way tool box, suitably tooled as follows:

(*a*) facing tool,
(*b*) roughing tool for sliding cut,
(*c*) recessing tool (facing outwards),
(*d*) finishing tool for diameter A and recess B.

Note carefully the rake angles on the tools. These are indicated by the direction of the arrows, and the value of these rake angles will be determined by the material from which the component is made.

Perhaps it may now be appreciated that the technique so far, in the roughing and finishing of the first datum face, differs little from the technique adopted in the machining of holes, counterbores and countersinks using a pillar drilling machine. This principle is common to the best use of most machine tools, and ensures that the geometrical movements inherent in the design and construction of the machine tool can be put to maximum use.

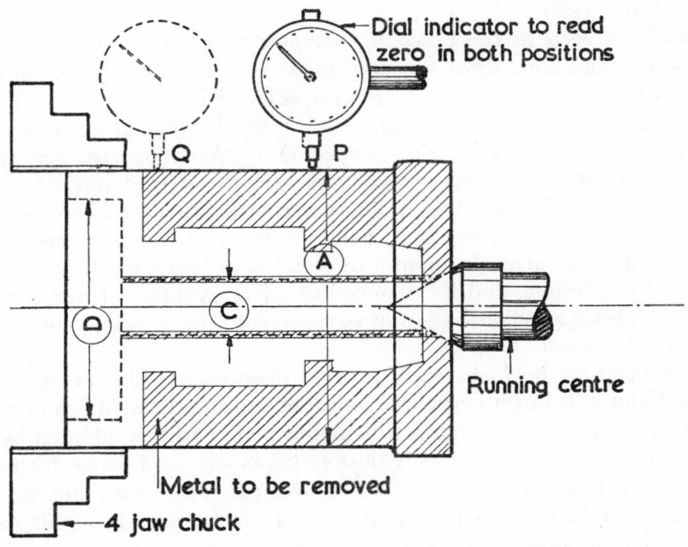

FIG. 138.—SECOND SETTING USING A 4-JAW CHUCK.

Second Setting

The object of the second setting is to hold the component in such a way that the centre line of the work is the same as that obtained during the machining of the first setting. Several methods of work holding are available, and we will choose a four-jaw chuck. Not only does a four-jaw chuck possess a greater gripping power than a three-jaw self-centring chuck, but it also possesses the great advantage of independent movement of each jaw. This means that the centre line of the work held in a four-jaw chuck can be adjusted.

Fig. 138 shows the technique adopted. Note the use of a dial indicator with the plunger locating on diameter A. The chuck is rotated by hand, and the jaws adjusted until the dial indicator reads zero for a full revolution of the work, not only at position P but also at position Q. With the work firmly gripped when these conditions have been achieved, the turner is assured that any machining carried out on this setting will be concentric with that carried out during the first setting.

Any movement of the work must be rigorously avoided, and increased rigidity can be obtained by machining a small chamfer of 60°, as shown in fig. 138, and supporting the end with a running centre. The remaining external diameters are now roughed down to within about 0·5 mm of finished size, together with the external taper.

Boring the Hole

We have seen in the preceding chapter that, owing to their weak cross-sectional area, drills are very liable to wander or deflect during the drilling operation, producing a mis-aligned hole.

Much greater accuracy of alignment is possible when holes are bored, the boring tool, provided it possesses the necessary rigidity, removing any imperfections of alignment. Note that the drilled hole is to be bored prior to the finishing of the external diameters. There is very good reason for this technique: another glance at the component will show that a considerable amount of metal is to be removed before the finished job results, and the removal of a large volume of metal tends to bring about a redistribution of stresses, resulting in slight distortion of the component.

The need for normalising to prevent distortion is illustrated in fig. 37 of Volume I, but it is not a practical measure to heat all bright mild steel stock prior to machining. The better plan, and that adopted by all skilled turners, is first to rough close to finish size, and allow the metal to distort. The finishing cuts will remove this distortion, and we see now an added advantage produced when the technique of roughing and finishing is adopted.

The set-up for the boring of the hole is shown in fig. 139, the boring bar having an inserted tool bit at the cutting end. It is certain that the turner will choose the largest-diameter boring bar that will pass through the hole, for we see from fig. 139 that the distance L is unsupported, and slight deflection or bending of the boring bar is inevitable should the boring bar be of small cross-section. Relatively small amounts of metal must be removed by the boring bar if a tapered hole, the product of bending of the boring bar, is to be avoided. For this reason the boring of holes on a centre lathe is a somewhat lengthy operation.

Machining the Tapers

In order to produce a tapered surface on a centre lathe it is necessary to change the line of action or path of the tool. Several methods of taper turning are possible on a centre lathe, and the method adopted depends on the type of taper required. The compound slide will be used to machine both the tapers, and the set-up is shown in fig. 140

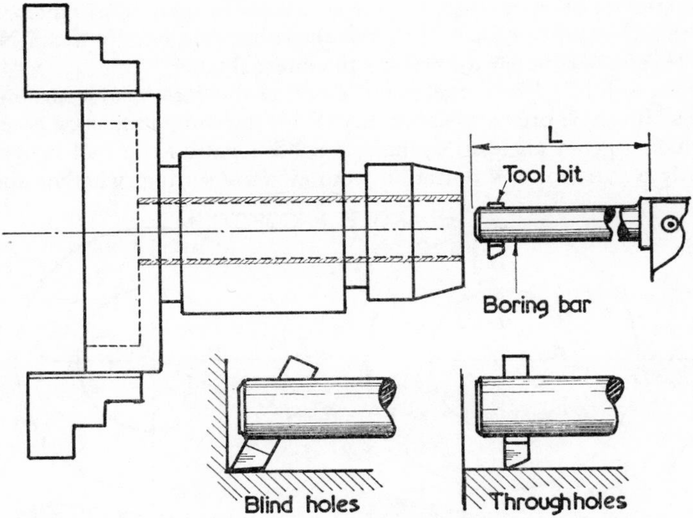

FIG. 139.—BORING THE HOLE.

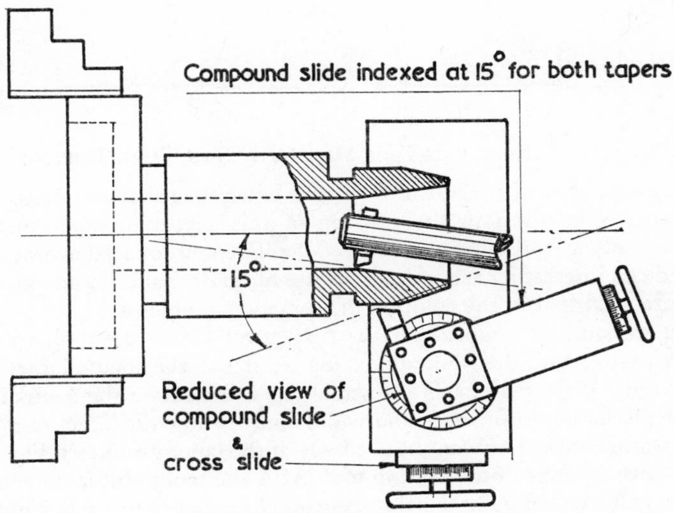

FIG. 140.—MACHINING THE TAPERS.

This method of taper turning is very suitable for fairly short tapers, but has the disadvantage that all the feeding must be done by hand. Note the use of a boring bar to machine the internal taper.

It is essential that the tool point be set dead centre for the turning of tapers. It can be proved theoretically that if the compound slide is set to produce a given angle, this angle is conditional on the tool being set exactly on centre; any deviation from a centre setting, whether above

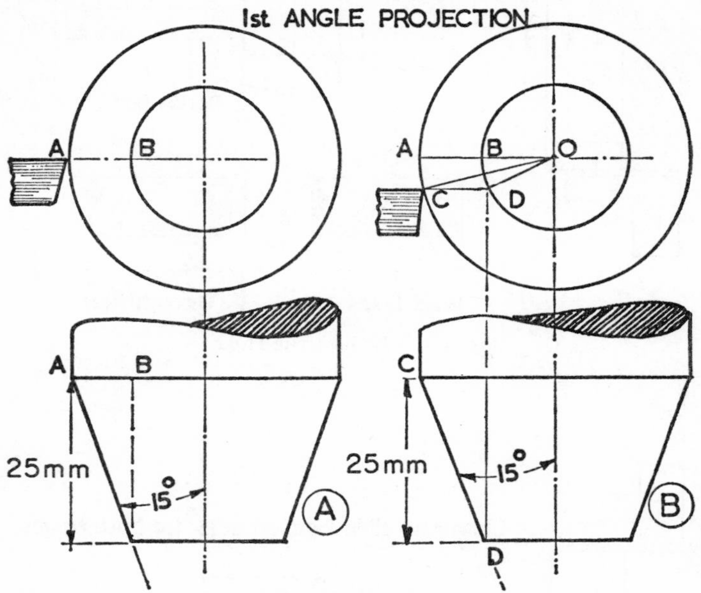

FIG. 141.—GEOMETRY OF TOOL MOVEMENT WHEN TAPER TURNING.

or below centre, will result in a smaller taper than that required. The calculations involved in the proving of this aspect of taper turning require only a working knowledge of the Theorem of Pythagoras, and provide an interesting example of the use of mathematics as an essential and practical tool in the solution of workshop problems.

Let us consider a taper that has been turned with the tool 2·5 mm below centre, with the compound slide set at 15°, the small diameter to be 40 mm. This of course is the actual taper present on the component under discussion in fig. 136, and we intend to show the effect of a tool set 2·5 mm below centre on the accuracy of the taper produced. Fig. 141 shows two settings of the cutting tool. At A the tool point is on centre, whilst at B the tool point is below centre. Note that in order to simplify the illustration we have omitted the bore and internal taper.

With the tool correctly set on centre as shown at A, then BA on the plan view represents the movement of the tool away from the centre line of the work, and is thus equal to one-half the actual taper. An included angle of 30° will require a setting on the compound slide of 15°: thus $BA = 25 \times \tan 15° = 25 \times 0{\cdot}2679 = 6{\cdot}697$ mm.

Assuming unit feed of 1 mm per revolution, the distance moved by the tool away from the centre line of the work will be 0·2679 mm per mm of traverse or feed.

With the tool set below centre, a different set of conditions exists, and reference to fig. 141B will help to make this clear. The tool com-

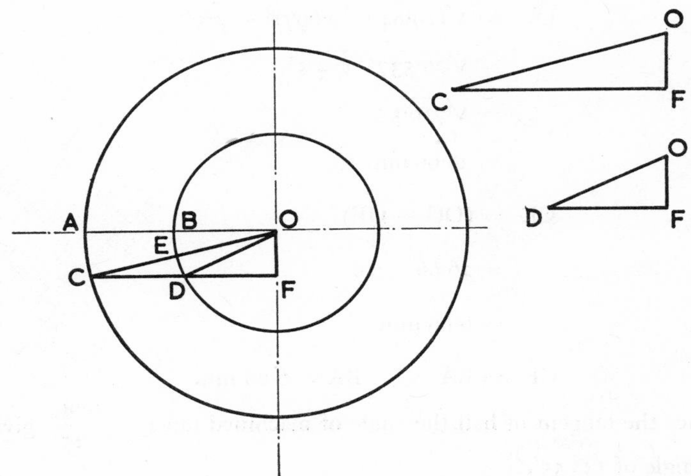

FIG. 142.—GEOMETRY REQUIRED TO CALCULATE ERROR WHEN TAPER TURNING.

mences to cut at D, and finishes its cut at C; the distance moved out from the centre line of the work being DC. Now DC is longer than BA, and this means that a different taper must result; for as we have stressed a taper is a conical surface, and the amount of taper is governed by the distance the tool moves away from the centre line of the work.

The problem now is to calculate the distance BA. When attempting to solve mathematical problems it is a good plan to make a neat enlarged sketch showing all the known information, and fig. 142 is an enlargement of fig. 141B, looking in the direction of the chuck. CD is the distance the tool moves away from the centre, and, as we have calculated, if the compound slide is set at 15°, this distance will be 0·2679 mm per mm of feed.

The calculations are set out below.

In $\triangle$ ODF $\quad DF^2 = (OD^2 - OF^2) = (20^2 - 2{\cdot}5^2)$

or $\quad DF = \sqrt{(400 - 6{\cdot}25)}$

$= \sqrt{393{\cdot}75}$

$= 19{\cdot}84$ mm

In $\triangle$ OCF $\quad OC^2 = CF^2 + OF^2$

$OC = \sqrt{(19{\cdot}84 + 6{\cdot}697)^2 + 2{\cdot}5^2}$

$= \sqrt{26{\cdot}537^2 + 2{\cdot}5^2}$

$= \sqrt{710{\cdot}55}$

$= 26{\cdot}66$ mm

$CE = (OC - OE)$

$= 26{\cdot}66 - 20$

$= 6{\cdot}66$ mm

and $\quad CE = BA \quad \therefore \quad BA = 6{\cdot}66$ mm

Hence the tangent of half the angle of machined taper $= \dfrac{6{\cdot}66,}{25}$ giving an angle of 14° 55′.

Thus the included angle will be 29° 50′, 10 minutes less than the required angle of 30°.

It is, of course, very unlikely that a turner would set a tool 2·5 mm below centre, and even should this unlikely event occur, the error of the included angle is only one-sixth of a degree. The important point is that a true taper can only result from accurate geometric movements, and all the geometric movements inherent in the lathe will be to little purpose if due care is not exercised when setting the cutting tool.

We will see in later work that toolsetting is a skilled and important operation, particularly when the machine tools are to be used for the mass production of engineering components. A toolsetter can rightly consider himself as a technician, and may well be responsible for several machines, or even a production line of capstan or automatic lathes.

Cutting the Thread

The cutting of threads on centre lathes is commonly known as screw cutting. It is a mistake to claim that the art of screw cutting represents the ultimate in turning technique, and a great deal of unnecessary prominence is often given to the operation of screw cutting using a centre lathe. Let it be clearly understood that every time a cut is taken on a centre lathe, the tool advances a certain linear amount for each revolution of the work. In effect most turning consists in the production

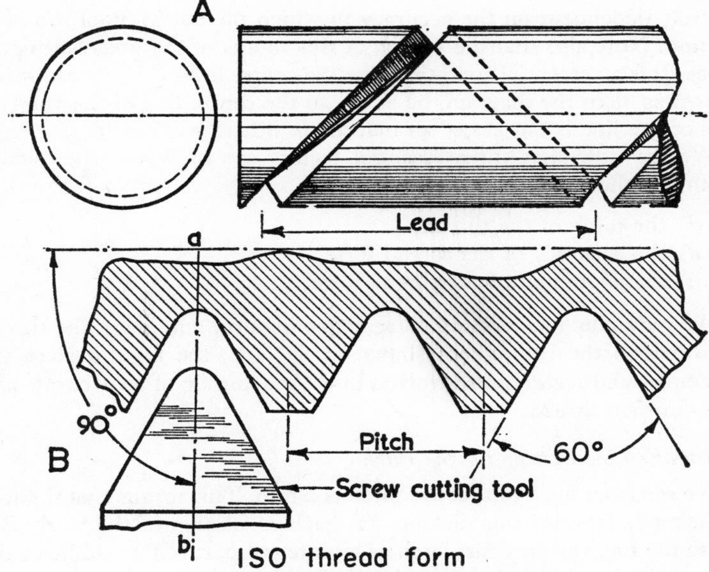

FIG. 143.—SCREW THREAD ELEMENTS.

of cylindrical surfaces generated by the combination of both tool and work movements. Cylindrical surfaces produced in this way are the result of screw threads of very fine pitch, and the smaller the pitch, the better or smoother the surface finish.

Screw Thread Essentials

Provided the essential requirements of a screw thread are appreciated, the machining of a screw thread on a centre lathe should present no greater problem than the machining of an ordinary cylindrical surface. There is, however, one important difference that must be appreciated, and this is that screw cutting is a combination of both **generating** and **forming** principles.

Fig. 143 illustrates this important feature. The lead of the thread is the distance moved by the tool for one revolution of the work, and results in the generation of a **helical** form on the work. If this is to be a true helix, the pitch, or linear movement of the tool, must be constant for the whole length of the helix. Thus the first problem to be solved before screw cutting is the selection or calculation of the gearing arrangements between spindle and lead screw.

Fig. 143B shows the thread form. Note that this form is in no way generated, but is an exact replica of the shape of the cutting tool. Thus the thread is formed or copied, and accuracy of the thread form will be entirely dependent on the accuracy to which the cutting tool has been ground. Note also that the setting of this tool is of the greatest importance. It is an essential condition that the centre line of the thread form, shown as *ab* in the diagram, be at 90° to the centre line of the work; if this centre line is not at 90° an inaccurate thread will result.

We see now that three essential factors are involved when screw cutting at the lathe:

(i) the pitch of the thread,
(ii) the accuracy of the thread form,
(iii) the alignment of the thread form.

We may now take each of these items in turn, and using the thread required on the component shown in fig. 136, see for ourselves the principles and techniques involved in the machining of an accurate and well-finished thread.

Calculating the Setting for the Pitch

We see from fig. 136 that the pitch is 2 mm. This means that the tool must move forward this distance for each revolution of the work. Because the tool can be considered as an integral part of the saddle of the lathe, it is the saddle that must be given this movement. A simple diagram is given in Volume I (fig. 137) showing clearly the use of spur gears to transmit motion from the lathe spindle to the lead screw. Fig. 138 in that volume shows also the use of a quadrant, permitting the changing of gears to allow for the cutting of threads of different pitches. The following calculations are intended mainly to show the necessary link between mathematics and workshop technique; it must be appreciated that there are very few lathes in use at the present moment which require the removal and changing of gears for the operation of screw cutting. Let us, at this stage, be perfectly clear about the purpose of a lathe.

A lathe, like any other machine tool, is only of value when it is actually removing metal. If the lathe has to be set, or gears changed, this is unproductive time, and must be kept to a minimum. If the cutting of threads requires the calculation, removal, and insertion of different gears, then the lathe must be considered as old-fashioned or out of date. The continued use of lathes of this type does not represent good machining technique.

Fig. 144 shows the essential gearing arrangement connected with the calculations which follow. The set-up is for the cutting of a right-hand thread; if a left-hand thread is required, another idler must be put into the train.

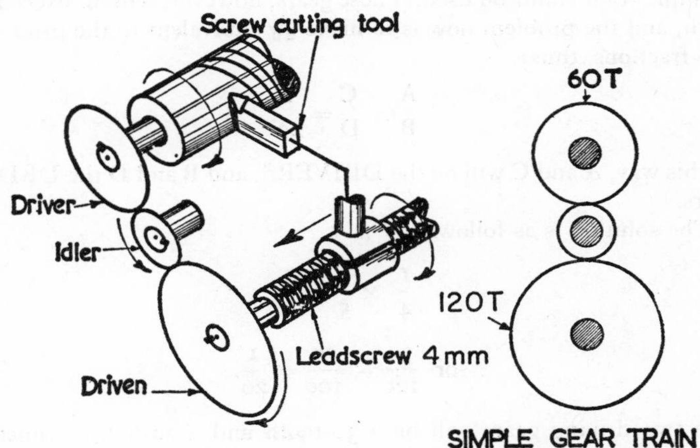

FIG. 144.—GEARING ARRANGEMENT TO CUT A RIGHT-HAND 2 MM PITCH THREAD.

Now $$\frac{\text{DRIVER}}{\text{DRIVEN}} = \frac{\text{PITCH to be CUT}}{\text{PITCH of LEAD SCREW}}$$

$$= \frac{2}{4}$$

This is the required ratio, and provided the gears used are of the same ratio, then a 60-tooth gear for the driver and a 120-tooth gear for the driven will produce the required thread. This is known as a **simple gear train**, and is illustrated in fig. 144, which indicates also the driving and driven gears.

Compound Gear Train

A compound gear train is used when the pitch required cannot be obtained with a simple gear train. A simple example will serve to illustrate the principle involved. Let us assume that we wish to cut a 3 mm dia 0·2 mm pitch thread on the same lathe.

$$\frac{\text{DRIVER}}{\text{DRIVEN}}=\frac{\text{PITCH to be CUT}}{\text{PITCH of LEAD SCREW}}$$

$$=\frac{0{\cdot}2}{4}.$$

We can reduce this ratio to $\frac{1}{20}$, and if a 400-tooth gear were available a simple train could be used. These gears, however, seldom exceed 120 teeth, and the problem now is to make $\frac{1}{20}$ equivalent to the product of two fractions, thus:

$$\frac{A}{B}\times\frac{C}{D}=\frac{1}{20}.$$

In this way, A and C will be the DRIVERS, and B and D the DRIVEN gears.

The solution is as follows:

$$\frac{1}{4}\times\frac{1}{5}=\frac{1}{20}$$

$$\text{or}\quad \frac{30}{120}\times\frac{20}{100}=\frac{1}{20}.$$

The two driving gears will be a 30-tooth and a 20-tooth, whilst the driven gears will be a 100-tooth and a 120-tooth. The compound train is shown in fig. 145; note that the 120- and 20-tooth gears are keyed to the same shaft. If a left-hand thread is to be cut, then an idler gear must be inserted between the 30-tooth driver and the 120 driven; this will reverse the rotation of the lead screw.

Calculations for English Threads

Before discussing the actual technique of cutting the thread it may be worthwhile to consider the calculation necessary if an English thread is required. Let us assume that it is required to cut a thread having 24 T.P.I., using the same lathe as before with a lead screw of 4 mm pitch.

Then
$$\frac{\text{DRIVERS}}{\text{DRIVEN}}=\frac{\text{T.P.I. on LEAD SCREW}}{\text{T.P.I. to be CUT}}$$

or
$$\frac{\text{DRIVERS}}{\text{DRIVEN}}=\frac{\text{PITCH to be CUT}}{\text{PITCH of LEAD SCREW}}$$

$$=\frac{\frac{1}{24}\text{ in}}{4\text{ mm}}.$$

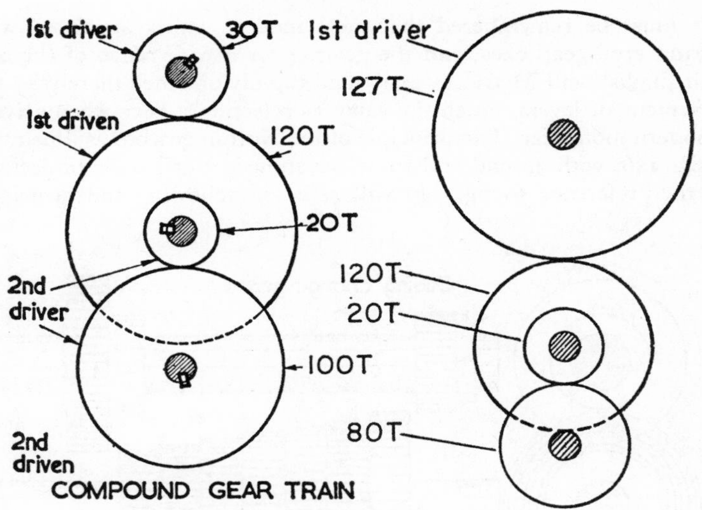

FIG. 145.—COMPOUND GEAR TRAINS.

Clearly we cannot have a ratio of dissimilar quantities, and the pitch of the lead screw is converted to mm using the Engineering Conversion Factor of 1 in = 25·4 mm, thus:

$$\frac{\text{DRIVERS}}{\text{DRIVEN}} = \frac{\frac{1}{24} \times 25{\cdot}4}{4}$$

$$= \frac{25{\cdot}4}{24 \times 4} = \frac{25{\cdot}4}{96}.$$

Provided the above conversion factor is always used, the numerator will always be 25·4, and division of this number by two will give us 12·7. A 127-tooth gear is supplied as standard equipment for the express purpose of the cutting of English threads, and all that now remains is to make up a suitable gear ratio with 127 as the numerator or product of the numerators, thus:

$$\frac{12{\cdot}7}{12} \times \frac{2}{8}$$

or

$$\frac{127}{120} \times \frac{20}{80}$$

A compound train can now be set up, having drivers of 127 and 20 teeth and driven gears of 120 and 80 teeth. This compound train is also shown in fig. 145

It must be remembered that most modern lathes are fitted with Norton type gearboxes, and the gearing for a wide range of threads, both English and Metric, is easily and rapidly obtained merely by the movement of levers, much the same as selecting a gear when driving a modern motor car. The principle of the Norton gearbox is illustrated in fig. 146, with an end and front elevation in third angle projection. Further reference to fig. 147 will assist in following the principles

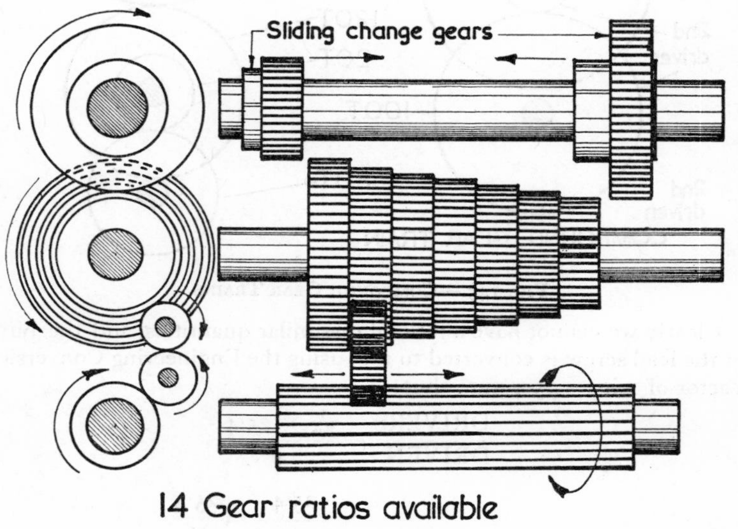

FIG. 146.—PRINCIPLE OF THE NORTON GEARBOX.

involved, and perhaps the student may now appreciate some of the high-quality work necessary in the design and manufacture of machine tools.

Setting the Cutting Tool

We may now return to the actual cutting of the thread, and it is certain that the turner will take only a few moments, using the Norton gearbox, to select the correct ratio. This ratio will represent a movement of the tool of 3 mm per revolution of the work. The accuracy of the thread form will depend on the accuracy to which the form on the tool has been ground, for the screw cutting tool is essentially a form tool. Assuming, then, that the tool has been correctly ground, the set-up for

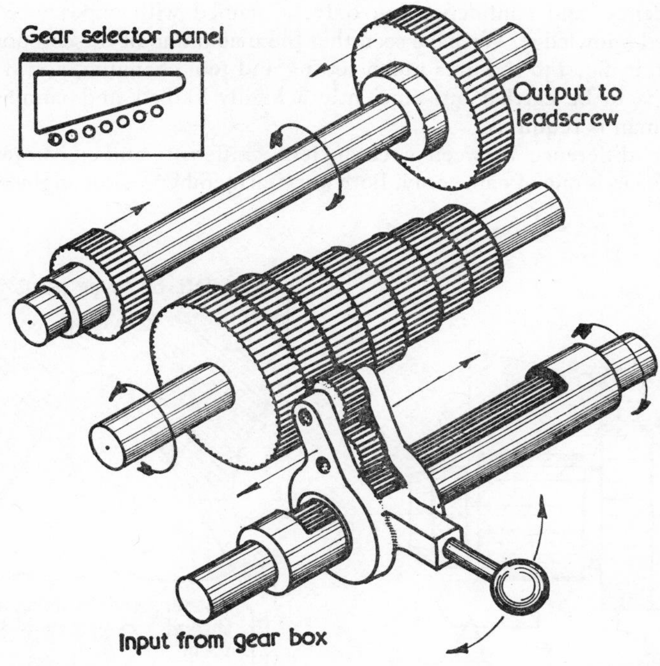

FIG. 147.—PICTORIAL VIEW OF NORTON GEARBOX PRINCIPLE.

accurate alignment is shown in fig. 148. Note the use of a screw cutting gauge to obtain accurate alignment of the tool.

The cutting of the thread is largely a matter of experience and confidence. Most turners prefer to feed directly into the work, although it is possible to set the compound slide at one-half the thread angle, and feed the tool into the work using this slide. It is customary also to reduce the depth of cut as the screw cutting proceeds, finishing with relatively small cuts, thus promoting a good finish.

It is possible to finish turn an ISO form screw thread at a lathe using a single-point cutting tool, because flat crests are permissible. However, rounded crests also are allowed, which in no way affect the thread performance. Fig. 149 shows the use of a hand chasing tool to produce rounded crests on a thread screw-cut at a centre lathe.

There is, of course, a great deal more involved in the machining of a screw thread at a centre lathe. We mentioned earlier the need for confidence, and confidence can only be gained with experience and applied knowledge. We have seen that the machining of the component shown in fig. 136 requires much setting and tool changing, and if this work is to be carried out efficiently a highly skilled and competent craftsman is required.

The difference between a competent craftsman and a competent technician is one of name only. Both are vital members of our engineering

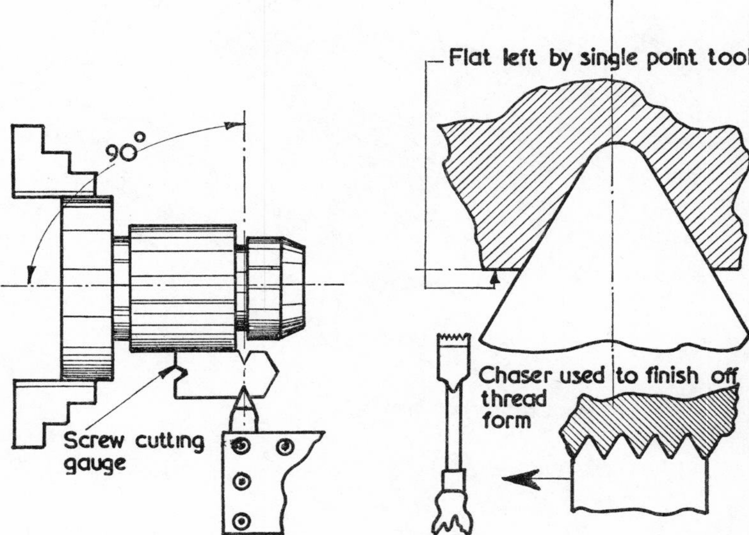

FIG. 148.—METHOD OF SETTING SCREW CUTTING TOOL.

FIG. 149.—THREAD CHASING.

community, and it is hoped that the examples of turning technique dealt with will enable the student technician to appreciate and understand the valuable contribution to engineering manufacture made by skilled craftsmen.

Alternative Methods of Work Holding

It must not be thought that the four-jaw chuck is the only way of holding a component for a second setting. It matters little which method of holding the work is adopted provided the finished component is produced within the limits laid down and in reasonable time. There are many centre lathe turners who are capable of remarkable improvisation, although the devices adopted are simplified versions of the following work holding principles.

Collets

Most centre lathes are provided with a set of collets, and these are very useful for the holding of standard diameters. The principle is shown in fig. 150; note the use of the taper principle to provide accurate location of both collet and work. Note also a typical component held in a collet, the part being a piercing punch for a press tool, turned from 13 mm diameter silver steel.

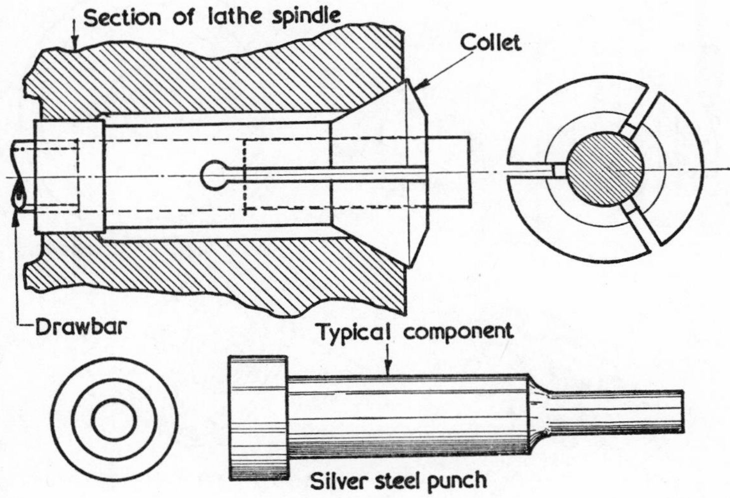

FIG. 150.—LATHE COLLET.

Mandrels

A mandrel is a work holding device intended to transmit its centre line to the work held. It is often used as a location device for bored work which requires external diameters true to the bored hole, and fig. 151 shows the use of a mandrel to turn the outside diameter of a flywheel. The mandrel is mounted between centres and is threaded to receive a tightening nut for the secure holding of the component. Mandrels are often tapered slightly, with the component carefully forced on to the mandrel, and held there by frictional force.

The Face Plate

The purpose of a face plate is to provide a datum face at 90° to the centre line of the lathe. This datum face is essentially a worktable, and T slots, together with other suitable openings, allow efficient clamping of the work. Great care must be exercised if heavy castings are clamped to the face plate of a centre lathe. It is essential that a reasonable measure of balance be obtained before machining is carried out, and under no circumstances should the lathe be rotated at high speed, because if the set-up on the face plate is out of balance considerable vibration will result, and at high speeds there is the grave danger of the set-up breaking away from the face plate.

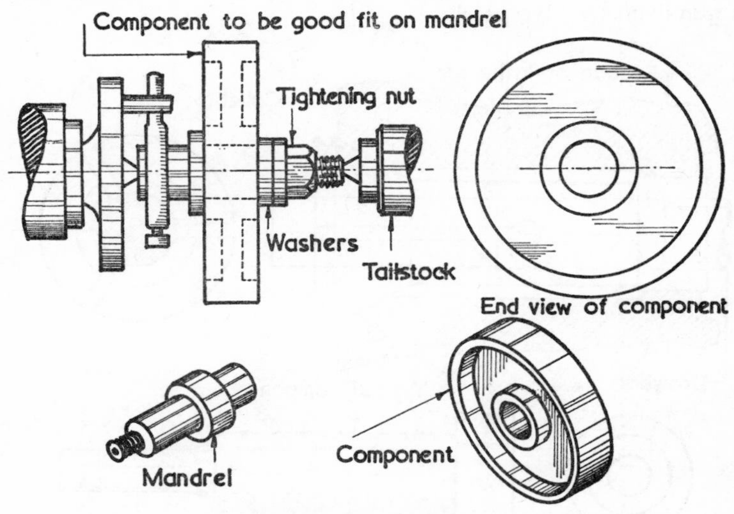

FIG. 151.—USE OF A MANDREL TO LOCATE FROM A BORED HOLE.

A typical example of a face plate set-up is shown in fig. 152. Note the use of an angle plate, together with a test bar and slip gauges to ensure that the distance A will be machined to very close limits. When the turner is satisfied with the setting, the test bar and centres are removed and the hole bored to size using a boring bar. Fig. 152A shows the set-up, whilst at B we see the casting in position ready for the machining of the bore. This is a good example of the use of end standards or slip gauges to ensure the machining of a hole, having the centre line of the hole to close dimensional accuracy to a datum face, which is in this case the base of the casting. It must be appreciated, however, that much time will be taken up by the setting-up operation, and this example will serve to emphasise further the high degree of skill and knowledge required by a centre lathe turner.

The 4-Jaw Chuck

Not only does a 4-jaw chuck provide a powerful gripping action, but also the independent movement of each of the four jaws allows the

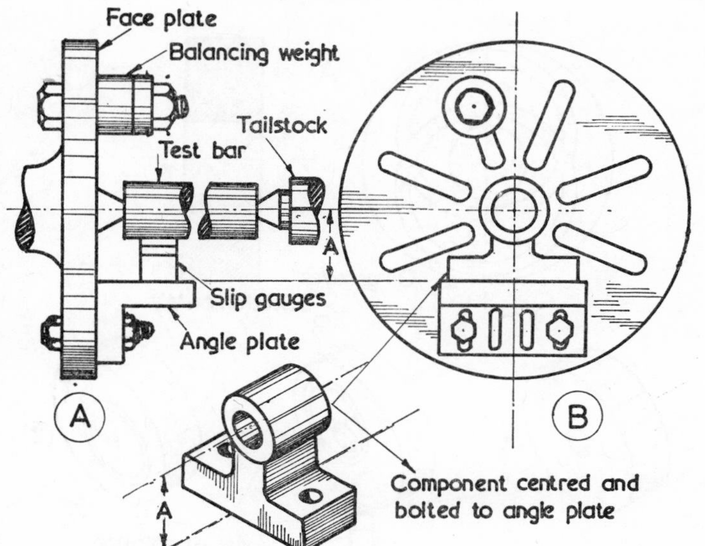

FIG. 152.—USE OF FACE PLATE FOR PRECISE BORING.

machining of eccentric work. A typical example of eccentric turning is shown in fig. 153A; this is a phosphor bronze pressure pad, having two eccentric oil grooves.

Clearly **three** lines of action of the work are required if the geometric surfaces of this component are to be produced on a centre lathe; this is shown in fig. 153B. Note that at C, a 3-jaw chuck may be used, for the object here is to produce a cylinder. At Y and Z, however, two different lines of action are required, one for each operation, and a 4-jaw chuck is ideal for this purpose. The independent movement of each of the jaws allows the turner to bring the centre-line of the work in line with the centre line of the lathe. A front elevation of the set-up is shown in fig. 153C. Note the use of a stick pin to pick up the scribed line, and that each oil groove will require a separate setting.

Lathe Steadies

Mention was made of lathe steadies in Volume I, where it was pointed out that their purpose is to support the revolving work, preventing bending or deflection under the influence of the cutting forces. Lathe steadies are seldom used for the average run of centre lathe work, and they are often to be found, neglected and unused, lying on the shop floor. The turning of long slender shafts, however, demands the use of a travelling steady, which is attached to the saddle of the lathe, and follows the tool as it traverses the work. Fixed steadies are used to

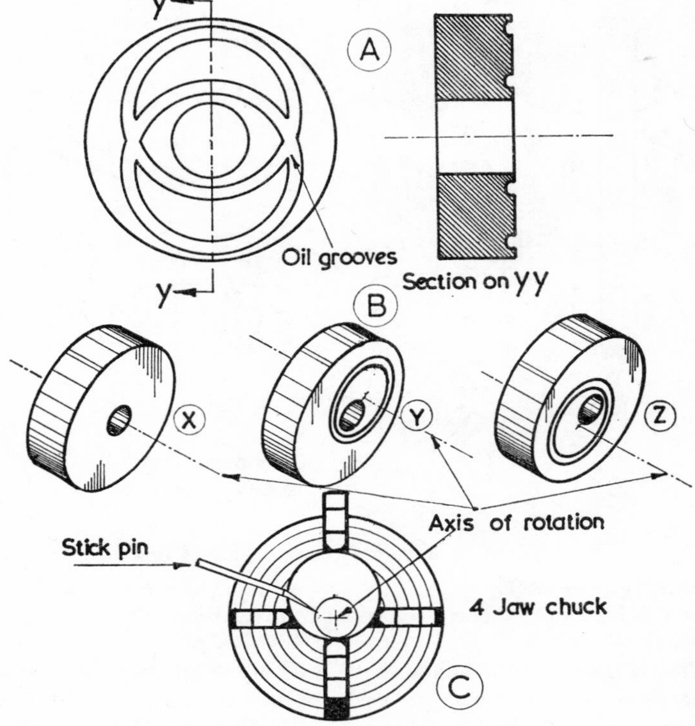

FIG. 153.—USE OF THE 4-JAW CHUCK.

support long shafts which require machining at some distance from the headstock. Both types of steadies are illustrated in fig. 154, and it must be remembered that the correct use and setting of these steadies is a highly-skilled job. A badly-adjusted steady may well cause serious damage to the work being turned.

Summary

We have seen that the use of a centre lathe involves much tool changing and tool setting. The principle underlying the best use of a centre lathe is similar to that underlying the use of a radial driller. This consists in secure holding of the work, and bringing as many cutting tools as possible to the work. In this way the geometrical alignments built into the machine are used to best advantage, and the non-linear functions of parallelism, concentricity, and alignment are assured.

We have seen also that the lathe is capable of a wide range of machining operations: screw cutting, drilling, reaming, and taper turning, to

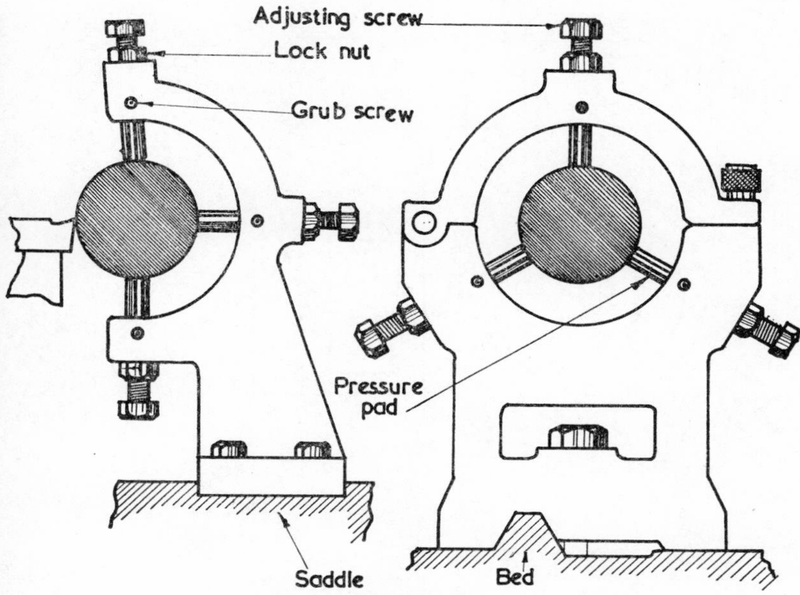

FIG. 154.—LATHE STEADIES.

mention only a few. It is not possible to cover in detail in the space of a single chapter the many techniques and principles necessary for the production of well-finished work in the minimum of time, neither is it expedient or proper to do so. The operation of a centre lathe is the province of a highly skilled craftsman, and we would be presumptuous to assume that the reading of one chapter of a book on Workshop Processes will replace the experience and skill gained through continued and intimate operation of a centre lathe.

It is essential, however, that the principles underlying the holding of work and tools, and the calculations involved in screw cutting and taper turning, be appreciated and understood; for we will find, in a later volume, that the machine tools used for the mass-production of engineering components are essentially simplified adaptations of the principles involved when machining on a centre lathe.

QUESTIONS ON CHAPTER NINE

1. Explain the advantages obtained if a job can be machined in one setting using a centre lathe.
2. Make a neat sketch of the set-up, showing clearly the work holding and tool holding, for the machining of **twelve** of the punches shown in fig. 155A.
3. Write down the relative advantages to be gained when using **each** of the following work holding devices: collet, 3-jaw chuck, 4-jaw chuck, centres, face plate.

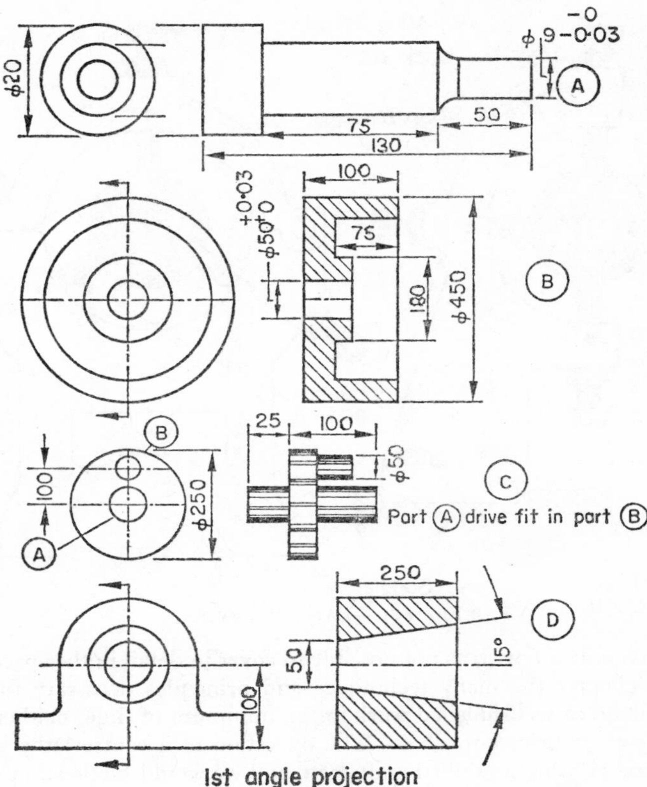

FIG. 155.—COMPONENTS TO BE TURNED ON A CENTRE LATHE.

4. Assuming that a fairly old-fashioned lathe, requiring the changing of gears is to be used, calculate the gears for cutting the following threads: 3 mm pitch, 10 mm pitch, 1.5 mm pitch.

The lead screw has a pitch of 2 mm, and gears from 20 to 100 teeth are available, together with a 127-tooth gear.

5. Describe briefly the sequence of operations for machining the component shown in fig. 155B on a centre lathe. (All dimensions are given in mm.)

6. Explain the need for a screw cutting gauge when setting a screw cutting tool. Why must a chaser be used if the thread cut is of Whitworth form?

7. Make a neat sketch showing the principle of a Norton gearbox. What advantages does the use of this gearbox offer the centre-lathe turner?

8. Describe briefly how the eccentric crank (fig. 155C) can be machined using a centre lathe.

9. Why are centre lathes never used for the mass-production of engineering components? Why are they still used in the engineering manufacturing industry?

10. Make neat sketches showing clearly the sequence of operations necessary for the machining of the tapered bore in the component shown in fig. 155D. The base has been machined, and a centre lathe is to be used for the boring of the hole.

10 Milling Machines

THERE is little doubt that milling machines are regarded as second to the centre lathe in their ability to perform a large number of machining operations. Their versatility is such that it is possible to generate plane, spherical, and internal cylindrical surfaces, whilst external cylindrical surfaces and contours may readily be machined by the forming or copying process. Milling machines are also widely used for production work, in conjunction with milling fixtures for accurate location and holding of the workpiece, and most toolrooms are equipped with them. We now see that the milling of metal is an important aspect of engineering manufacture, and can range from the mass-production of milled components to the milling of a spiral-fluted reamer in the toolroom.

Principles of Milling

Unlike the centre lathe, which operates on the principle of rotation of the work and feed of the tool to generate a cylindrical surface, the milling machine operates by rotation of the tool and feeding of the work. Two main types of milling are in general use:

(i) vertical milling,
(ii) horizontal milling.

Vertical Milling

When vertical milling, the axis of the cutter is vertical to the work-table of the machine. This principle is illustrated in fig. 156. Note that in order to simplify the principle we show a single-point tool, with the cutting point at a radius R from the axis of rotation. In this way the tool point is offset from the centre line or axis of rotation, and rotation of the tool causes the tool point to generate a circle. If now the workpiece shown in fig. 156 is fed in the direction of arrow A, a plane surface is generated. This surface is plane provided the axis of tool rotation is truly vertical in **all** planes. Any deviation from 90° will result in a slightly concave surface. This is shown in fig. 157; at A we see a view at 90° to the feed, and it will be noted that the tool point is lower at P than it is at Q. At B we see the view in the direction of arrow X, which is in

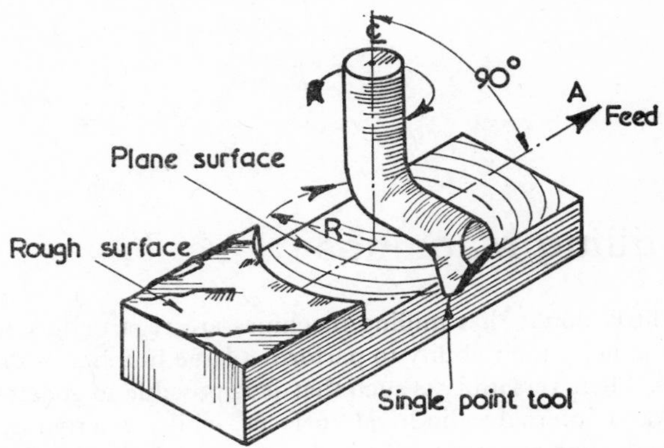

FIG. 156.—PRINCIPLE OF VERTICAL MILLING.

effect a third angle projection of the end elevation of the large view A. Note that the surface generated by the single-point tool is not plane but elliptical.

Once again the importance of the essential geometry inherent in a machine tool is amply illustrated by this simple example of the effect

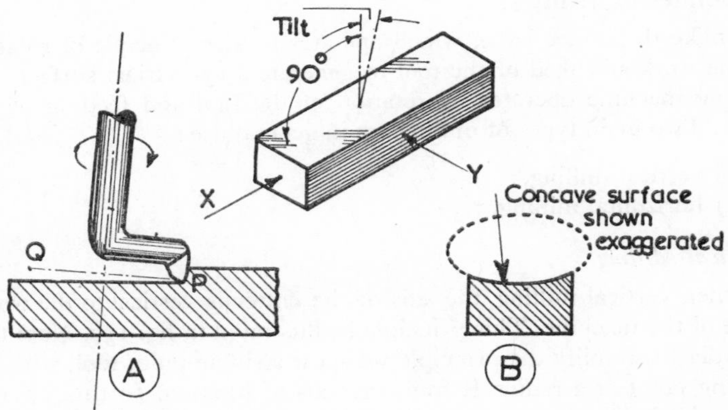

FIG. 157.—SURFACE PRODUCED WHEN CENTRE LINE OF TOOL IS NOT VERTICAL.

on the generated surface produced by a geometrical error in the line of action of the tool. We are now approaching the end of the second year of our study of Workshop Processes, and perhaps it is now evident that the main quality of a machine tool is the geometrical accuracy of the moving parts.

Before leaving the principle of the vertical milling action, it is worthwhile to have a look at the method of generating an internal cylindrical surface, or in other words boring a hole.

We have seen, in our discussion on the drilling machine, that the drilling of holes is no easy matter with respect to accuracy of diameter and the linear dimensions of the hole centres. If the movement of the worktable can be controlled with the use of the indexing dial principle, linear accuracy is possible, and if a workpiece is clamped or held on the table it is a simple matter to present the workpiece to the tool with linear control over the distances moved.

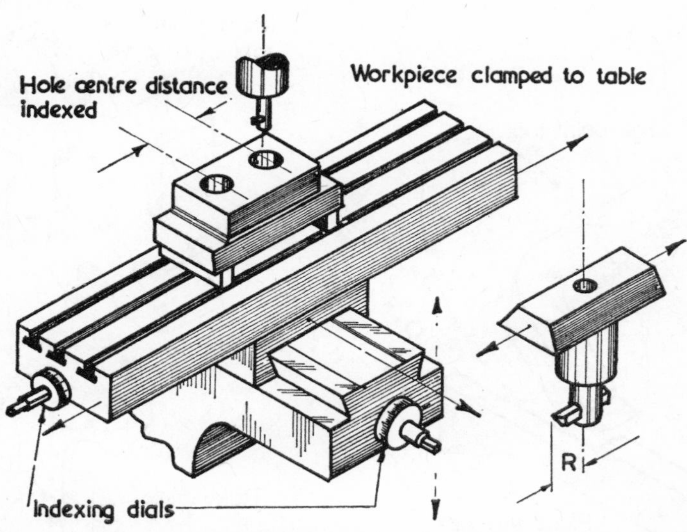

FIG. 158.—VERTICAL MILLING MACHINE. MOVEMENTS AND PRINCIPLE OF THE BORING HEAD.

If in addition the distance of the tool point shown as R in fig. 156 could be accurately adjusted for both inward and outward movement, this would permit the machining of holes to precise diameters.

This is exactly the sort of work that can be carried out on a vertical miller, and the essential movements are shown in fig. 158. We see at once the marked similarity to the movements available on a shaping machine, and the relationship to the saddle and cross slide movements of a centre lathe. The principle of a **boring head** is also shown in fig. 158, and most boring heads are fitted with a micrometer adjusting device permitting the machining of holes to very close limits. It is evident that a vertical milling machine will be a rigid structure, allowing the movements shown in fig. 158, and the methods adopted to obtain accurate guiding of the moving parts, and to bring about the necessary movements, will differ little from those we have discussed in Volume I.

Horizontal Milling

The difference between horizontal and vertical milling lies only in the position of the axis of rotation. This is clearly shown in fig. 159*a*, and once again we show a simple single-point tool. The axis of rotation is PQ, and the point of the tool describes a circle. With the workpiece fed in the direction of arrow A a plane surface is generated, as shown in the

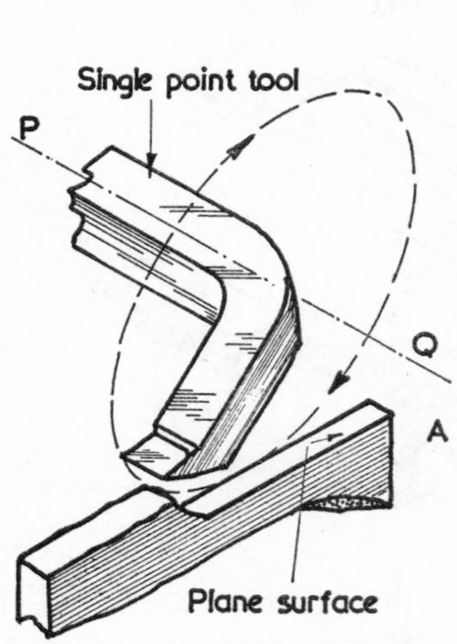

FIG. 159*a*.—PRINCIPLE OF HORIZONTAL MILLING.

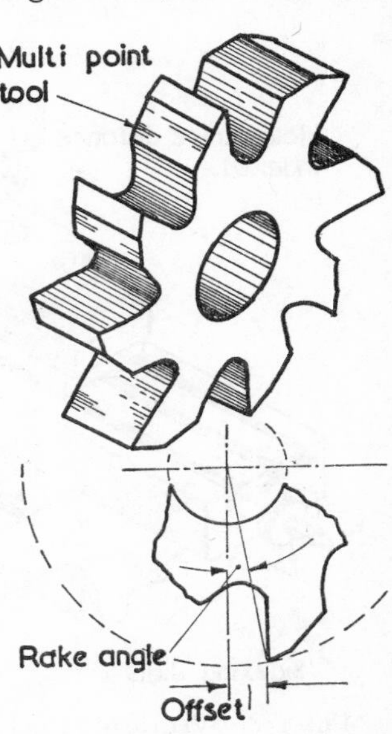

FIG. 159*b*.—PRINCIPLE OF THE MILLING CUTTER.

diagram. Clearly a horizontal milling machine will have movements similar to those of the vertical milling machine shown in fig. 158. There is, however, one serious limitation of the horizontal miller, namely that there is no movement of the tool along its axis of rotation. This means that once the tool has been set in position no further movement or adjustment of it is possible.

Before leaving the principles underlying both vertical and horizontal milling, it is worthwhile to consider the type of cutting tools to be used in the milling machines we have described. Fig. 159*a* shows a single-point cutter, and its similarity to a lathe tool is clearly seen. Thus all we have said regarding the importance of the rake and clearance angles with regard to lathe tools is also true for milling cutters, for a milling cutter intended for use on a horizontal milling machine is little more than a number of lathe tool points arranged in a circular manner.

This is clearly shown in fig. 159*b*, and it is clear that the milling cutter shown is a multi-point cutting tool. Note also that the method of obtaining a rake angle on the cutting teeth is similar to the method adopted when providing a rake angle on the cutting edges of a hand tap. This principle of offsetting the flutes of a hand tap was described in Volume I, and once again we see the continued application of simple but well-proven principles.

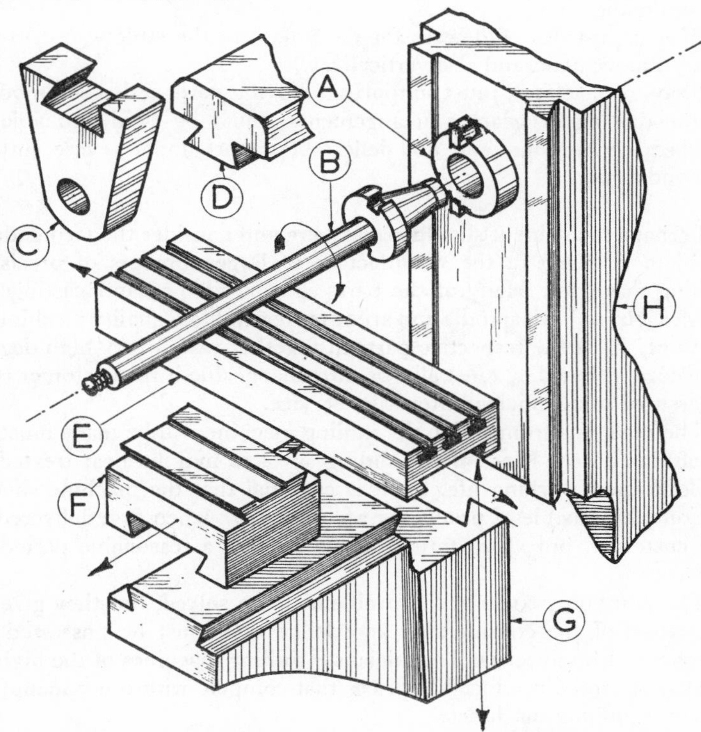

FIG. 160.—ESSENTIAL PARTS OF THE HORIZONTAL MILLING MACHINE.

The Horizontal Milling Machine

A simple but informative view of the essential parts of a horizontal milling machine is shown in fig. 160, and the essential parts are listed below, together with their purpose.

A Spindle; provides axis of rotation and locates work holding device; must have a range of speeds.

B Arbor; a work holding device; locates in spindle nose.

C Arbor supporting bracket; prevents bending or deflection of arbor under cutting loads; must be adjustable.

D Overarm; provides support and guideways for arbor supporting bracket; locates and is adjustable in body of machine.

E Table; provides clamping of work holding devices, and both horizontal and vertical movement; feed should be automatic.

F Saddle; guides table for the feed movement, and has guideways to provide for movement at 90° to feed movement; should have automatic feed.

G Knee; provides guideways for movement of the table at 90° to the feed movement, and also vertically.

H Body of machine; must support all moving parts and accommodate the driving or gearing arrangements; must be rigid and able to absorb vibrations, and not deflect or distort under severe cutting conditions.

Perhaps the student should pause here and consider the tremendous problem involved in the manufacture of large numbers of precision milling machines. Many of the parts shown will be sand castings in grey cast iron; both spindle and arbor represent high-quality machining. Not only must the respective parts fit together with a very high degree of accuracy, but they must also be interchangeable if the customer is to be assured of an efficient after-sales service.

The materials from which the milling machine will be made must be carefully chosen. Most of the sliding surfaces may be heat treated to prolong their working life, for it is essential that the machine should not only be capable of producing accurate work when first delivered to the customer, but also continue to do so over a reasonable period of time.

These are only some of the problems to be solved, but they give an indication of the considerable knowledge that must be possessed by Mechanical Engineering Technicians if milling machines of the highest quality are to be produced at prices that compete with other manufacturers of milling machines.

Advantages of the Horizontal Miller

The great advantage possessed by the horizontal miller over the vertical miller is that much greater support is afforded to the cutting tool. We have already stressed that maximum rigidity is an essential feature of efficient machining, and correct use of the arbor and arbor support permits considerable metal removal on the horizontal milling machine. Fig. 161 makes a comparison between the two milling machines under discussion, and it will be clear that the use of an **end mill** in the vertical machine is not likely to produce accuracy with respect to the linear dimension A. This is due to the relatively long unsupported length of cutter shown as L, and any attempt to remove a large amount of metal must result in bending or deflection of the cutter in the direction of the

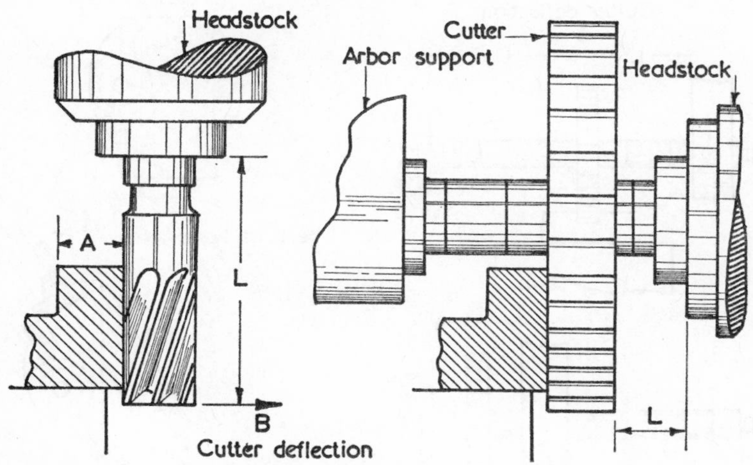

FIG. 161.—ADVANTAGE OF THE HORIZONTAL MILLER WITH REGARD TO CUTTER RIGIDITY.

arrow B. Thus, if the table is indexed a given amount using the indexing dial, it is certain that some of this movement will be lost through bending of the cutter, and error and confusion must result.

It is seldom that vertical milling machines are used on production lines, where the emphasis is on maximum metal removal in the minimum of time and with consistent accuracy. Clearly the horizontal miller is best suited for this kind of work, and fig. 161 shows the same operation carried out on a horizontal milling machine. Note the fact that the milling cutter is located as close as possible to the headstock of the machine. This promotes maximum rigidity, and is good milling practice. The same applies to the position of the arbor support, which is kept as close as possible to the cutter. Yet it is surprising how often one sees the horizontal milling set-up shown in fig. 162.

This is the worst possible position to mount the cutter, for the bending of the arbor will be at a maximum with the cutter in the position shown. There is no excuse for a set-up of this kind, and it is a certain indication of indifferent machining technique. It is, of course, possible that the size of the clamping arrangements does not permit the ideal condition also shown in fig. 162, but at all times the cutter should be placed as close to the headstock as possible, and the arbor support as close to the cutter as possible.

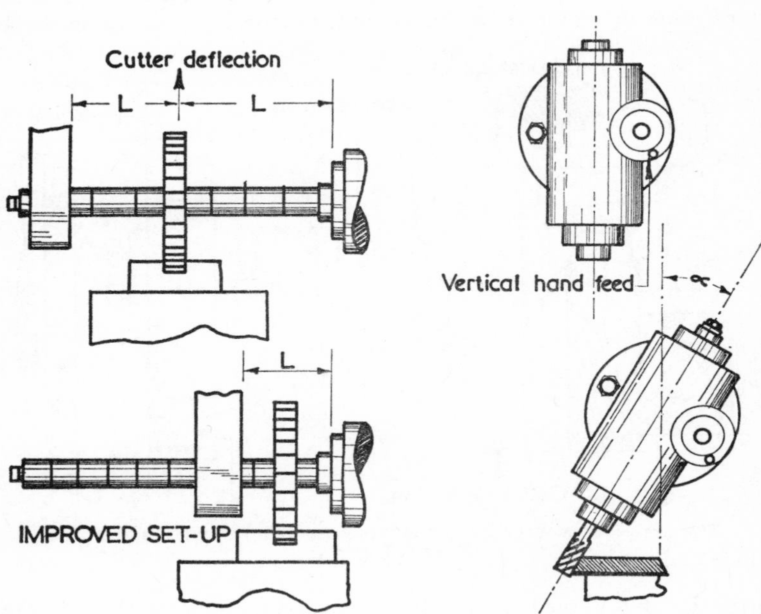

FIG. 162.—IMPORTANCE OF CORRECT CUTTER POSITIONING.

FIG. 163.—TILTING THE VERTICAL HEAD.

The Vertical Milling Machine

The essential parts of a vertical milling machine are almost identical with those of a horizontal milling machine. We have seen that the difference consists in a vertical axis of rotation of the cutter, together with provision for vertical feed of the cutting tool. This principle is similar in all respects to the vertical feed provided on all drilling machines, and differs little from the head slide of the shaping machine. Similar to the shaping machine head slide, most vertical millers have swivelling heads, thus permitting the feeding of the tool at an angle inclined to the vertical. This principle is illustrated in fig. 163, and a graduated scale in degrees allows reasonably accurate setting to a given angle.

Advantages of the Vertical Miller

Although the vertical miller finds little use on production lines, it is nevertheless a most useful and versatile machine tool when used to best advantage by an experienced and skilled toolroom miller. We have already seen that a boring head will permit the accurate boring of holes with respect to diameter, whilst the indexing dials will permit accurate positioning of the hole centres. It is perhaps in the milling of small slots that the vertical miller offers the greatest scope, and fig. 164 illustrates the sort of work readily carried out on a vertical milling machine. Note that as the table feed is at 90° this angle will be transmitted to the work,

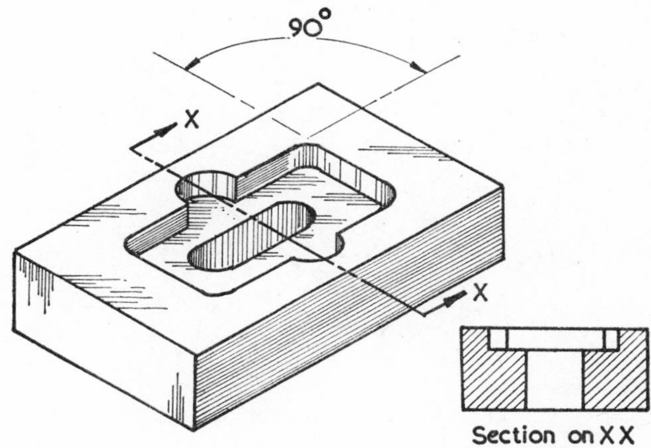

FIG. 164.—TYPICAL COMPONENT MACHINED ON A VERTICAL MILLER.

resulting in equivalent accuracy of the milled faces. The section of the workpiece shown at B clearly demonstrates the advantages offered by vertical milling when profiles of the type shown are to be machined.

This type of work is an essential feature of the forming dies used in plastic moulding, and also in the drop forging of metal components. The manufacture of the dies used in the pressure die casting process is certain to include the sort of work illustrated in fig. 164, and it is hoped that the student may now appreciate the practical value of all the matters discussed in this book.

Milling Cutters

A milling cutter is a multi-point cutting tool, and the principle underlying the design of a cutter for use on a horizontal milling machine is shown in fig. 159. Let us first consider a milling cutter as a number of wedge-like points; fig. 165 illustrates a typical **plain milling cutter.** Note carefully that a cutter of this type is unable to cut on the sides shown as A in the diagram; a typical use for this cutter would be the milling of a slot as shown in the diagram. This cutter is often known as a **slotting** cutter.

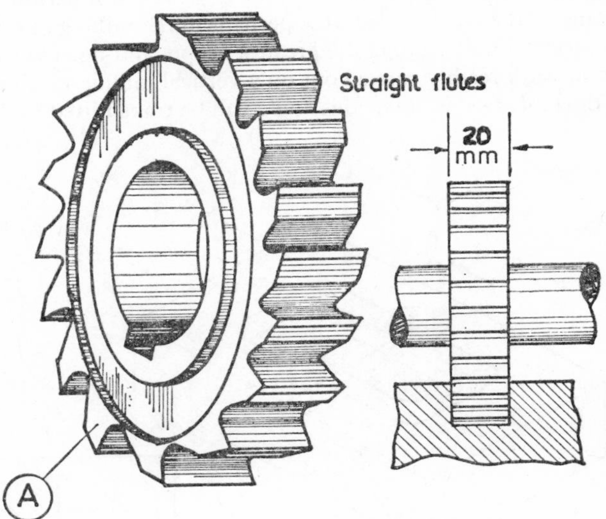

FIG. 165.—PLAIN MILLING CUTTER.

Side and Face Cutter

This cutter is provided with cutting edges on both sides as well as on its face or periphery. This means that it is capable of cutting on both its face and sides; fig. 166 illustrates this cutter and shows also some typical applications of its use. Note that we have shown on the diagram that the maximum width of the tooth is limited to 20 mm, if the cutter is to have straight teeth.

Helical or Fluted Cutters

If the cutting face of a miller cutter exceeds 20 mm it is usual to provide side rake by giving the teeth a spiral angle. Let us consider a milling cutter that is to be used to generate a plane surface on the component shown in fig. 167. If the width of the cutter is made 75 mm, it will be possible to machine the top surface of the component in one pass, the use of a simple milling fixture permitting the operation to be carried out on a production basis, using semi-skilled labour.

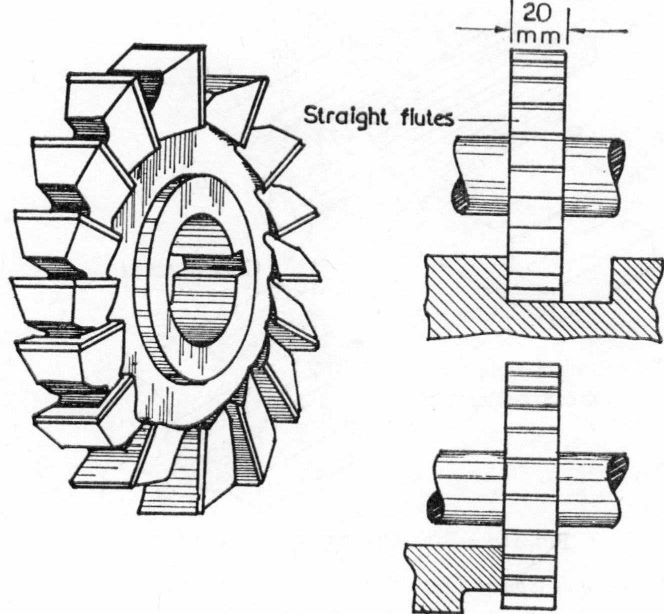

FIG. 166.—SIDE AND FACE MILLING CUTTER.

Fig. 167 shows the milling cutter with straight teeth, and this is not a particularly good cutter. If the cutter is provided with straight teeth as shown, then each tooth will remove a slice or chip of metal of length PQ. In effect, the work will be subjected to a series of sudden impacts as the tooth makes contact with the work over the whole of its length. This principle is further shown in fig. 167B, and clearly this is an undesirable state of affairs, leading to severe vibration of the set-up.

Fig. 168 illustrates the answer to this problem of large work-cutter contact area. At A we see a spiral-tooth milling cutter, sometimes known as a **slab** or **helical** mill. At B we see the great advantage offered by the spiral flutes; one tooth only is shown, the cut commencing at P and finishing at Q. The spacing of the teeth is so arranged that the following tooth starts cutting before the preceding tooth finishes its cut, and in this way the metal is removed smoothly with no hammering effect.

Note that the principle of helical flutes is also found in the **end mills** used in the vertical milling machine, for if the cutting conditions are as shown in fig. 168C the distance RS is also considerable, and the use of a straight-fluted cutter would lead to much vibration.

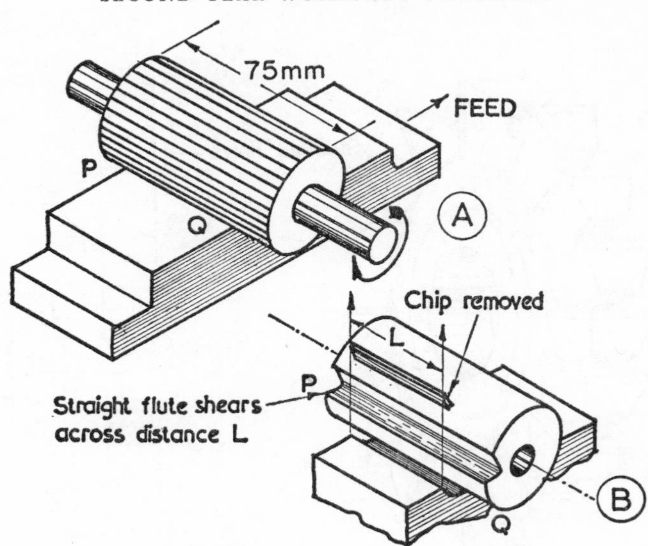

FIG. 167.—STRAIGHT-FLUTED MILLING CUTTER.

Disadvantage of Spiral Teeth

There is a slight disadvantage experienced when reasonably heavy cuts are taken with milling cutters possessing spiral or helical teeth. Fig. 169 shows a plan view of the milling operation illustrated in fig. 167. The dotted lines show the spiral flutes on the underside of the cutter; the cutter will be rotating with a certain torque, transmitted from the arbor to the cutter through the keyway shown in fig. 169B. As **torque = force × radius**, each tooth will exert a force on the metal as the cutter rotates against the table feed. This force acts at 90° to the helical flute; the direction is indicated by arrow R in fig. 169A.

An equal and opposite force must now act on the tooth of the cutter, and this is shown as *ab* in the diagram. It is not difficult to resolve this one force component into the two components *ac* and *cb*. Clearly *bc* is the force opposing the table feed, whilst the force *ac* tends to drive the cutter along the arbor against the headstock. As shown the set-up is acceptable, but it is considered bad practice if the cutter is forced against the arbor support.

If the cutter shown as P were mounted alone on the arbor, it would tend to move towards the arbor support, as shown in fig. 169C. Thus if two slab mills are to be mounted side by side to mill a relatively large area, they would be mounted as shown. Note that the forces are now cancelled out, as each tends to move towards the other.

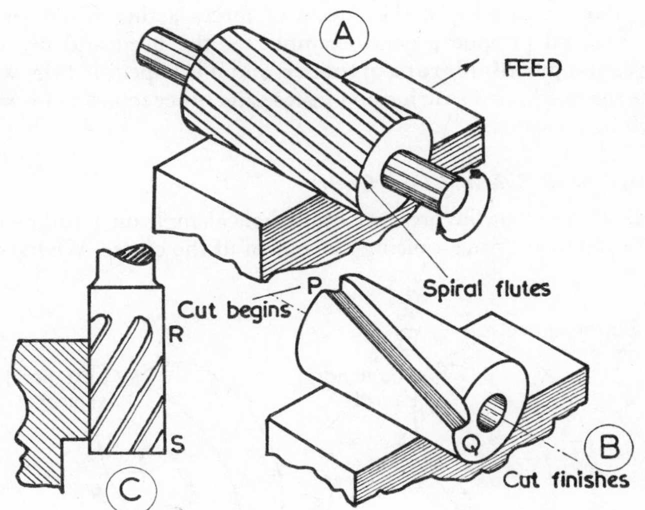

Fig. 168.—Spiral-fluted Milling Cutter.

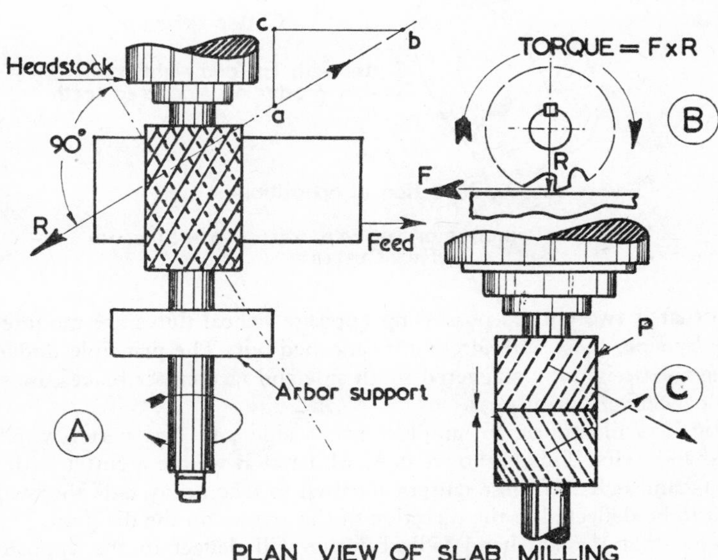

Fig. 169.—Effect of Spiral-fluted Teeth on the Cutting Forces.

The above examples of the effects of forces acting whilst metal is being removed provide a good example for the need and use of the **triangle** and **parallelogram of forces**, and it is hoped that the student will see the need for the inclusion of these and other topics in his studies for technician status.

Staggered-tooth Side and Face Cutters

We have seen that the presence of the helical angle on a milling cutter ends to produce a force causing movement of the cutter. We have seen

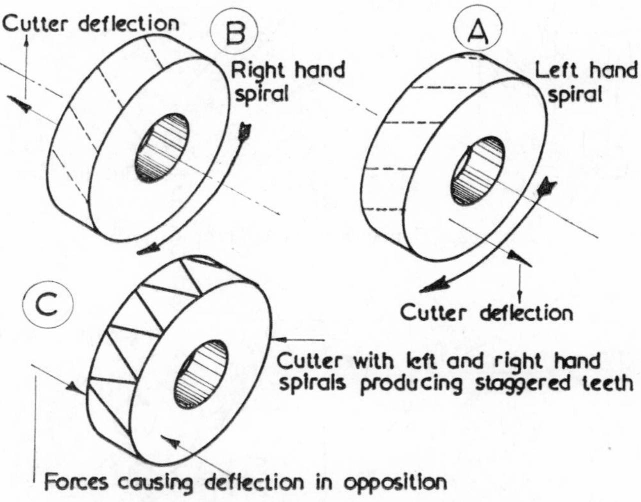

FIG. 170.—PRINCIPLE OF THE STAGGERED-TOOTH SIDE AND FACE CUTTER.

also that if two cutters possessing opposite helical flutes are mounted side by side, these side forces are cancelled out. The principle underlying the design of a staggered-tooth side and face cutter makes use of this cancelling-out process.

Fig. 170 illustrates, in simple form, a side and face cutter with a left-hand helix. This is shown at A, whilst at B we see a cutter with a right-hand helix. If these cutters are used to take heavy cuts they will tend to be deflected in the direction of the arrows on the diagram.

Note that the left-hand helical cutter will deflect in the opposite direction to the right-hand helical cutter. Clearly now, if we could design a cutter having both right- and left-hand helical teeth, the side forces would cancel out, and a smooth-action cutter must result, capable of taking heavy cuts with little or no distortion or vibration.

This is precisely what a staggered-tooth cutter can achieve, and the essential design is shown in fig. 170C. The metal removal capabilities of these cutters are very good indeed, provided both cutter and work are rigidly mounted or supported, and once again we see the necessity for a knowledge of both science and mathematics, for there will be an application of both in the design and manufacture of the cutter.

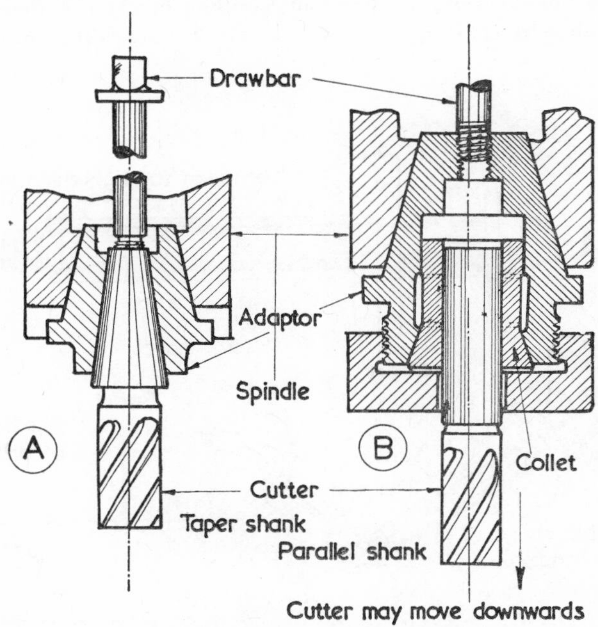

FIG. 171.—CUTTER HOLDING.

Tool or Cutter Holding

As in all machine tools, provision must exist for the accurate holding of the milling cutter, and as in the drilling operation, it is an essential condition of cutter holding on both horizontal and vertical machines that the cutter rotates about its axis.

Because the vertical milling machine is not unlike a drilling machine with regard to tool holding, perhaps it is not unexpected to find the taper principle used for the accurate location of the milling cutter. Both parallel- and taper-shank end mills may be used, and the principle underlying their location is illustrated in fig. 171. The use of the collet-type holding device is not advisable if heavy cuts are to be taken using a right-hand spiral end mill. There will be a tendency for the cutter to be forced downwards, resulting in an increased depth of cut with possible scrapping of the work. It is better to use the taper-shank end mill, for as shown at fig. 171A vertical movement of the cutter is not possible because of the use of a draw bar to pull the cutter tightly into the taper.

The Use of the Arbor

The arbor as used on a horizontal milling machine is essentially a tool holding device. It must be appreciated at the outset that the accuracy

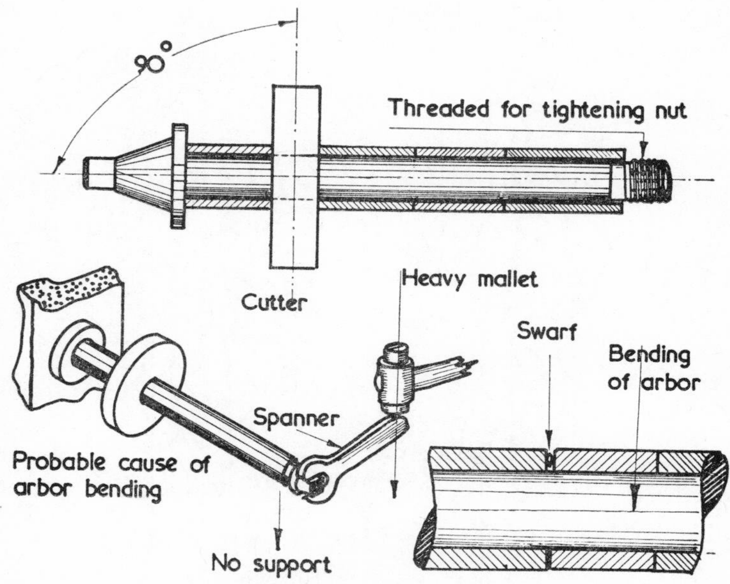

FIG. 172.—THE MILLING MACHINE ARBOR AS A TOOL HOLDING DEVICE.

of the rotation of the cutter about its axis will be the accuracy of the rotation of the arbor about its axis. In other words if the arbor is not running true, the cutter will not run true. Thus there is no excuse for the continued use of a bent arbor. As we have stated, an arbor is a tool holding device and must be treated with care and respect. It is exceedingly bad practice to attempt removal of the tightening nut using a spanner and mallet on an unsupported arbor. This undesirable technique is illustrated in fig. 172 and is certain to cause bending of the arbor. Note the use of spacing collars; it is again necessary to ensure that these collars are kept clean and free from damage or swarf. The presence of a piece of swarf, as shown in the diagram, will cause bending of the arbor when the nut is tightened.

Milling Techniques

Milling machines are machine tools, and it cannot be stated too often that the best use of a machine tool involves the maximum use of the geometrical movements built into the machine tool. At the same time the set-up must be as rigid as possible, with as much work carried out in the one setting as possible. Perhaps a few examples will serve to demonstrate not only the correct approach to the art of milling, but also the sort of set-up likely to give the best results on a production line.

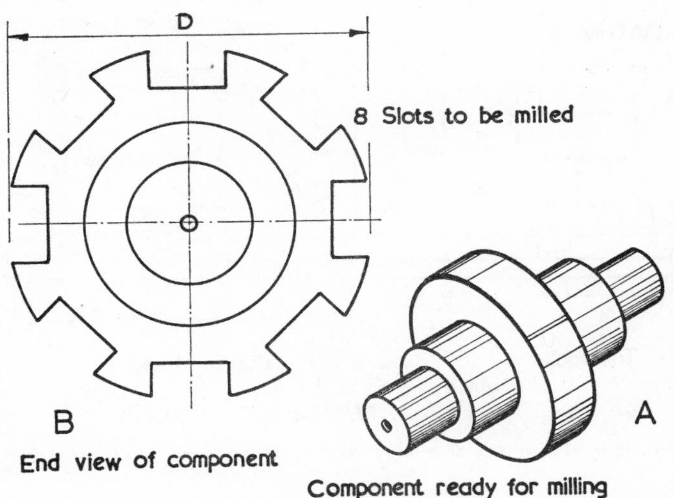

FIG. 173.—COMPONENT REQUIRING MILLED SLOTS.

Fig. 173 shows a turned blank requiring the milling of eight equi-spaced slots on the diameter shown as D. An end view of the finished component is shown at B. Let us keep in mind the fact that the part will be sent to an inspector for checking when we have completed the milling, and we must ensure that the dimensions are within the limits laid down. We can take it that the turning has already been checked and passed, and all that now remains is the milling of the slots shown.

The slots will possess the linear dimensions of width and depth; the non-linear functions of both concentricity and alignment are also involved, together with the angular dimensions between the centre lines of the slots.

The Centres as a Datum

The concentricity of the slots is governed by their distance from the centre line of the component. Provided the centre lathe turner used the centres as a datum when turning the outside diameters of the component, the continued use of the centres as a datum must result in slots which are milled at equal distances from the centre line and are thus concentric.

We need, then, a work holding device which will not only permit the rotation of the work about its axis, but also allow accurate indexing or

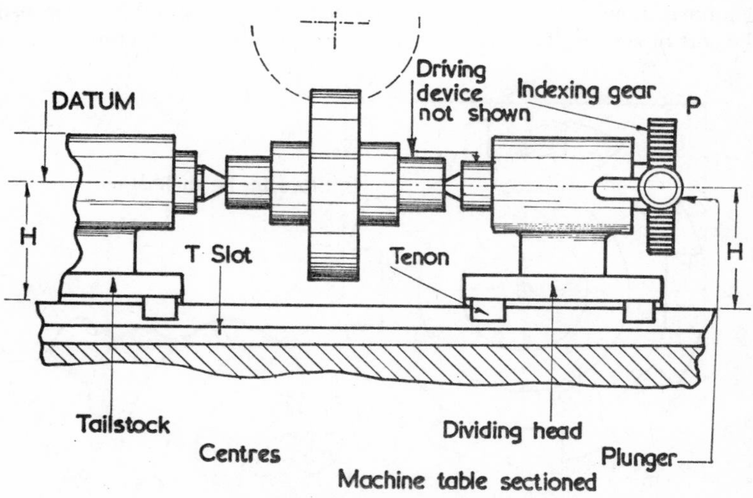

FIG. 174.—PRINCIPLE AND APPLICATION OF A SIMPLE DIVIDING HEAD.

positioning at required angles. Such a work holding device is known as a **dividing head.** A simple dividing head is illustrated in fig. 174, and shows the work in position for the milling of the slots. The indexing device illustrated consists of an accurate spindle carrying an indexing gear in which a plunger locates. This principle is known as **direct indexing.** There are no gear ratios; the angular divisions are obtained by the rotation and location of the indexing plate indicated in the diagram as P. It is, in effect, not unlike an accurate gear.

Note the use of registers or tenons to locate both dividing head and tailstock, thus ensuring that the movement or feed of the table is at 90° to the axis of the arbor. Any deviation from 90°, as we have previously stated, will produce a concave surface at the bottom of the milled slot. The tenons locate in the T slots machined in the table of the milling machine. It is worthwhile testing the height H using a dial indicator, as this will ensure alignment of the milled slots.

The problem now remaining is the alignment of the slots with respect to the centre line of the component, and the required condition is shown in fig. 175. It will be seen that the centre of the cutter face must lie on the centre line of the work; many methods are used to bring the cutter in this position, and the method adopted will depend on the degree of accuracy required. One such technique is illustrated in fig. 175, together with the method of indexing for the eight slots.

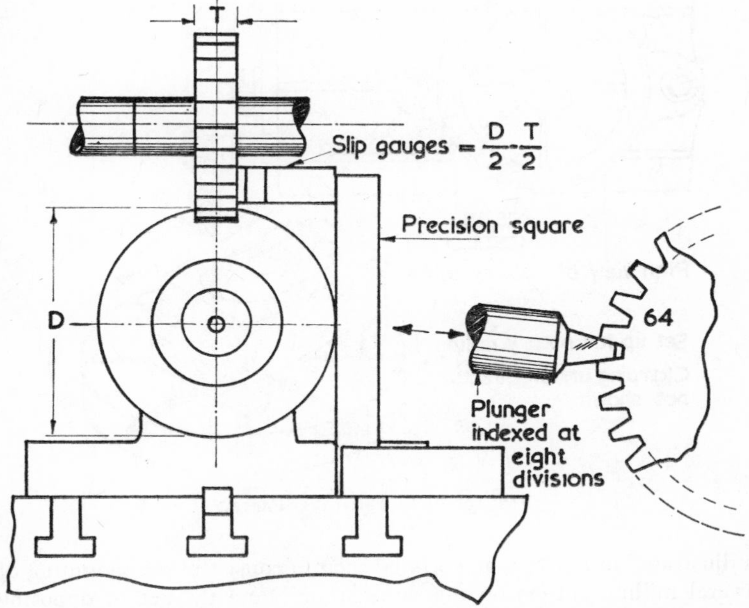

FIG. 175.—SETTING WORK TO CENTRE, AND METHOD OF INDEXING.

It must be remembered that other dividing heads are available, most of which have a 40:1 reduction ratio, and these dividing heads permit both simple and compound or differential indexing.

The Rotary Table

We can consider a rotary table as a dividing head mounted with the axis of rotation vertical, and fitted with a work table. This table is provided with T slots to allow clamping of the work, and the circumference of the table is graduated in degrees. Rotary tables are widely used for the end milling of radii, and fig. 176 illustrates a typical application. The stick pin method, illustrated in fig. 223 of Volume I, may be used to pick up the scribed line.

Gang Milling

This principle is mainly used on production work, and is seldom adopted for the milling of single or one-off components. The technique

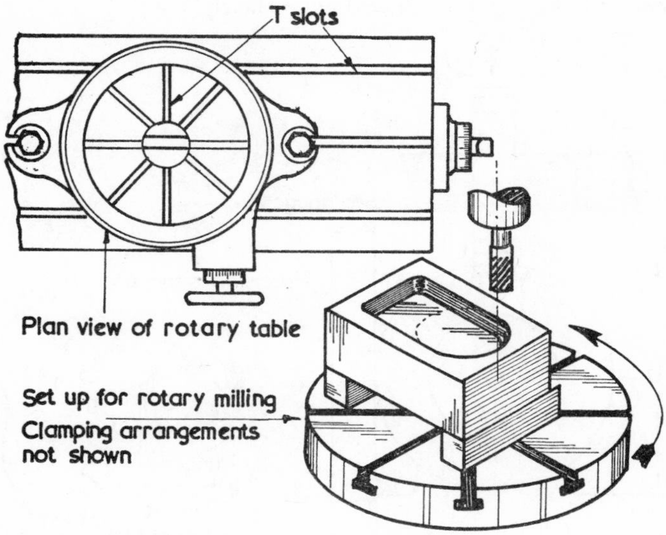

FIG. 176.—THE ROTARY TABLE.

is illustrated in fig. 177, and will be seen to consist in the mounting of several milling cutters on the same arbor. Note the use of opposing spirals in the two slab mills. The surfaces shown at A are generated, but it is a simple matter to produce contoured surfaces using the forming or copying principle. A typical example is shown at B, and provides some idea of the versatility of the milling machine in its ability to produce geometrical surfaces.

Use of Shell End Mills

A shell end mill is illustrated in fig. 178. The use of this milling cutter is to be encouraged, for it promotes the principle of maximum rigidity of the cutting tool. It can be used on both vertical and horizontal milling machines, and is ideal for the machining of relatively large plane

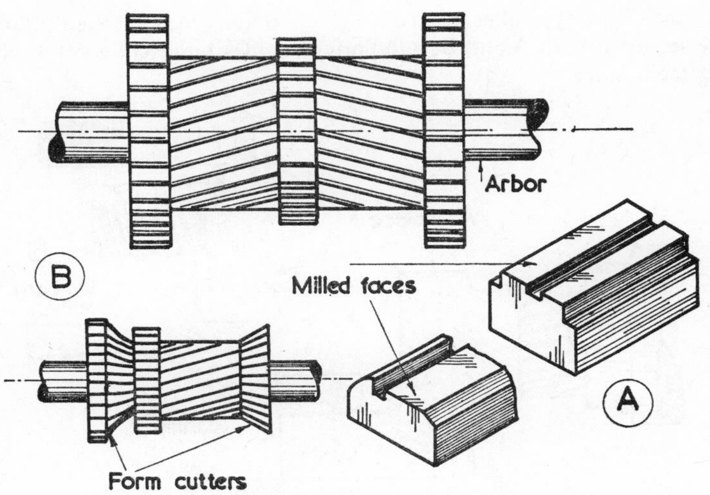

FIG. 177—EXAMPLES OF GANG MILLING.

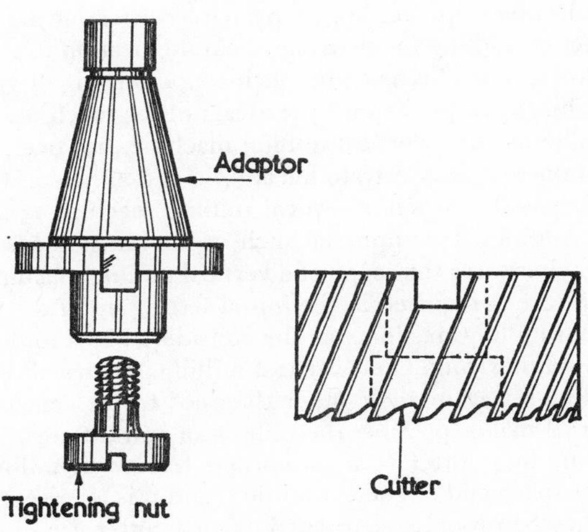

FIG. 178.—SHELL END MILL AND ADAPTOR.

surfaces. Two typical examples are given in fig. 179; note the rigidity of the set-up at both A and B; and both examples represent good machining technique.

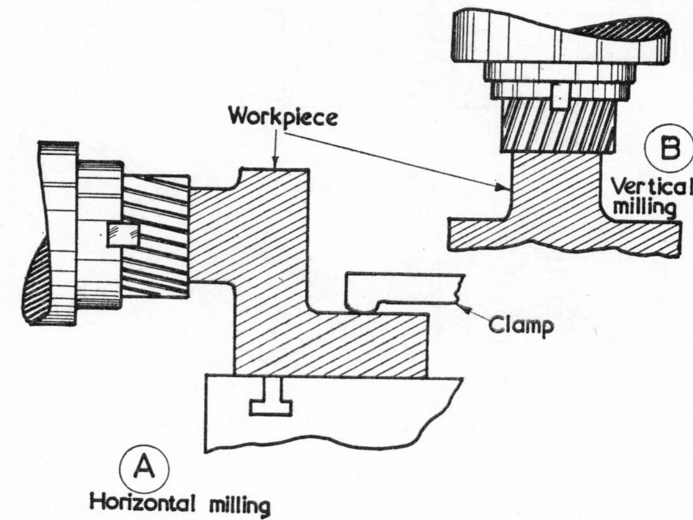

FIG. 179.—TYPICAL USES FOR A SHELL END MILL.

Summary

Milling machines operate on the principle of taking the work to the tool. Production milling involves the accurate location of the work in a milling fixture, and because of their superior rigidity, horizontal milling machines are preferred to vertical milling machines on production runs. The use of a vertical milling machine, however, enables the skilled machinist to demonstrate his ability, and accurate work to close tolerances is possible when a vertical milling machine is used to best advantage. Additional equipment such as dividing heads and rotary tables greatly increases the scope of a vertical milling machine, although considerable care is required in the initial setting up of the work.

A universal milling machine can be considered as a milling machine capable of both horizontal and vertical milling. A special device allows the table to be set at an angle other than 90° to the centre line of the arbor, and this makes possible the milling of spiral flutes. The correct choice of a milling cutter is an important feature of milling. Cutters must be kept sharp and in good condition, and it is an essential requirement that they be properly sharpened using a cutter grinding machine. This is the work of a skilled craftsman.

The use of a bent arbor or damaged spacing collars leads to a considerable reduction in the efficiency of the milling cutter. This is due to the fact that the centre line of rotation of the cutter will be slightly eccentric, resulting in an uneven distribution of the cutting load on the teeth of the cutter.

QUESTIONS ON CHAPTER TEN

PART A

1. Make neat sketches to show the principle of generating a plane surface when milling.
2. What is the essential difference between vertical and horizontal milling?
3. With the aid of a neat diagrammatic sketch, show the essential movements of a vertical milling machine.
4. Write down the purpose of the following:
arbor, knee, overarm, arbor supporting bracket.
5. Why are vertical millers seldom used on production lines? Why is it usually possible to take heavy cuts using a horizontal miller?
6. Make neat sketches showing a typical application for each of the following cutters: plain milling cutter, end mill, slab mill, staggered-tooth side and face cutter.
7. Explain why heavy cuts can be taken using a staggered-tooth side and face cutter.
8. What advantages are gained by providing milling cutters with helical or spiral teeth? What are the disadvantages?
9. Make neat sketches illustrating the principles of tool holding on a vertical milling machine.
10. With neat diagrams illustrate a typical use for each of the following: rotary table, dividing head, shell end mill, gang milling.

PART B

1. Make neat sketches showing a typical application of each of the following devices:
(i) rotary table,
(ii) dividing head,
(iii) engineers' parallels.

W.J.E.C (1963)

Synopsis

We have now completed the first two years of our study of Workshop Processes. It is hoped that the student will have appreciated that the purpose of Volume I was to provide a basic knowledge of the principles underlying the many techniques and processes carried out not only in engineering workshops, but also in a great number of our manufacturing industries.

This knowledge is essential if the second year of our course is to be pursued with profit, and now that we have reached the end of Volume II, we must consider whether we have sufficient knowledge and interest to continue and proceed to the third and fourth years. Perhaps it is as well to point out that entry into the third year of the course is conditional on a successful result in the forthcoming examination at Ordinary level. This can only be achieved if the student possesses the necessary knowledge.

Let us consider the assembly illustrated in fig. 180. This is a most important assembly, and its correct functioning is a matter of great import to all users of internal combustion engines. Let us take each chapter of this volume in turn, and see whether its contents help us to appreciate some of the problems involved in the manufacture of the assembly shown.

1. *The Casting of Metals*

The **piston** must be light, yet strong, and must be produced at a high production rate and as cheaply as possible.

It will therefore be pressure die cast in aluminium alloy.

2. *The Forging of Metals*

The **connecting rod** must be as strong and as tough as possible, and mass-produced at an economic rate.

It will therefore be drop forged from alloy steel.

3. *The Testing of Metals*

The **gudgeon pin** is subject to severe shear stress; the **connecting rod** to stress reversals. The hardness of the gudgeon pin and the

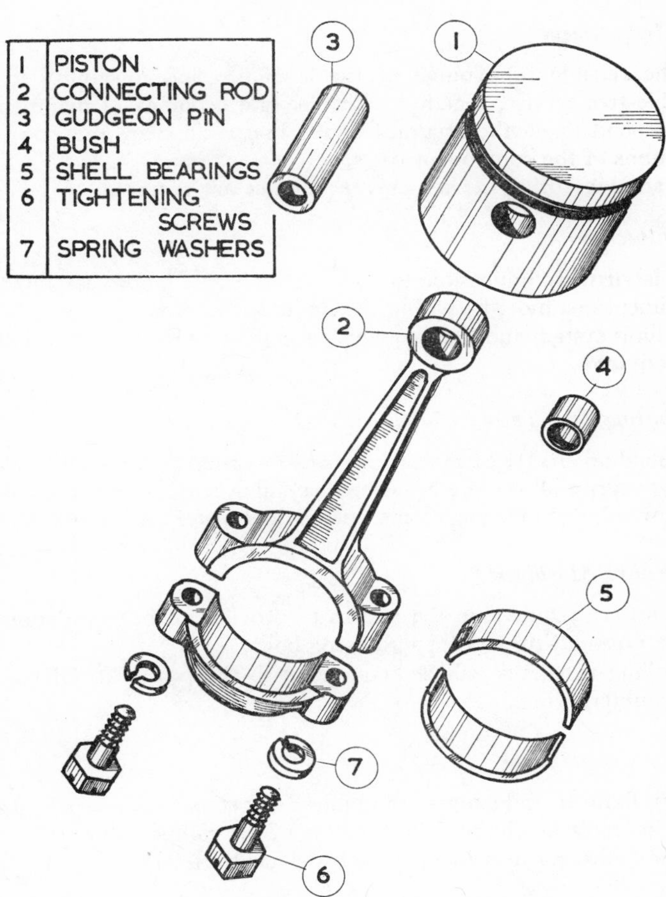

FIG. 180.—PRECISION ENGINEERING ASSEMBLY.

toughness of the connecting rod must be of the quality or standard required.

All these properties must be tested.

4. *Heat Treatments*

The **gudgeon pin** must have a hard outside surface and a tough core, the **connecting rod** must have a refined grain to promote maximum strength.

Heat treatments are required to improve the structures of these components.

5. *Measurement*

The reliable functioning of the assembly and its ability to give trouble-free service, together with ease and economy of manufacture, are dependent on the accuracy of the linear, angular, and non-linear functions of the component parts.

Many measuring devices and techniques are required.

6. *Inspection*

It is virtually impossible to measure each part before assembly, yet all dimensions must be within the limits laid down.

A limit system and limit gauges, or alternative inspection technique, are required.

7. *Cutting Tool Theory and Practice*

Outside diameter of **piston**, grooves for **piston rings**, and hole for **gudgeon pin** all require accurate machining with good surface finish. A knowledge of rake angles and cutting tool materials is required.

8. *Drilling Machines*

Holes are required in the **piston** to provide for oil circulation and in the **connecting rod** for tightening bolts.

Drilling machines will be required with the possibility of reaming and counterboring.

9. *The Centre Lathe*

Jigs, fixtures, and gauges are required, together with special-purpose machine tools for the mass-production of the component parts.

The toolroom must be equipped with centre lathes.

10. *Milling Machines*

Two parallel plane surfaces are required at big end of connecting rod; also at small end.

A gang milling operation is required.

The examples chosen are simple, for there are a great number of additional problems to be solved if the assembly shown is to be produced economically; but it is hoped that both this and the preceding volume have served, not only to assist the student to pass his examination, but also to stimulate or awaken a real interest in the fascinating art of engineering manufacture, and perhaps more important, to encourage him to greater achievements.

Appendix

SPECIMEN EXAMINATION PAPER

Reproduced by kind permission of the City and Guilds of London Institute

CITY AND GUILDS OF LONDON INSTITUTE

Mechanical Engineering Technicians

Part 1.—Workshop Processes and Practice

This paper contains nine questions: answer any FIVE.

Where possible illustrate your answers with pencil sketches in the answer book.

Logarithmic tables are supplied. At the end of the examination, they should be handed to the Invigilator.

A sheet of graph paper is supplied; drawing instruments may be used if desired.

The attached sheet shows the Figures referred to in the questions. All questions carry equal marks.

1. (*a*) What sort of grinding equipment should be used when grinding (*i.e.* re-sharpening)
either (i) single point lathe tools,
or (ii) twist drills,
in order to ensure the necessary finish and accuracy? It is not necessary to draw the equipment, but line diagrams may be used if desired.

(*b*) Outline the steps which should be taken to prevent accidents in the use of the above equipment, indicating some of the main causes of injury.

2. Two of the main reasons for the efficiency of the standard straight-edged lathe tool is that the cutting edge is at the same height and the cutting angles are constant over the whole depth of cut.

Use sketches to show the meaning of this statement and so explain the disadvantages of badly shaped cutting tools, such as round-nosed "hooked" tools.

3. (*a*) Describe a practical thermo-couple pyrometer outfit, as supplied with muffle furnaces operating up to 1000° C. Show how the equipment is arranged relative to the furnace.

(*b*) What precautions are necessary for the protection of the pyrometer equipment?

(*c*) State briefly what is meant by re-calibration and why it is necessary.

4. (*a*) To what accuracy and degree of finish can the following products usually be made:

(i) sand castings; (ii) die castings; (iii) drop forgings?

Give reasons for the differences in the values for these products.

(*b*) Explain briefly which of the above products would be best for

(i) the steering drop arm of a motor car,

(ii) a vee-belt pulley for the drive of a power hacksaw.

5. (*a*) Describe the main difficulties encountered when parting-off in a centre-lathe and state how they can be minimised or overcome.

(*b*) Discuss the relative advantages of using material in the form of sawn-off billets or in the form of bar stock when producing quantities of similar components on the centre lathe, taking into account size of work, size of machine and any other relevant factors.

6. The disc shown in *Fig.* 1 is the indexing plate for a milling fixture.
Assuming that other machining is completed, explain how you would machine the slots, giving details of the settings required, the cutting tool or tools to be used and the method of holding the work. Note that the slots must be accurately spaced to within ± 10 min.

7. When the indexing plate shown in *Fig.* 1 is in use, a tapered plunger engages in the slots which tend to wear and should be hardened.

(*a*) Give the approximate composition of the material which you consider most suitable for the plate.

(*b*) State what heat-treatment would be given to the plate and give details of the equipment and temperatures needed.

(*c*) In view of possible distortion during heat-treatment, what steps should be taken to ensure the accuracy of the finished work?

8. (*a*) Describe, with the aid of a simple line diagram, the line of drive through which power is transmitted from the motor to the tool or the work on *either* a centre-lathe *or* a milling machine. Put on the diagram the names of the main units of the drive.

DIMENSIONS GIVEN ARE IN MM UNLESS OTHERWISE STATED
FIRST ANGLE PROJECTION

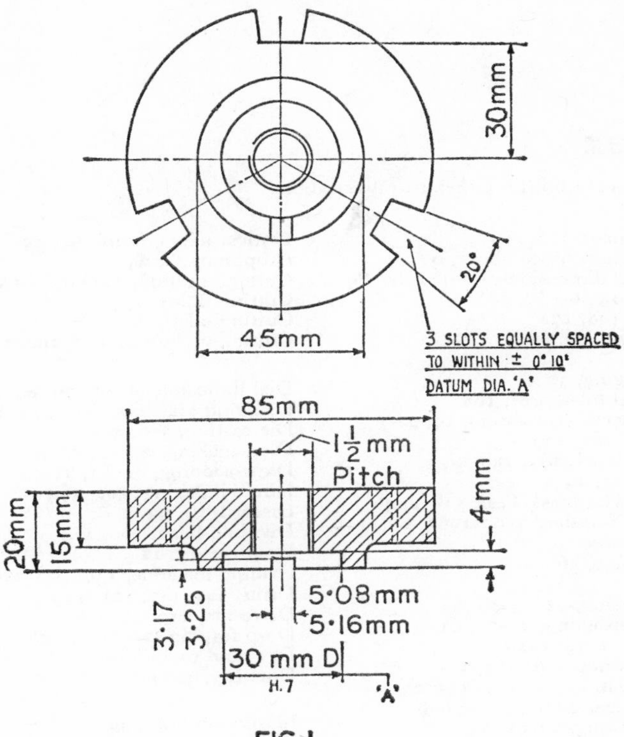

FIG. 1

(*b*) Explain what arrangements are usually made, on the machine chosen, for

(i) feed, stating the units in which the feed is normally reckoned,

(ii) accurate movement of the tool and the work, giving an example to show how a typical setting is carried out.

9. (*a*) What is the essential difference between a measuring instrument and a gauge?

(*b*) Explain what steps must be taken in a works to ensure that equipment such as micrometers and gauges give continued accuracy.

(*c*) Describe how to check either a micrometer or a plug gauge for accuracy; name two common faults which might account for any inaccuracies found.

Index

Numbers in **bold** type refer to illustrations